KU-677-411

Topic 4 — Natural Selection and Genetic Modification

Topic 5 — Health, Disease and the Development of Medicines

Topic 6 — Plant Structures and Their Functions

Topic 7 — Animal Coordination, Control and Homeostasis

Published by CGP

Editors: Luke Bennett, Ellen Burton, Mary Falkner, Daniel Fielding and Emily Forsberg.

Contributors: Paddy Gannon

From original material by Richard Parsons.

With thanks to Phil Armstrong, Chris Lindle and Hayley Thompson for the proofreading.

With thanks to Jan Greenway for the copyright research.

Percentile growth chart on page 43 copyright © 2009 Royal College of Paediatrics and Child Health.

Definition of health on page 95 from: Preamble to the Constitution of the World Health Organization as adopted by the International Health Conference, New York, 19 June - 22 July 1946; signed on 22 July 1946 by the representatives of 61 States (Official Records of the World Health Organization, no. 2, p. 100) and entered into force on 7 April 1948.

With thanks to EYE OF SCIENCE/SCIENCE PHOTO LIBRARY for permission to reproduce the image of blood cells on page 230.

With thanks to SCIENCE PHOTO LIBRARY for permission to reproduce the image of a contraceptive implant on page 240.

With thanks to iStock.com/AbelBrata for permission to reproduce the image of a condom on page 240.

Every effort has been made to locate copyright holders and obtain permission to reproduce sources. For those sources where it has been difficult to trace the originator of the work, we would be grateful for information. If any copyright holder would like us to make an amendment to the acknowledgements, please notify us and we will gladly update the book at the next reprint. Thank you.

ISBN: 978 1 78294 880 3

Printed by Elanders Ltd, Newcastle upon Tyne.

Clipart from Corel®

Illustrations by: Sandy Gardner Artist, email sandy@sandygardner.co.uk

GCSE
Biology

There's a lot to learn in GCSE Biology... but this fantastic CGP book explains the facts, theory and practical skills with the clearest study notes around!

On top of all that, there are exam-style questions for every topic — plus a set of practice exam papers to *really* test you on what you've learned.

We've also included fully-worked answers, so it's easy to mark your work and learn from any mistakes. Everything you need for a top grade!

Complete
Revision & Practice
Everything you need to pass the exams!

Contents

Throughout this book you'll see grade stamps like these:

These grade stamps help to show how difficult the questions are.

Remember — to get a top grade you need to be able to answer **all** the questions, not just the hardest ones.

In the real exams, some questions test how well you can structure an answer (as well as your scientific knowledge). In this book, we've marked these questions with an asterisk (*).

What to Expect in the Exams

Before you get cracking with your revision and exam practice, here's a handy guide to what you'll have to face in the exams — and the special features of this book that we've included especially to help you. You're welcome.

1. Topics are Covered in Different Papers

For GCSE Biology, you'll sit two exam papers at the end of your course.

Paper	Time	No. of marks	Topics Assessed
1	1 hr 45 mins	100	1, 2, 3, 4 and 5
2	1 hr 45 mins	100	1, 6, 7, 8 and 9

2. There are Different Question Types

In each exam, you'll be expected to answer a mixture of multiple-choice questions, calculations, short answer questions, and two longer, open response questions.

We've marked open response questions in this book with an asterisk (*).

For open response questions, you'll be marked on the structure of your answer, not just its scientific content. So...

Always make sure:
- Your answer is clear and has a logical structure.
- The points you make link together and form a sensible line of reasoning (if appropriate for the question).
- You include detailed, relevant information.

Fortunately, we've included loads of questions in this book, as well as a set of practice papers to give you the best possible preparation for the exams.

3. You'll be Tested on Your Maths...

At least 10% of the total marks for GCSE Biology will come from questions that test your maths skills. For these questions, always remember to:

EXAMPLE:

Look out for these worked examples in this book — they show you maths skills you'll need in the exam.

- Show your working — you could get marks for this, even if your final answer's wrong.
- Check that you're using the right units.
- Make sure your answer is given to an appropriate number of significant figures.

4. ...and on Your Practical Skills

Whenever one of the core practicals crops up in this book, it's marked up with stamps like these...

...and there's a whole section on Practical Skills on pages 194-198.

- GCSE Biology contains 8 mandatory core practicals that you'll do during the course. You can be asked about these, and the practical skills involved in them, in the exams.
- At least 15% of the total marks will be for questions that test your understanding of the practical activities and practical skills.
- For example, you might be asked to comment on the design of an experiment (the apparatus and method), make predictions, analyse or interpret results... Pretty much anything to do with planning and carrying out the investigations.

5. You'll Need to Know About Working Scientifically

Working Scientifically is all about how science is applied in the outside world by real scientists.

For example, you might be asked about ways that scientists communicate an idea to get their point across without being biased, or about the limitations of a scientific theory.

Working Scientifically is covered on pages 2-16.

You need to think about the situation that you've been given and use all your scientific savvy to answer the question. Always read the question and any data you've been given really carefully before you start writing your answer.

The Scientific Method

This section isn't about how to 'do' science — but it does show you the way most scientists work.

Scientists Come Up With **Hypotheses** — Then **Test** Them

1) Scientists try to explain things. They start by observing something they don't understand.

2) They then come up with a hypothesis — a possible explanation for what they've observed.

3) The next step is to test whether the hypothesis might be right or not. This involves making a prediction based on the hypothesis and testing it by gathering evidence (i.e. data) from investigations. If evidence from experiments backs up a prediction, you're a step closer to figuring out if the hypothesis is true.

Hundreds of years ago, we thought demons caused illness.

Several Scientists Will **Test** a Hypothesis

1) Normally, scientists share their findings in peer-reviewed journals, or at conferences.

2) Peer-review is where other scientists check results and scientific explanations to make sure they're 'scientific' (e.g. that experiments have been done in a sensible way) before they're published. It helps to detect false claims, but it doesn't mean that findings are correct — just that they're not wrong in any obvious way.

Then we thought it was caused by 'bad blood' (and treated it with leeches).

3) Once other scientists have found out about a hypothesis, they'll start basing their own predictions on it and carry out their own experiments. They'll also try to reproduce the original experiments to check the results — and if all the experiments in the world back up the hypothesis, then scientists start to think the hypothesis is true.

4) However, if a scientist does an experiment that doesn't fit with the hypothesis (and other scientists can reproduce the results) then the hypothesis may need to be modified or scrapped altogether.

If **All** the **Evidence** Supports a Hypothesis, It's **Accepted** — For Now

1) Accepted hypotheses are often referred to as theories. Our currently accepted theories are the ones that have survived this 'trial by evidence' — they've been tested many times over the years and survived.

2) However, theories never become totally indisputable fact. If new evidence comes along that can't be explained using the existing theory, then the hypothesising and testing is likely to start all over again.

Now we've collected more evidence, we know that illnesses that can be spread between people are due to microorganisms.

Scientific models are constantly being refined...

The scientific method has been developed over time. Aristotle (a Greek philosopher) was the first person to realise that theories need to be based on observations. Muslim scholars then introduced the ideas of creating a hypothesis, testing it, and repeating work to check results.

Models and Communication

Once scientists have made a <u>new discovery</u>, they <u>don't</u> just keep it to themselves. Oh no. Time to learn about how scientific discoveries are <u>communicated</u>, and the <u>models</u> that are used to represent theories.

Theories Can Involve Different Types of Models

Scientists test models by carrying out experiments to check that the predictions made by the model happen as expected.

1) A <u>representational model</u> is a <u>simplified description</u> or <u>picture</u> of what's going on in real life. Like all models, it can be used to <u>explain observations</u> and <u>make predictions</u>. E.g. the <u>lock and key model</u> of enzyme action is a simplified way of showing how <u>enzymes</u> work (see p.26). It can be used to explain why enzymes only catalyse particular reactions.

2) <u>Computational models</u> use computers to make <u>simulations</u> of complex real-life processes, such as climate change. They're used when there are a <u>lot</u> of different <u>variables</u> (factors that change) to consider, and because you can easily <u>change their design</u> to take into account <u>new data</u>.

3) All models have <u>limitations</u> on what they can <u>explain</u> or <u>predict</u>. <u>Climate change models</u> have several limitations — for example, it's hard to take into account <u>all</u> the biological and chemical processes that influence climate. It can also be difficult to include <u>regional variations</u> in climate.

Scientific Discoveries are Communicated to the General Public

Some scientific discoveries show that people should <u>change their habits</u>, or they might provide ideas that could be <u>developed</u> into new <u>technology</u>. So scientists need to <u>tell the world</u> about their discoveries.

<u>Gene technologies</u> are used in <u>genetic engineering</u> to produce <u>genetically modified crops</u>. Information about these crops needs to be communicated to <u>farmers</u> who might <u>benefit</u> from growing them and to the <u>general public</u>, so they can make <u>informed decisions</u> about the food they buy and eat.

Scientific Evidence can be Presented in a Biased Way

1) Scientific discoveries that are reported in the <u>media</u> (e.g. newspapers or television) <u>aren't</u> peer-reviewed.

2) This means that, even though news stories are often <u>based</u> on data that has been peer-reviewed, the data might be <u>presented</u> in a way that is <u>over-simplified</u> or <u>inaccurate</u>, making it open to <u>misinterpretation</u>.

3) People who want to make a point can sometimes <u>present data</u> in a <u>biased way</u> (sometimes <u>without knowing</u> they're doing it). For example, a scientist might overemphasise a relationship in the data, or a newspaper article might describe details of data <u>supporting</u> an idea without giving any evidence <u>against</u> it.

Companies can present biased data to help sell products...

Sometimes a company may only want you to see half of the story so they present the data in a <u>biased way</u>. For example, a pharmaceutical company may want to encourage you to buy their drugs by telling you about all the <u>positives</u>, but not report the results of any <u>unfavourable studies</u>.

Issues Created by Science

Science has helped us make progress in loads of areas, from medicine to space travel. But science still has its issues. And it can't answer everything, as you're about to find out.

Scientific Developments are Great, but they can Raise Issues

Scientific knowledge is increased by doing experiments. And this knowledge leads to scientific developments, e.g. new technologies or new advice. These developments can create issues though. For example:

Economic issues: Society can't always afford to do things scientists recommend (e.g. investing in alternative energy sources) without cutting back elsewhere.

Social issues: Decisions based on scientific evidence affect people — e.g. should alcohol be banned (to prevent health problems)? Would the effect on people's lifestyles be acceptable?

Personal issues: Some decisions will affect individuals. For example, someone might support alternative energy, but object if a wind farm is built next to their house.

Environmental issues: Human activity often affects the natural environment. For example, genetically modified crops may help us to produce more food — but some people think they could cause environmental problems (see p.90).

Science Can't Answer Every Question — Especially Ethical Ones

1) We don't understand everything. We're always finding out more, but we'll never know all the answers.

2) In order to answer scientific questions, scientists need data to provide evidence for their hypotheses.

3) Some questions can't be answered yet because the data can't currently be collected, or because there's not enough data to support a theory.

4) Eventually, as we get more evidence, we'll answer some of the questions that currently can't be answered, e.g. what the impact of global warming on sea levels will be. But there will always be the "Should we be doing this at all?"-type questions that experiments can't help us to answer...

Think about new drugs which can be taken to boost your 'brain power'.
- Some people think they're good as they could improve concentration or memory. New drugs could let people think in ways beyond the powers of normal brains.
- Other people say they're bad — they could give some people an unfair advantage in exams. And people might be pressured into taking them so that they could work more effectively, and for longer hours.

There are often issues with new scientific developments...

The trouble is, there's often no clear right answer where these issues are concerned. Different people have different views, depending on their priorities. These issues are full of grey areas.

Risk

Scientific discoveries are often great, but they can prove risky. With dangers all around, you've got to be aware of hazards — this includes how likely they are to cause harm and how serious the effects may be.

Nothing is Completely **Risk-Free**

1) A hazard is something that could potentially cause harm.

2) All hazards have a risk attached to them — this is the chance that the hazard will cause harm.

3) The risks of some things seem pretty obvious, or we've known about them for a while, like the risk of causing acid rain by polluting the atmosphere, or of having a car accident when you're travelling in a car.

4) New technology arising from scientific advances can bring new risks, e.g. scientists are unsure whether nanoparticles that are being used in cosmetics and suncream might be harming the cells in our bodies. These risks need to be considered alongside the benefits of the technology, e.g. improved sun protection.

5) You can estimate the size of a risk based on how many times something happens in a big sample (e.g. 100 000 people) over a given period (e.g. a year). For example, you could assess the risk of a driver crashing by recording how many people in a group of 100 000 drivers crashed their cars over a year.

6) To make decisions about activities that involve hazards, we need to take into account the chance of the hazard causing harm, and how serious the consequences would be if it did. If an activity involves a hazard that's very likely to cause harm, with serious consequences if it does, that activity is considered high risk.

People Make Their **Own Decisions** About Risk

1) Not all risks have the same consequences, e.g. if you chop veg with a sharp knife you risk cutting your finger, but if you go scuba-diving you risk death. You're much more likely to cut your finger during half an hour of chopping than to die during half an hour of scuba-diving. But most people are happier to accept a higher probability of an accident if the consequences are short-lived and fairly minor.

2) People tend to be more willing to accept a risk if they choose to do something (e.g. go scuba diving), compared to having the risk imposed on them (e.g. having a nuclear power station built next door).

3) People's perception of risk (how risky they think something is) isn't always accurate. They tend to view familiar activities as low-risk and unfamiliar activities as high-risk — even if that's not the case. For example, cycling on roads is often high-risk, but many people are happy to do it because it's a familiar activity. Air travel is actually pretty safe, but a lot of people perceive it as high-risk.

4) People may over-estimate the risk of things with long-term or invisible effects, e.g. ionising radiation.

The pros and cons of new technology must be weighed up...

The world's a dangerous place and it's impossible to rule out the chance of an accident altogether. But if you can recognise hazards and take steps to reduce the risks, you're more likely to stay safe.

Designing Investigations

Dig out your lab coat and dust off your badly-scratched safety goggles... it's <u>investigation time</u>.

Evidence Can Support or Disprove a Hypothesis

1) Scientists <u>observe</u> things and come up with <u>hypotheses</u> to explain them (see p.2). You need to be able to do the same. For example:

> <u>Observation</u>: People with big feet have spots. <u>Hypothesis</u>: Having big feet causes spots.

2) To <u>determine</u> whether or not a hypothesis is <u>right</u>, you need to do an <u>investigation</u> to gather evidence. To do this, you need to use your hypothesis to make a <u>prediction</u> — something you think <u>will happen</u> that you can test. E.g. people who have bigger feet will have more spots.

Investigations include experiments and studies.

3) Investigations are used to see if there are <u>patterns</u> or <u>relationships</u> between <u>two variables</u>, e.g. to see if there's a pattern or relationship between the variables 'number of spots' and 'size of feet'.

Evidence Needs to be Repeatable, Reproducible and Valid

1) <u>Repeatable</u> means that if the <u>same person</u> does an experiment again using the <u>same methods</u> and equipment, they'll get <u>similar results</u>.

2) <u>Reproducible</u> means that if <u>someone else</u> does the experiment, or a <u>different</u> method or piece of equipment is used, the results will still be <u>similar</u>.

3) If data is <u>repeatable</u> and <u>reproducible</u>, it's <u>reliable</u> and scientists are more likely to <u>have confidence</u> in it.

4) <u>Valid results</u> are both repeatable and reproducible AND they <u>answer the original question</u>. They come from experiments that were designed to be a <u>FAIR TEST</u>...

Make an Investigation a Fair Test By Controlling the Variables

1) In a lab experiment you usually <u>change one variable</u> and <u>measure</u> how it affects <u>another variable</u>.

2) To make it a fair test, <u>everything else</u> that could affect the results should <u>stay the same</u> — otherwise you can't tell if the thing you're changing is causing the results or not.

3) The variable you <u>CHANGE</u> is called the <u>INDEPENDENT</u> variable.

4) The variable you <u>MEASURE</u> when you change the independent variable is the <u>DEPENDENT</u> variable.

5) The variables that you <u>KEEP THE SAME</u> are called <u>CONTROL</u> variables.

> You could find how <u>temperature</u> affects the rate of an <u>enzyme-controlled reaction</u>. The <u>independent variable</u> is the <u>temperature</u>. The <u>dependent variable</u> is the <u>rate of reaction</u>. <u>Control variables</u> include the <u>concentration</u> and <u>amounts</u> of reactants, <u>pH</u>, the <u>time period</u> you measure, etc.

6) Because you can't always control all the variables, you often need to use a <u>control experiment</u>. This is an experiment that's kept under the <u>same conditions</u> as the rest of the investigation, but <u>doesn't</u> have anything <u>done</u> to it. This is so that you can see what happens when you don't change anything at all.

Designing Investigations

The **Bigger** the **Sample Size** the **Better**

1) Data based on <u>small samples</u> isn't as good as data based on large samples.
   A sample should <u>represent</u> the <u>whole population</u> (i.e. it should share as many
   of the characteristics in the population as possible) — a small sample can't do
   that as well. It's also harder to spot <u>anomalies</u> if your sample size is too small.

2) The <u>bigger</u> the sample size the <u>better</u>, but scientists have to be <u>realistic</u> when choosing how big.
   For example, if you were studying how <u>lifestyle</u> affects people's <u>weight</u> it'd be great to study
   everyone in the UK (a huge sample), but it'd take ages and cost a lot. It's more realistic to study
   a thousand people, with a <u>mixture</u> of ages, gender and race.

Your **Equipment** has to be **Right for the Job**

1) The measuring equipment you use has to be <u>sensitive enough</u> to measure the changes you're looking for.
   For example, if you need to measure changes of 1 cm^3 you need to use a <u>measuring cylinder</u> that
   can measure in <u>1 cm^3</u> steps — it'd be no good trying with one that only measures 10 cm^3 steps.

2) The <u>smallest change</u> a measuring instrument can <u>detect</u> is called its <u>resolution</u>. E.g. some mass balances
   have a resolution of 1 g, some have a resolution of 0.1 g, and some are even more sensitive.

3) Also, equipment needs to be <u>calibrated</u> by measuring a known value. If there's a <u>difference</u> between
   the <u>measured</u> and <u>known value</u>, you can use this to <u>correct</u> the inaccuracy of the equipment.

Data Should be **Repeatable**, **Reproducible**, **Accurate** and **Precise**

1) To <u>check repeatability</u> you need to <u>repeat</u> the readings and check that the results are similar.
   You need to repeat each reading at least <u>three times</u>.

2) To make sure your results are <u>reproducible</u> you can cross check them by taking
   a <u>second set of readings</u> with <u>another instrument</u> (or a <u>different observer</u>).

3) Your data also needs to be <u>accurate</u>. Really accurate
   results are those that are <u>really close</u> to the <u>true answer</u>.
   The accuracy of your results usually depends on your
   <u>method</u> — you need to make sure you're measuring the
   right thing and that you don't <u>miss anything</u> that should
   be included in the measurements. E.g. estimating the
   <u>amount of gas</u> released from a reaction by <u>counting
   the bubbles</u> isn't very accurate because you might <u>miss</u>
   some of the bubbles and they might have different
   <u>volumes</u>. It's <u>more accurate</u> to measure the volume
   of gas released using a <u>gas syringe</u> (see p.198).

4) Your data also needs to be <u>precise</u>. Precise results are
   ones where the data is <u>all really close</u> to the <u>mean</u>
   (average) of your repeated results (i.e. not spread out).

Repeat	Data set 1	Data set 2
1	12	11
2	14	17
3	13	14
Mean	<u>13</u>	<u>14</u>

Data set 1 is more precise than data set 2.

Designing Investigations

You Need to Look out for **Errors** and **Anomalous Results**

1) The results of your experiment will always <u>vary a bit</u> because of <u>random errors</u> — unpredictable differences caused by things like <u>human errors</u> in <u>measuring</u>. E.g. the errors you make when reading from a measuring cylinder are <u>random</u>. You have to <u>estimate</u> or <u>round</u> the distance when it's between two marks — so sometimes your figure will be a bit above the real one, and sometimes it will be a bit below.

2) You can <u>reduce</u> the effect of random errors by taking <u>repeat readings</u> and finding the <u>mean</u>. This will make your results <u>more precise</u>.

If there's no systematic error, then doing repeats and calculating a mean could make your results more accurate.

3) If a measurement is wrong by the <u>same amount every time</u>, it's called a <u>systematic error</u>. For example, if you measured from the very end of your ruler instead of from the 0 cm mark every time, all your measurements would be a bit small. Repeating the experiment in the exact same way and calculating a mean <u>won't</u> correct a systematic error.

4) Just to make things more complicated, if a systematic error is caused by using <u>equipment</u> that <u>isn't zeroed properly</u>, it's called a <u>zero error</u>. For example, if a mass balance always reads 1 gram before you put anything on it, all your measurements will be 1 gram too heavy.

5) You can <u>compensate</u> for some systematic errors if you know about them, e.g. if a mass balance always reads 1 gram before you put anything on it, you can subtract 1 gram from all your results.

6) Sometimes you get a result that <u>doesn't fit in</u> with the rest at all. This is called an <u>anomalous result</u>. You should investigate it and try to <u>work out what happened</u>. If you can work out what happened (e.g. you measured something wrong) you can <u>ignore</u> it when processing your results.

Investigations Can be **Hazardous**

1) <u>Hazards</u> from science experiments might include:

- <u>Microorganisms</u>, e.g. some bacteria can make you ill.
- <u>Chemicals</u>, e.g. sulfuric acid can burn your skin and alcohols catch fire easily.
- <u>Fire</u>, e.g. an unattended Bunsen burner is a fire hazard.
- <u>Electricity</u>, e.g. faulty electrical equipment could give you a shock.

You can find out about potential hazards by looking in textbooks, doing some internet research, or asking your teacher.

2) Part of planning an investigation is making sure that it's <u>safe</u>.

3) You should always make sure that you <u>identify</u> all the hazards that you might encounter. Then you should think of ways of <u>reducing the risks</u> from the hazards you've identified. For example:

- If you're working with <u>sulfuric acid</u>, always wear gloves and safety goggles. This will reduce the risk of the acid coming into contact with your skin and eyes.
- If you're using a <u>Bunsen burner</u>, stand it on a heat proof mat. This will reduce the risk of starting a fire.

Designing an investigation is an involved process...

Collecting <u>data</u> is what investigations are all about. Designing a good investigation is really important to make sure that any data collected is <u>accurate</u>, <u>precise</u>, <u>repeatable</u> and <u>reproducible</u>.

Processing Data

Processing your data means doing some <u>calculations</u> with it to make it <u>more useful</u>.

Data Needs to be Organised

1) <u>Tables</u> are really useful for <u>organising data</u>.

2) When you draw a table <u>use a ruler</u> and make sure <u>each column</u> has a <u>heading</u> (including the <u>units</u>).

There are Different Ways of Processing Your Data

1) When you've done repeats of an experiment you should always calculate the <u>mean</u> (a type of average). To do this <u>add together</u> all the data values and <u>divide</u> by the total number of values in the sample.

2) You might also need to calculate the <u>range</u> (how spread out the data is). To do this find the <u>largest</u> number and <u>subtract</u> the <u>smallest</u> number from it.   *Ignore anomalous results when calculating the mean and the range.*

 The results of an experiment to find the volume of gas produced in an enzyme-controlled reaction are shown below. Calculate the mean volume and the range.

Repeat 1 (cm³)	Repeat 2 (cm³)	Repeat 3 (cm³)	Mean (cm³)	Range (cm³)
28	37	32	(28 + 37 + 32) ÷ 3 = 32	(37 − 28) = 9

3) You might also need to calculate the <u>median</u> or <u>mode</u> (two more types of average). To calculate the <u>median</u>, put all your data in <u>numerical order</u> — the median is the <u>middle value</u>. The number that appears <u>most often</u> in a data set is the <u>mode</u>.   *If you have an even number of values, the median is halfway between the middle two values.*

> E.g. If you have the data set: 1 2 1 1 3 4 2
> The <u>median</u> is: 1 1 1 <u>2</u> 2 3 4. The <u>mode</u> is <u>1</u> because 1 appears most often.

Round to the Lowest Number of Significant Figures

The <u>first significant figure</u> of a number is the first digit that's <u>not zero</u>. The second and third significant figures come <u>straight after</u> (even if they're zeros). You should be aware of significant figures in calculations.

1) In <u>any</u> calculation where you need to round, you should round the answer to the <u>lowest number of significant figures</u> (s.f.) given.

2) Remember to write down <u>how many</u> significant figures you've rounded to after your answer.

3) If your calculation has multiple steps, <u>only</u> round the <u>final</u> answer, or it won't be as accurate.

 A plant produces 10.2 cm³ of oxygen in 6.5 minutes whilst photosynthesising. Calculate the rate of photosynthesis.

rate = 10.2 cm³ ÷ 6.5 min = 1.5692... = 1.6 cm³/min (2 s.f.)

3 s.f.   2 s.f.   *Final answer should be rounded to 2 s.f.*

 ## Don't forget your calculator...

In the exam you could be given some <u>data</u> and be expected to <u>process it</u> in some way. Make sure you keep an eye on <u>significant figures</u> in your answers and <u>always write down your working</u>.

Presenting Data

Once you've processed your data, e.g. by calculating the mean, you can present your results in a nice <u>chart</u> or <u>graph</u>. This will help you to <u>spot any patterns</u> in your data.

Bar Charts Can be Used to Show Different Types of Data

Bar charts can be used to display:

1) <u>Categoric data</u> — data that comes in <u>distinct categories</u>, e.g. flower colour, blood group.

2) <u>Discrete data</u> — data that can be counted in <u>chunks</u>, where there's no in-between value, e.g. number of bacteria is discrete because you can't have half a bacterium.

3) <u>Continuous data</u> — <u>numerical data</u> that can have <u>any value</u> within a <u>range</u>, e.g. length, volume.

There are some <u>golden rules</u> you need to follow for <u>drawing</u> bar charts:

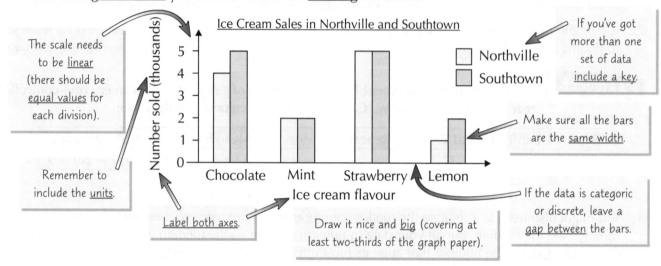

The scale needs to be <u>linear</u> (there should be <u>equal values</u> for each division).

Remember to include the <u>units</u>.

<u>Label both axes</u>.

Draw it nice and <u>big</u> (covering at least two-thirds of the graph paper).

If you've got more than one set of data <u>include a key</u>.

Make sure all the bars are the <u>same width</u>.

If the data is categoric or discrete, leave a <u>gap between</u> the bars.

Graphs Can be Used to Plot Continuous Data

1) If both variables are <u>continuous</u> you should use a <u>graph</u> to display the data.

2) Here are the <u>rules</u> for plotting points on a graph:

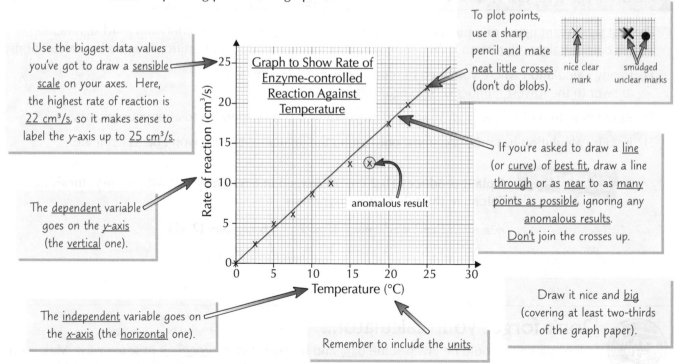

Use the biggest data values you've got to draw a <u>sensible</u> <u>scale</u> on your axes. Here, the highest rate of reaction is <u>22 cm³/s</u>, so it makes sense to label the y-axis up to <u>25 cm³/s</u>.

The <u>dependent</u> variable goes on the <u>y-axis</u> (the <u>vertical</u> one).

The <u>independent</u> variable goes on the <u>x-axis</u> (the <u>horizontal</u> one).

To plot points, use a sharp pencil and make <u>neat little crosses</u> (don't do blobs).

nice clear mark

smudged unclear marks

If you're asked to draw a <u>line</u> (or <u>curve</u>) of <u>best fit</u>, draw a line <u>through</u> or as <u>near</u> to as <u>many</u> <u>points as possible</u>, ignoring any <u>anomalous results</u>. <u>Don't</u> join the crosses up.

anomalous result

Remember to include the <u>units</u>.

Draw it nice and <u>big</u> (covering at least two-thirds of the graph paper).

More on Graphs

Graph's aren't just fun to plot, they're also really useful for showing <u>trends</u> in your data.

Graphs Can Give You a Lot of Information About Your Data

1) The <u>gradient</u> (slope) of a graph tells you how quickly the <u>dependent variable</u> changes if you change the <u>independent variable</u>.

$$\text{gradient} = \frac{\text{change in } y}{\text{change in } x}$$

The <u>graph</u> below shows the <u>volume of gas</u> produced in a reaction against <u>time</u>. The graph is <u>linear</u> (it's a straight line graph), so you can simply calculate the <u>gradient</u> of the line to find out the <u>rate of reaction</u>.

1) To calculate the gradient, pick <u>two points</u> on the line that are easy to read and a <u>good distance</u> apart.

2) <u>Draw a line down</u> from one of the points and a <u>line across</u> from the other to make a <u>triangle</u>. The line drawn down the side of the triangle is the <u>change in y</u> and the line across the bottom is the <u>change in x</u>.

Change in y = 6.8 − 2.0 = 4.8 cm³   Change in x = 5.2 − 1.6 = 3.6 s

Rate = gradient = $\dfrac{\text{change in } y}{\text{change in } x}$ = $\dfrac{4.8 \text{ cm}^3}{3.6 \text{ s}}$ = <u>1.3 cm³/s</u> or <u>1.3 cm³ s⁻¹</u>

The units of the gradient are (units of y)/(units of x). cm³/s can also be written as cm³ s⁻¹.

You can use this method to calculate any rates from a graph, not just the rate of a reaction.
Just remember that a rate is how much something changes over time, so x needs to be the time.

2) The <u>intercept</u> of a graph is where the line of best fit crosses one of the <u>axes</u>. The <u>x-intercept</u> is where the line of best fit crosses the x-axis and the <u>y-intercept</u> is where it crosses the <u>y-axis</u>.

Graphs Show the Relationship Between Two Variables

1) You can get <u>three</u> types of <u>correlation</u> (relationship) between variables:

<u>POSITIVE correlation:</u>
as one variable <u>increases</u>
the other <u>increases</u>.

<u>INVERSE (negative) correlation:</u>
as one variable <u>increases</u>
the other <u>decreases</u>.

<u>NO correlation:</u>
<u>no relationship</u> between
the two variables.

2) Just because there's correlation, it doesn't mean the change in one variable is <u>causing</u> the change in the other — there might be <u>other factors</u> involved (see page 14).

Units

Graphs and maths skills are all very well, but the numbers don't mean much if you don't get the <u>units</u> right.

S.I. Units Are Used All Round the World

1) It wouldn't be all that useful if I defined volume in terms of <u>bath tubs</u>, you defined it in terms of <u>egg-cups</u> and my pal Fred defined it in terms of <u>balloons</u> — we'd never be able to compare our data.

2) To stop this happening, scientists have come up with a set of <u>standard units</u>, called S.I. units, that all scientists use to measure their data. Here are some S.I. units you'll see in biology:

Quantity	S.I. Base Unit
mass	kilogram, kg
length	metre, m
time	second, s

Always Check The Values Used in Equations Have the Right Units

1) Formulas and equations show <u>relationships</u> between <u>variables</u>.

2) To <u>rearrange</u> an equation, make sure that whatever you do to <u>one side</u> of the equation you also do to the <u>other side</u>.

For example, you can find the <u>magnification</u> of something using the equation: <u>magnification = image size ÷ real size</u> (see p.23). You can <u>rearrange</u> this equation to find the <u>image size</u> by <u>multiplying each side</u> by the real size: <u>image size = magnification × real size</u>

3) To use a formula, you need to know the values of <u>all but one</u> of the variables. <u>Substitute</u> the values you do know into the formula, and do the calculation to work out the final variable.

4) Always make sure the values you put into an equation or formula have the <u>right units</u>. For example, if you're calculating the magnification of something, but your image size is in <u>mm</u> and the real size is in <u>μm</u>, you'll have to convert both measurements into the <u>same unit</u> (either mm or μm) before you start.

5) To make sure your units are <u>correct</u>, it can help to write down the <u>units</u> on each line of your <u>calculation</u>.

S.I. units help scientists to compare data...

You can only really <u>compare</u> things if they're in the <u>same units</u>. E.g. if the rate of blood flow was measured in ml/min in one vein and in l/day in another vein, it'd be hard to know which was faster.

Converting Units

You can <u>convert units</u> using <u>scaling prefixes</u>. This can save you from having to write a lot of 0's...

Scaling Prefixes Can Be Used for Large and Small Quantities

1) Quantities come in a huge <u>range</u> of sizes. For example, the volume of a swimming pool might be around 2 000 000 000 cm³, while the volume of a cup is around 250 cm³.

2) To make the size of numbers more <u>manageable</u>, larger or smaller units are used. These are the <u>S.I. base units</u> (e.g. metres) with a <u>prefix</u> in front:

Prefix	tera (T)	giga (G)	mega (M)	kilo (k)	deci (d)	centi (c)	milli (m)	micro (μ)	nano (n)
Multiple of Unit	10^{12}	10^9	1 000 000 (10^6)	1000	0.1	0.01	0.001	0.000001 (10^{-6})	10^{-9}

3) These <u>prefixes</u> tell you <u>how much bigger</u> or <u>smaller</u> a unit is than the base unit. So one <u>kilo</u>metre is <u>one thousand</u> metres.

4) To <u>swap</u> from one unit to another, all you need to know is what number you have to divide or multiply by to get from the original unit to the new unit — this is called the <u>conversion factor</u>.

The conversion factor is the number of times the smaller unit goes into the larger unit.

- To go from a <u>bigger unit</u> (like m) to a <u>smaller unit</u> (like cm), you <u>multiply</u> by the conversion factor.
- To go from a <u>smaller unit</u> (like g) to a <u>bigger unit</u> (like kg), you <u>divide</u> by the conversion factor.

5) Here are some conversions that'll be useful for GCSE biology:

Length can have lots of units including mm, μm and nm.

mm ×1000 / ÷1000 μm ×1000 / ÷1000 nm

Mass can have units of kg and g.

kg ×1000 / ÷1000 g

Volume can have units of m³, dm³ and cm³.

m³ ×1000 / ÷1000 dm³ ×1000 / ÷1000 cm³

Time can have units of min and s.

min ×60 / ÷60 s

To convert from bigger units to smaller units...

MATHS TIP

...<u>multiply</u> by the <u>conversion factor</u>, and to convert from <u>smaller units</u> to <u>bigger units</u>, <u>divide</u> by the <u>conversion factor</u>. Don't go getting this the wrong way round or you'll get some odd answers.

Drawing Conclusions

Once you've carried out an experiment and processed your data, it's time to work out what your data shows.

You Can **Only Conclude** What the Data Shows and **No More**

1) Drawing conclusions might seem pretty straightforward — you just look at your data and say what pattern or relationship you see between the dependent and independent variables.

The table on the right shows heights of pea plant seedlings grown for three weeks with different fertilisers.

Fertiliser	Mean growth / mm
A	13.5
B	19.5
No fertiliser	5.5

CONCLUSION: Fertiliser B makes pea plant seedlings grow taller over a three week period than fertiliser A.

2) But you've got to be really careful that your conclusion matches the data you've got and doesn't go any further.

> You can't conclude that fertiliser B makes any other type of plant grow taller than fertiliser A — the results could be totally different.

3) You also need to be able to use your results to justify your conclusion (i.e. back up your conclusion with some specific data).

> Over the three week period, fertiliser B made the pea plants grow 6 mm more on average than fertiliser A.

4) When writing a conclusion you need to refer back to the original hypothesis and say whether the data supports it or not:

> The hypothesis for this experiment might have been that adding fertiliser would increase the growth of plants and that different types of fertiliser would affect growth by different amounts. If so, the data supports the hypothesis.

Correlation **DOES NOT** Mean **Cause**

If two things are correlated (i.e. there's a relationship between them) it doesn't necessarily mean a change in one variable is causing the change in the other — this is REALLY IMPORTANT — DON'T FORGET it. There are three possible reasons for a correlation:

1) CHANCE: It might seem strange, but two things can show a correlation purely due to chance.

> For example, one study might find a correlation between people's hair colour and how good they are at frisbee. But other scientists don't get a correlation when they investigate it — the results of the first study are just a fluke.

2) LINKED BY A 3RD VARIABLE: A lot of the time it may look as if a change in one variable is causing a change in the other, but it isn't — a third variable links the two things.

> For example, there's a correlation between water temperature and shark attacks. This isn't because warmer water makes sharks crazy. Instead, they're linked by a third variable — the number of people swimming (more people swim when the water's hotter, and with more people in the water you get more shark attacks).

3) CAUSE: Sometimes a change in one variable does cause a change in the other. You can only conclude that a correlation is due to cause when you've controlled all the variables that could affect the result.

> For example, there's a correlation between smoking and lung cancer. This is because chemicals in tobacco smoke cause lung cancer. This conclusion was only made once other variables (such as age and exposure to other things that cause cancer) had been controlled and shown not to affect people's risk of getting lung cancer.

Uncertainty

Uncertainty is how sure you can really be about your data. There's a little bit of maths to do, and also a formula to learn. But don't worry too much — it's no more than a simple bit of subtraction and division.

Uncertainty is the Amount of Error Your Measurements Might Have

1) When you repeat a measurement, you often get a slightly different figure each time you do it due to random error. This means that each result has some uncertainty to it.

2) The measurements you make will also have some uncertainty in them due to limits in the resolution of the equipment you use (see page 7).

3) This all means that the mean of a set of results will also have some uncertainty to it. You can calculate the uncertainty of a mean result using the equation:

$$\text{uncertainty} = \frac{\text{range}}{2}$$

The range is the largest value minus the smallest value (see p.9).

4) The larger the range, the less precise your results are and the more uncertainty there will be in your results. Uncertainties are shown using the '±' symbol.

EXAMPLE:

The table below shows the results of a respiration experiment to determine the volume of carbon dioxide produced. Calculate the uncertainty of the mean.

Repeat	1	2	3	mean
Volume of CO_2 produced (cm³)	20.2	19.8	20.0	20.0

1) First work out the range:

Range = 20.2 − 19.8 = 0.4 cm³

2) Use the range to find the uncertainty:

Uncertainty = range ÷ 2 = 0.4 ÷ 2 = 0.2 cm³

So the uncertainty of the mean = 20.0 ± 0.2 cm³

5) Measuring a greater amount of something helps to reduce uncertainty.

For example, in a rate of reaction experiment, measuring the amount of product formed over a longer period compared to a shorter period will reduce the percentage uncertainty in your results.

The smaller the uncertainty, the more precise your results...

Remember that equation for uncertainty. You never know when you might need it — you could be expected to use it in the exams. You need to make sure all the data is in the same units though. For example, if you had some measurements in metres, and some in centimetres, you'd need to convert them all into either metres or centimetres before you set about calculating uncertainty.

Evaluations

Hurrah! The end of another investigation. Well, now you have to work out all the things you did <u>wrong</u>. That's what <u>evaluations</u> are all about I'm afraid. Best get cracking with this page...

Evaluations — Describe **How** Investigations Could be **Improved**

An evaluation is a <u>critical analysis</u> of the whole investigation.

1) You should comment on the <u>method</u> — was it <u>valid</u>? Did you control all the other variables to make it a <u>fair test</u>?

2) Comment on the <u>quality</u> of the <u>results</u> — was there <u>enough evidence</u> to reach a valid <u>conclusion</u>? Were the results <u>repeatable</u>, <u>reproducible</u>, <u>accurate</u> and <u>precise</u>?

3) Were there any <u>anomalous</u> results? If there were <u>none</u> then <u>say so</u>. If there were any, try to <u>explain</u> them — were they caused by <u>errors</u> in measurement? Were there any other <u>variables</u> that could have <u>affected</u> the results? You should comment on the level of <u>uncertainty</u> in your results too.

4) All this analysis will allow you to say how <u>confident</u> you are that your conclusion is <u>right</u>.

5) Then you can suggest any <u>changes</u> to the <u>method</u> that would <u>improve</u> the quality of the results, so that you could have <u>more confidence</u> in your conclusion. For example, you might suggest <u>changing</u> the way you controlled a variable, or <u>increasing</u> the number of <u>measurements</u> you took. Taking more measurements at <u>narrower intervals</u> could give you a <u>more accurate result</u>.

<u>Enzymes</u> have an <u>optimum temperature</u> (a temperature at which they <u>work best</u>). Say you do an experiment to find an enzyme's optimum temperature and take measurements at 10 °C, 20 °C, 30 °C, 40 °C and 50 °C. The results of this experiment tell you the optimum is <u>40 °C</u>. You could then <u>repeat</u> the experiment, <u>taking more measurements around 40 °C</u> to a get a <u>more accurate</u> value for the optimum.

6) You could also make more <u>predictions</u> based on your conclusion, then <u>further experiments</u> could be carried out to test them.

When suggesting improvements to the investigation, always make sure that you say why you think this would make the results better.

Always look for ways to improve your investigations

So there you have it — <u>Working Scientifically</u>. Make sure you know this stuff like the back of your hand. It's not just in the lab or the field, when you're carrying out your groundbreaking <u>investigations</u>, that you'll need to know how to work scientifically. You can be asked about it in the <u>exams</u> as well. So swot up...

Cells

When someone first peered down a microscope at a slice of cork and drew the <u>boxes</u> they saw, little did they know that they'd seen the <u>building blocks</u> of <u>every organism on the planet</u>...

Organisms can be **Prokaryotes** or **Eukaryotes**

1) <u>All living things</u> are made of <u>cells</u>.

2) Cells can be either <u>prokaryotic</u> or <u>eukaryotic</u>. Eukaryotic cells are <u>complex</u> and include all <u>animal</u> and <u>plant</u> cells. Prokaryotic cells are <u>smaller</u> and <u>simpler</u>, e.g. bacteria (see next page).

You might see the sizes of cells written in standard form — see p.24 for more on this.

3) <u>Eukaryotes</u> are organisms that are made up of <u>eukaryotic cells</u>.

4) A <u>prokaryote</u> is a <u>prokaryotic cell</u> (it's a single-celled organism).

Plant and **Animal** Cells have **Similarities** and **Differences**

Animal Cells

Subcellular structures are also known as organelles.

The different parts of a cell are called <u>subcellular structures</u>. Most <u>animal</u> cells have the following subcellular structures — make sure you know them all:

<u>Nucleus</u> — contains <u>genetic material</u> that controls the activities of the cell. Genetic material is arranged into <u>chromosomes</u>.

<u>Cytoplasm</u> — gel-like substance where most of the <u>chemical reactions</u> happen. It contains <u>enzymes</u> (see page 26) that control these chemical reactions.

<u>Mitochondria</u> — these are where most of the reactions for <u>aerobic respiration</u> take place (see page 159). Respiration transfers <u>energy</u> that the cell needs to work.

<u>Cell membrane</u> — holds the cell together and controls what goes <u>in</u> and <u>out</u>.

<u>Ribosomes</u> — these are involved in <u>translation of genetic material</u> in the <u>synthesis of proteins</u>.

Subcellular structures are all the different parts of a cell

Make sure you get to grips with the different <u>subcellular structures</u> that animal cells contain before you move on to the next page. There are more subcellular structures coming up that you <u>need to know</u>...

Cells

Plant Cells

Plant cells usually have all the bits that animal cells have,
plus a few extra things that animal cells don't have:

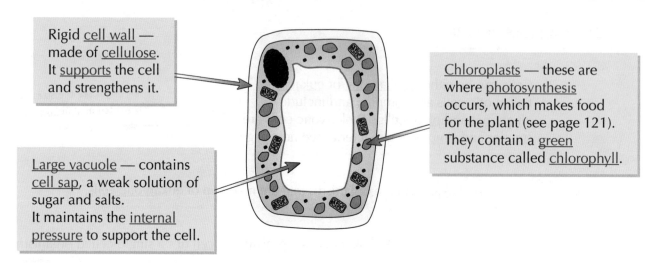

Rigid cell wall — made of cellulose. It supports the cell and strengthens it.

Large vacuole — contains cell sap, a weak solution of sugar and salts. It maintains the internal pressure to support the cell.

Chloroplasts — these are where photosynthesis occurs, which makes food for the plant (see page 121). They contain a green substance called chlorophyll.

Bacterial Cells Have No Nucleus

Bacterial cells are a lot smaller than plant or animal cells and have these subcellular structures:

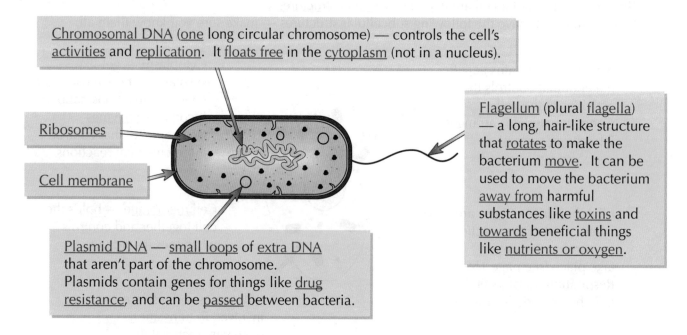

Chromosomal DNA (one long circular chromosome) — controls the cell's activities and replication. It floats free in the cytoplasm (not in a nucleus).

Ribosomes

Cell membrane

Flagellum (plural flagella) — a long, hair-like structure that rotates to make the bacterium move. It can be used to move the bacterium away from harmful substances like toxins and towards beneficial things like nutrients or oxygen.

Plasmid DNA — small loops of extra DNA that aren't part of the chromosome. Plasmids contain genes for things like drug resistance, and can be passed between bacteria.

REVISION TIP

There's quite a bit to learn in biology — but that's life, I guess...

On these pages are a typical animal cell, plant cell and bacterial cell. Make sure you're familiar with all their structures. A good way to check that you know what all the bits and pieces are is to copy out the diagrams and see if you can remember all the labels. No cheating.

Specialised Cells

The previous pages show the structure of some <u>typical cells</u>. However, most cells are <u>specialised</u> for a particular function, so their <u>structure</u> can vary...

Different Cells Have Different Functions

1) <u>Multicellular organisms</u> contain lots of different <u>types</u> of cells (i.e. cells with different <u>structures</u>).

2) Cells that have a structure which makes them <u>adapted</u> to their function are called <u>specialised cells</u>.

3) You need to know how <u>egg</u>, <u>sperm</u> and <u>ciliated epithelial cells</u> are <u>adapted</u> to their functions.

Egg Cells and Sperm Cells Are Specialised for Reproduction

1) In <u>sexual reproduction</u>, the <u>nucleus</u> of an egg cell <u>fuses</u> with the nucleus of a <u>sperm cell</u> to create a <u>fertilised egg</u>, which then develops into an <u>embryo</u>. Both the nucleus of an egg cell and of a sperm cell only contain <u>half</u> the number of chromosomes that's in a <u>normal</u> body cell — so they are called 'haploid'.

2) This is important as it means that when an egg and sperm nucleus <u>combine</u> at <u>fertilisation</u>, the resulting cell will have the <u>right number</u> of chromosomes.

There's more about sexual reproduction on page 56.

Egg Cells

The main functions of an <u>egg</u> are to carry the female DNA and to <u>nourish</u> the developing embryo in the early stages. This is how it's adapted to its function:

1) It contains <u>nutrients</u> in the <u>cytoplasm</u> to feed the embryo.

2) It has a <u>haploid nucleus</u>.

3) Straight after <u>fertilisation</u>, its <u>membrane</u> changes <u>structure</u> to stop any more sperm getting in. This makes sure the offspring end up with the <u>right amount</u> of DNA.

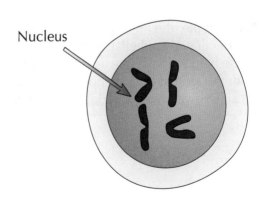

Nucleus

Specialised Cells

Sperm Cells

The <u>function</u> of a sperm is to <u>transport</u> the <u>male's DNA</u> to the <u>female's egg</u>.

1) A sperm cell has a <u>long tail</u> so it can <u>swim</u> to the egg.

2) It has lots of <u>mitochondria</u> in the middle section to provide the <u>energy</u> (from respiration) needed to <u>swim</u> this distance.

3) It also has an <u>acrosome</u> at the front of the 'head', where it stores <u>enzymes</u> needed to <u>digest</u> its way through the <u>membrane</u> of the egg cell.

4) It also contains a <u>haploid nucleus</u>.

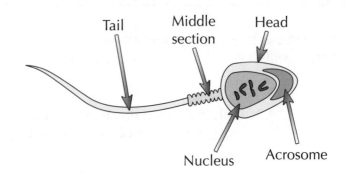
Tail   Middle section   Head   Nucleus   Acrosome

Ciliated Epithelial Cells Are Specialised for Moving Materials

1) Epithelial cells <u>line the surfaces</u> of organs.

2) Some of them have <u>cilia</u> (hair-like structures) on the <u>top surface</u> of the cell.

3) The function of these <u>ciliated epithelial cells</u> is to <u>move substances</u> — the cilia beat to <u>move</u> substances in <u>one direction</u>, <u>along the surface</u> of the tissue.

Cilia

For example, the <u>lining of the airways</u> contains <u>lots</u> of ciliated epithelial cells. These help to move <u>mucus</u> (and all of the particles from the air that it has trapped) up to the <u>throat</u> so it can be <u>swallowed</u> and <u>doesn't reach</u> the lungs.

Cells have the same basic bits but are specialised for their function

Nearly every cell in your body is <u>specialised</u> to carry out some kind of function, but the ones on these pages — egg cells, sperm cells and ciliated epithelial cells — are the examples you need to <u>learn</u> for your exams.

Microscopy

Without <u>microscopes</u> we would never have discovered cells. We can even use them to look <u>inside</u> cells.

Cells are **Studied** Using **Microscopes**

Microscopes use lenses to <u>magnify</u> images (make them look bigger). They also increase the <u>resolution</u> of an image. <u>Resolution</u> means how well a microscope distinguishes between <u>two points</u> that are <u>close together</u>. A <u>higher resolution</u> means that the image can be seen <u>more clearly</u> and in <u>more detail</u>.

<u>Light microscopes</u> were invented in the 1590s. They work by passing <u>light</u> through the specimen. They let us see things like <u>nuclei</u> and <u>chloroplasts</u> and we can also use them to study <u>living cells</u>.

<u>Electron microscopes</u> were invented in the 1930s. They use <u>electrons</u> rather than <u>light</u>. Electron microscopes have a higher <u>magnification</u> and <u>resolution</u> than light microscopes, so they let us see much <u>smaller things</u> in <u>more detail</u> like the <u>internal structure</u> of mitochondria and chloroplasts. This has allowed us to have a much <u>greater understanding</u> of <u>how cells work</u> and the <u>role of subcellular structures</u> (although they can't be used to view living cells).

You Can Create a **Scientific Drawing** of a **Specimen**

PRACTICAL

1) Using a <u>sharp</u> pencil, draw <u>outlines</u> of the <u>main features</u> using <u>clear, unbroken lines</u>. Don't include any <u>colouring</u> or <u>shading</u>.

2) Make sure that your drawing takes up <u>at least half</u> of the space available and remember to keep all the parts <u>in proportion</u>.

3) <u>Label</u> the <u>important features</u> of your diagram with <u>straight lines</u> which <u>don't cross over</u> each other, and include the <u>magnification</u> used and a <u>scale</u>.

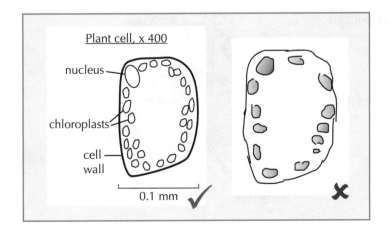

Plant cell, x 400
nucleus
chloroplasts
cell wall
0.1 mm ✓
✗

PRACTICAL TIP

Take your time when you're doing scientific drawings

When you look at a <u>real specimen</u> down a microscope, it often doesn't look exactly like what you'd expect from seeing diagrams in books. But don't be put off — just <u>draw what you can see</u>.

Microscopy

It's all very well knowing what microscopes <u>do</u> — you also have to know how to actually <u>use</u> one.

This is How to **View** a **Specimen** Using a **Light Microscope:**

1) Your specimen needs to <u>let light through it</u> so you'll need to take a <u>thin slice</u> of it to start with.

2) Next, take a clean <u>slide</u> and use a <u>pipette</u> to put one drop of water in the middle of it — this will <u>secure</u> the specimen in place. Then use <u>tweezers</u> to place your specimen on the slide.

3) Add a drop of <u>stain</u> if your <u>specimen</u> is completely <u>transparent</u> or <u>colourless</u> — this makes the specimen <u>easier to see</u> (different stains highlight different structures within cells, e.g. methylene blue stains DNA).

4) Place a <u>cover slip</u> at one end of the specimen, holding it at an <u>angle</u> with a <u>mounted needle</u> and carefully <u>lower</u> it onto the slide. Press it down <u>gently</u> so that no <u>air bubbles</u> are trapped under it. Then <u>clip</u> the slide onto the <u>stage</u>.

5) Select the <u>lowest-powered objective lens</u>.

6) Use the <u>coarse adjustment knob</u> to move the stage <u>up</u> so that the slide is <u>just underneath</u> the objective lens. Then, <u>looking</u> down the <u>eyepiece</u>, move the stage <u>downwards</u> (so you don't accidently crash it into the lens) until the specimen is <u>nearly in focus</u>.

7) Then <u>adjust the focus</u> with the <u>fine adjustment knob</u>, until you get a <u>clear image</u>. Position a <u>clear ruler</u> on the stage and use it to measure the <u>diameter</u> of the circular area visible — your <u>field of view</u> (<u>FOV</u>).

8) If you need to see your specimen with <u>greater magnification</u>, swap to a <u>higher-powered objective lens</u>, <u>refocus</u> and <u>recalculate</u> your <u>FOV</u> accordingly (e.g. if your FOV was 5 mm then you swap to a lens that is 10 times more powerful, your FOV will now be 5 mm ÷ 10 = 0.5 mm).

Measuring your field of view allows you to estimate the size of your specimen.

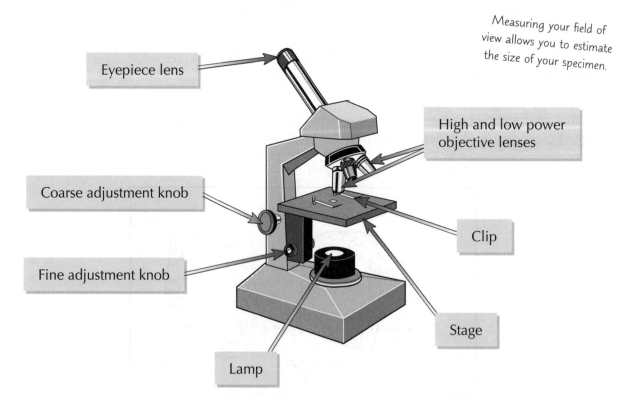

Your microscope might look a bit different

 The appearance of light microscopes can <u>vary</u> (e.g. they might have two eyepieces rather than one) but they should have the <u>same basic features</u> shown on this page.

More Microscopy

Sometimes you need to do a bit of <u>maths</u> with microscope images.

Magnification is **How Many Times Bigger** the Image is

1) If you know the <u>power</u> of the lenses used by a microscope to view an image, you can work out the <u>total magnification</u> of the image using this simple formula:

> **total magnification = eyepiece lens magnification × objective lens magnification**

 An image is viewed with an eyepiece lens magnification of × 10 and an objective lens magnification of × 40. What is the total magnification?

Total magnification = eyepiece lens magnification × objective lens magnification = 10 × 40 = × 400

2) If you don't know which lenses were used, you can still work out the magnification of an image as long as you can <u>measure the image</u> and know the <u>real size of the specimen</u>. This is the <u>formula</u> you need:

$$\text{magnification} = \frac{\text{image size}}{\text{real size}}$$

Both measurements should have the same units. If they don't, you'll need to convert them first (see next page).

 A magnified image is 2 mm wide, and the specimen is 0.02 mm wide. What is the magnification?

$$\text{magnification} = \frac{\text{image size}}{\text{real size}} = \frac{2}{0.02} = \times 100$$

3) If you're working out the <u>image size</u> or the <u>real size</u> of the object, you can rearrange the equation using this <u>formula triangle</u>. <u>Cover up</u> the thing you're trying to find. The parts you can <u>still see</u> are the formula you need to use.

4) <u>Estimating</u> can help you to <u>check</u> that your answer is <u>correct</u>. To estimate an answer, <u>round</u> the numbers so you can do the maths in your <u>head</u>.

 The real size of a specimen is 21.5 µm. The size of an image of the specimen is 9800 µm. Estimate the magnification used.

1) First, <u>round</u> both numbers to <u>1 significant figure</u>.
   - 21.5 µm = 20 µm to 1 significant figure.
   - 9800 µm = 10 000 µm to 1 significant figure.

2) Then do the calculation.
   - magnification = image size ÷ real size = 10 000 ÷ 20 = × 500

Learn these formulas

You might need to use that formula triangle in the exam, so make sure you know it off by heart. You only really need to remember that <u>image size</u> goes at the <u>top</u> of the triangle, which shouldn't be too tricky, since it comes first when you put the three things in <u>alphabetical order</u>.

More Microscopy

There's <u>more maths</u> coming up on this page — it might look a bit complicated, but really it's just a handy way of writing really small numbers a bit more neatly.

You Might Need to Work in **Standard Form** and **Convert Units**

1) Because microscopes can see such <u>tiny objects</u>, sometimes it's useful to write figures in <u>standard form</u>.

2) This is where you change <u>very big</u> or <u>small</u> numbers with <u>lots of zeros</u> into something more manageable, e.g. 0.017 can be written 1.7×10^{-2}. To do this you just need to <u>move</u> the <u>decimal point</u> left or right.

3) The number of places the decimal point moves is then represented by a <u>power of 10</u> — this is <u>positive</u> if the decimal point's moved to the <u>left</u>, and <u>negative</u> if it's moved to the <u>right</u>.

4) You can also use <u>different units</u> to express very big or very small numbers. E.g. <u>0.0007 m</u> could be written as <u>0.7 mm</u>. The <u>table</u> shows you how to <u>convert between different units</u>. The right hand column of the table shows you how each unit can be expressed as a <u>metre</u> in <u>standard form</u>.

To convert	Unit	To convert	In standard form:
× 1000	Millimetre (mm)	÷ 1000	$\times 10^{-3}$ m
× 1000	Micrometre (µm)	÷ 1000	$\times 10^{-6}$ m
× 1000	Nanometre (nm)	÷ 1000	$\times 10^{-9}$ m
	Picometre (pm)		$\times 10^{-12}$ m

So 1 pm = 0.000000000001 m.

Here's an example of a calculation in standard form:

 A specimen is 5×10^{-6} m wide. Calculate the width of the image of the specimen under a magnification of × 100. Give your answer in standard form.

1) <u>Rearrange</u> the magnification formula.

image size = magnification × real size

2) Fill in the <u>values</u> you know.

image size = 100 × (5×10^{-6} m)

3) Write out the values <u>in full</u> (i.e. don't use standard form).

= 100 × 0.000005 m

4) Carry out the calculation and then <u>convert back</u> into standard form.

= 0.0005 m

= 5×10^{-4} m

0.0005 m could also be written as 0.5 mm or 500 µm.

 ## Make sure you pay close attention to the number of zeros

If you've got a <u>scientific calculator</u>, you can put <u>standard form</u> numbers into it using the 'EXP' or the '×10ˣ' button. For example, enter 2.67×10^{15} by pressing 2.67 then 'EXP' or '×10ˣ', then 15.

Warm-Up and Exam Questions

So, hopefully you've read the last eight pages. But could you cope if a question on cells or microscopes came up in the exam? With amazing new technology we can simulate that very situation...

Warm-Up Questions

1) Name the subcellular structures where aerobic respiration takes place.
2) Give two ways that a sperm cell is adapted to its function.
3) What type of microscope should be used to look at the internal structure of chloroplasts?
4) Write the number 0.00045 µm in standard form.

Exam Questions

1   Which of the following subcellular structures would you not expect to find in a prokaryotic cell?

☐   **A**   plasmid   ☐   **B**   nucleus   ☐   **C**   cell wall   ☐   **D**   cell membrane

[1 mark]

2   **Figure 1** shows a typical plant cell.

Figure 1

(a)   Which label points to a chloroplast?

☐   **A**   ☐   **B**   ☐   **C**   ☐   **D**

[1 mark]

(b)   Describe the function of a chloroplast.

[1 mark]

(c)   **Figure 1** also shows ribosomes.
Describe the function of a ribosome.

[1 mark]

PRACTICAL

3   A light microscope can be used to observe a layer of onion cells on a slide.

(a)* Describe how you would use a light microscope to view onion cells.
Include how you would prepare the slide.

[6 marks]

(b)   When the onion cell is viewed with × 100 magnification, the image of the cell is 7.5 mm wide.
Calculate the real width of the onion cell using the formula:

$$\text{magnification} = \frac{\text{image size}}{\text{real size}}$$

Give your answer in µm.

[3 marks]

Enzymes

Chemical reactions are what make you work. And enzymes are what make them work.

Enzymes Are Catalysts Produced by Living Things

1) Living things have thousands of different chemical reactions going on inside them all the time.
2) These reactions need to be carefully controlled — to get the right amounts of substances.
3) You can usually make a reaction happen more quickly by raising the temperature.
   This would speed up the useful reactions but also the unwanted ones too... not good.
4) So... living things produce enzymes which act as biological catalysts. Enzymes reduce the need for
   high temperatures and we only have enzymes to speed up the useful chemical reactions in the body.

> A CATALYST is a substance which INCREASES the speed of a reaction,
> without being CHANGED or USED UP in the reaction.

Enzymes Have Special Shapes So They Can Catalyse Reactions

1) Chemical reactions usually involve things either being split apart or joined together.
2) The substrate is the molecule changed in the reaction.
3) Every enzyme has an active site — the part where it joins on to its substrate to catalyse the reaction.
4) Enzymes usually only work with one substrate. They are said to have a high specificity for their substrate.
5) This is because, for the enzyme to work, the substrate has to fit into the active site. If the substrate's
   shape doesn't match the active site's shape, then the reaction won't be catalysed. This is called the
   'lock and key' mechanism, because the substrate fits into the enzyme just like a key fits into a lock.

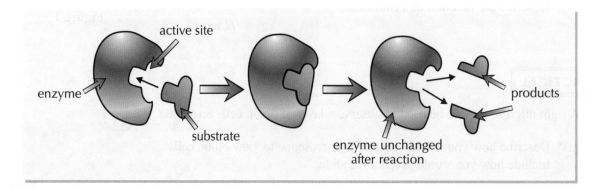

Enzymes speed up chemical reactions

Just like you've got to have the correct key for a lock, you've got to have the right substance for an enzyme.
If the substance doesn't fit into the active site, the enzyme won't be able to catalyse the reaction...

Enzymes

Enzymes are clearly very clever, but they're <u>not</u> very versatile. They need just the right <u>conditions</u> if they're going to work properly.

Enzymes Need the **Right Temperature**...

1) Changing the <u>temperature</u> changes the <u>rate</u> of an enzyme-catalysed reaction.

2) Like with any reaction, a higher temperature <u>increases</u> the rate at first.

3) But if it gets <u>too hot</u>, some of the <u>bonds</u> holding the enzyme together <u>break</u>. This changes the shape of the enzyme's <u>active site</u>, so the substrate <u>won't fit</u> any more. The enzyme is said to be <u>denatured</u>.

4) All enzymes have an <u>optimum temperature</u> that they work best at.

Enzymes denature at different temperatures. Most human enzymes denature at around 45 °C.

... and the **Right pH**...

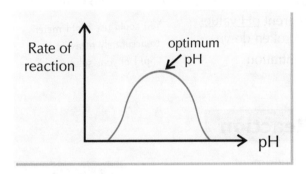

1) The <u>pH</u> also affects enzymes. If it's too high or too low, the pH interferes with the <u>bonds</u> holding the enzyme together.

2) This changes the <u>shape</u> of the <u>active site</u> and <u>denatures</u> the enzyme.

3) All enzymes have an <u>optimum pH</u> that they work best at. It's often <u>neutral pH 7</u>, but <u>not always</u> — e.g. <u>pepsin</u> is an enzyme used to break down <u>proteins</u> in the <u>stomach</u>. It works best at <u>pH 2</u>, which means it's well-suited to the <u>acidic conditions</u> there.

... and the **Right Substrate Concentration**

1) <u>Substrate concentration</u> also affects the rate of reaction — the higher the <u>substrate concentration</u>, the <u>faster the reaction</u>. This is because it's more likely that the enzyme will <u>meet up</u> and <u>react</u> with a substrate molecule.

2) This is only true <u>up to a point</u> though. After that, there are so many substrate molecules that the enzymes have about as much as they can cope with (<u>all the active sites are full</u>), and adding more makes <u>no difference</u>.

Most enzymes catalyse just one reaction

The <u>optimum temperature</u> for most human enzymes is around <u>normal body temperature</u>. And <u>stomach enzymes</u> work best at <u>low pH</u>, but the enzymes in your <u>small intestine</u> like a <u>higher pH</u>.

Investigating Enzyme Activity

You Can **Investigate** the Effect of **pH** on **Enzyme Activity**

PRACTICAL

The enzyme amylase catalyses the breakdown of starch to maltose. It's easy to detect starch using iodine solution — if starch is present, the iodine solution will change from browny-orange to blue-black. This is how you can investigate how pH affects amylase activity:

You could use an electric water bath, instead of a Bunsen and a beaker of water, to control the temperature.

1) Put a drop of iodine solution into every well of a spotting tile.

2) Place a Bunsen burner on a heat-proof mat, and a tripod and gauze over the Bunsen burner. Put a beaker of water on top of the tripod and heat the water until it is 35 °C (use a thermometer to measure the temperature). Try to keep the temperature of the water constant throughout the experiment.

3) Use a syringe to add 3 cm³ of amylase solution and 1 cm³ of a buffer solution with a pH of 5 to a boiling tube. Using test tube holders, put the tube into the beaker of water and wait for five minutes.

amylase, starch and buffer solution

mixture sampled every 10 seconds

dropping pipette

drop of iodine solution

spotting tile

4) Next, use a different syringe to add 3 cm³ of a starch solution to the boiling tube.

5) Immediately mix the contents of the boiling tube and start a stop clock.

6) Use continuous sampling to record how long it takes for the amylase to break down all of the starch. To do this, use a dropping pipette to take a fresh sample from the boiling tube every ten seconds and put a drop into a well. When the iodine solution remains browny-orange, starch is no longer present.

7) Repeat the whole experiment with buffer solutions of different pH values to see how pH affects the time taken for the starch to be broken down.

You could use a pH meter to accurately measure the pH of your solutions.

8) Remember to control any variables each time (e.g. concentration and volume of amylase solution) to make it a fair test.

Here's How to **Calculate** the **Rate of Reaction**

1) It's often useful to calculate the rate of reaction after an experiment. Rate is a measure of how much something changes over time.

2) For the experiment above, you can calculate the rate of reaction using this formula:

$$\text{Rate} = \frac{1000}{\text{time}}$$

E.g. at pH 6, the time taken for amylase to break down all of the starch in a solution was 90 seconds. So the rate of the reaction = 1000 ÷ 90 = 11 s⁻¹ (2 s.f.)

The units are in s⁻¹ since rate is given per unit time.

You could also use the formula '1/time' but '1000/time' will give you a bigger number that's easier to plot on a graph.

3) If an experiment measures how much something changes over time, you calculate the rate of reaction by dividing the amount that it has changed by the time taken.

EXAMPLE: The enzyme catalase catalyses the breakdown of hydrogen peroxide into water and oxygen. During an investigation into the activity of catalase, 24 cm³ of oxygen was released in 50 seconds (s). Calculate the rate of the reaction. Write your answer in cm³ s⁻¹.

Amount of product formed = change = 24 cm³

Rate of reaction = change ÷ time = 24 cm³ ÷ 50 s = **0.48 cm³ s⁻¹**

cm³ s⁻¹ is another way of writing cm³/s.

You can investigate other factors too...

PRACTICAL TIP

You could easily adapt this experiment to investigate how factors other than pH affect the rate of amylase activity. For example, you could use a water bath to investigate the effect of temperature.

Enzymes in Breakdown and Synthesis

Organisms use <u>enzymes</u> to help <u>break down large molecules</u> and to <u>build them back up</u> again.

Enzymes Break Down Big Molecules

1) <u>Proteins</u>, <u>lipids</u> and some <u>carbohydrates</u> are big molecules.   *Lipids are fats and oils.*

2) It's important that organisms are able to break them down into their <u>smaller components</u> so they can be used for <u>growth</u> and other <u>life processes</u>. For example:

> • Many of the molecules in the food we eat are <u>too big</u> to pass through the walls of our digestive system, so <u>digestive enzymes</u> break them down into <u>smaller</u>, <u>soluble</u> molecules. These can <u>pass easily</u> through the walls of the digestive system, allowing them to be <u>absorbed</u> into the <u>bloodstream</u>. They can then <u>pass into cells</u> to be used by the body.
>
> • Plants <u>store energy</u> in the form of <u>starch</u> (a carbohydrate). When plants need energy, <u>enzymes</u> break down the starch into smaller molecules (sugars). These can then be <u>respired</u> to transfer energy to be used by the cells (see p.159).

Different Enzymes Break Down Carbohydrates, Proteins and Lipids

Enzymes called <u>carbohydrases</u> convert <u>carbohydrates</u> into <u>simple sugars</u>. E.g. <u>amylase</u> is an example of a <u>carbohydrase</u>. It breaks down <u>starch</u>.

starch → amylase enzyme → maltose and other sugars, e.g. dextrins

<u>Proteases</u> convert <u>proteins</u> into <u>amino acids</u>.

proteins → protease enzymes → amino acids

<u>Lipases</u> convert <u>lipids</u> into <u>glycerol</u> and <u>fatty acids</u>.

lipid → lipase enzymes → glycerol and fatty acids

When lipids are broken down, the fatty acids will lower the pH of the solution they are in.

Some Enzymes Join Molecules Together

Organisms need to be able to <u>synthesise carbohydrates, proteins and lipids</u> from their <u>smaller components</u>. Again, <u>enzymes</u> are used in this process.

• <u>Carbohydrates</u> can be synthesised by joining together <u>simple sugars</u>.

> <u>Glycogen synthase</u> is an enzyme that joins together lots of chains of <u>glucose</u> molecules to make <u>glycogen</u> (a molecule used to <u>store energy</u> in animals).

• <u>Proteins</u> are made by <u>joining</u> amino acids together (see page 60). <u>Enzymes</u> catalyse the reactions needed to do this.

• Lots of enzymes are also involved in the <u>synthesis of lipids</u> from <u>fatty acids</u> and <u>glycerol</u>.

Different types of enzymes act on different molecules

Make sure you know all the <u>smaller components</u> that make up <u>carbohydrates</u>, <u>proteins</u> and <u>lipids</u> and understand that enzymes play a role in both the <u>breakdown</u> and <u>synthesis</u> of these bigger molecules.

PRACTICAL | Testing for Biological Molecules

Carbohydrates, lipids and proteins are all <u>biological molecules</u> (molecules found in living organisms). You need to know how you can <u>test for them</u> using different <u>chemicals</u>.

You Can Test for **Sugars** Using **Benedict's Reagent**

There are lots of different types of <u>sugar molecules</u>. Due to their <u>chemical properties</u>, many sugars (e.g. glucose) are called <u>reducing sugars</u>. You don't need to know exactly what reducing sugars are, but you do need to know how to <u>test</u> for them:

1) Add <u>Benedict's reagent</u> (which is <u>blue</u>) to a sample and <u>heat</u> it in a water bath that's set to <u>75 °C</u>. If the test's <u>positive</u> it will form a <u>coloured precipitate</u> (solid particles suspended in the solution).

2) The <u>higher</u> the <u>concentration</u> of reducing sugar, the <u>further</u> the colour change goes — you can use this to <u>compare</u> the amount of reducing sugar in different solutions.

The colour of the precipitate changes from:

blue ⇒ green ⇒ yellow ⇒ orange ⇒ brick red

Benedict's reagent

water bath

food sample

colour change if reducing sugar present

higher sugar concentration

The **Biuret Test** is Used for **Proteins**

If you needed to find out if a substance contained <u>protein</u> you'd use the <u>biuret test</u>.

1) First, add a few drops of <u>potassium hydroxide</u> solution to make the solution <u>alkaline</u>.

2) Then add some <u>copper(II) sulfate</u> solution (which is <u>bright blue</u>).

   • If there's <u>no protein</u>, the solution will stay <u>blue</u>.

   • If protein <u>is present</u>, the solution will turn <u>purple</u>.

Negative result

test solution, potassium hydroxide and copper(II) sulfate solution

Positive result

The colours are quite pale so you'll need to look carefully.

solution staying blue indicates no protein

purple colour indicates protein

Testing for Biological Molecules PRACTICAL

There are a couple more tests coming up on this page — for lipids and starch.

Use the **Emulsion Test** for **Lipids**

To find out if there are any lipids in a sample:

1) Shake the test substance with ethanol for about a minute until it dissolves, then pour the solution into water.

2) If there are any lipids present, they will precipitate out of the liquid and show up as a milky emulsion.

3) The more lipid there is, the more noticeable the milky colour will be.

An emulsion is when one liquid doesn't dissolve in another — it just forms little droplets.

Test substance and ethanol — Shake — Add to water — Milky colour indicates lipid

Starch is Tested for with **Iodine**

Just add iodine solution to the test sample.

1) If starch is present, the sample changes from browny-orange to a dark, blue-black colour.

2) If there's no starch, it stays browny-orange.

Iodine solution is iodine dissolved in potassium iodide solution.

iodine

colour changes to blue-black if starch is present

colour remains browny-orange if starch isn't present

food sample

Make sure you think about all of the hazards...

 PRACTICAL TIP

Iodine is an irritant to the eyes, and the chemicals used in the biuret test are dangerous, so wear safety goggles when carrying out food tests. If you spill any of the chemicals on your skin, wash it off straight away. Be careful around the water bath in the Benedict's test, too.

Energy in Food

Here's another <u>experiment</u> — this one can be used to work out how much <u>energy</u> different foods contain.

Food Can be Burnt to See How Much Energy it Contains

The posh name for this is <u>calorimetry</u>. You need to know how to do it with a <u>simple experiment</u>:

First You Need a Dry Food, Water and a Flame...

1) You need a <u>food</u> that'll <u>burn easily</u> — something that's dry, e.g. dried beans or pasta, will work best.
2) <u>Weigh</u> a small amount of the food and then <u>skewer</u> it on a <u>mounted needle</u>.
3) Next, add <u>a set volume</u> of water to a boiling tube (held with a clamp) — this will be used to <u>measure</u> the amount of <u>energy</u> that's transferred when the food is <u>burnt</u>.
4) Measure the <u>temperature</u> of the <u>water</u>, then <u>set fire</u> to the food using a <u>Bunsen burner flame</u>. Make sure the Bunsen isn't near the water or it may affect your results.
5) Immediately <u>hold</u> the burning food <u>under</u> the boiling tube until it <u>goes out</u>. Then <u>relight</u> the food and <u>hold</u> it under the tube — <u>keep doing this</u> until the food <u>won't</u> catch fire again.
6) The last thing to do is measure the <u>temperature</u> of the <u>water</u> again. Then you're ready for a bit of <u>maths</u>...

thermometer

clamp

water

dried bean

mounted needle

...Then You Can Calculate the Amount of Energy in the Food

1) First work out how many <u>joules</u> (J) of energy the food contains using this formula:

$$\text{Energy in Food (in J)} = \text{Mass of water (in g)} \times \text{Temperature change of water (in °C)} \times 4.2$$

Quite a bit of the energy in the food is transferred to the environment. You can minimise this by insulating the boiling tube, e.g. with foil.

2) Then work out how many joules are in <u>each gram</u> of the food. You need to do this calculation so you can <u>compare</u> the energy values of different foods <u>fairly</u>.

1 cm³ of water is the same as 1 g of water.

$$\text{Energy per gram of food (in J/g)} = \frac{\text{Energy in food (in J)}}{\text{Mass of food (in g)}}$$

EXAMPLE: A student burned 0.2 g of popcorn and 0.5 g of bread separately under 20 cm³ of water. During the experiment, the temperature of the water increased by 28.6 °C when the popcorn was burnt and 38.7 °C when the bread was burnt. Which food has more energy per unit mass?

1) First find the amount of energy in each type of food:

Energy in the popcorn =
20 g × 28.6 °C × 4.2 = 2402.4 J

Energy in the bread =
20 g × 38.7 °C × 4.2 = 3250.8 J

2) Then convert this into joules per gram:

Popcorn: 2402.4 ÷ 0.2
= 12 012.0 J/g

Bread: 3250.8 ÷ 0.5
= 6501.6 J/g

Answer: the popcorn has more energy per unit mass.

The more energy there is in the food, the hotter the water will get

Food scientists use machines called <u>calorimeters</u> to measure the energy content of our food — they're insulated and sealed so produce much more <u>accurate</u> results than the experiment on this page.

Warm-Up and Exam Questions

Doing well in exams isn't just about remembering all the facts, although that's important. You have to get used to the way the questions are phrased and make sure you always read the question carefully.

Warm-Up Questions

1) What is meant by the term 'active site'?
2) What is meant by the optimum pH of an enzyme?
3) Name two other variables that affect the rate of enzyme activity.
4) Which enzyme breaks down: (a) starch   (b) protein   (c) lipids?
5) What are the products of the breakdown of: (a) starch   (b) protein
6) What type of molecule do enzymes join together to synthesise proteins?

Exam Questions

1   **Figure 1** represents the action of an enzyme in catalysing a biological reaction.

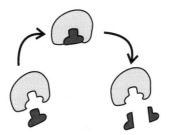

Figure 1

(a)   In terms of the enzyme's shape, explain why an enzyme only catalyses one reaction.

[1 mark]

(b)   Describe how the rate of an enzyme-catalysed reaction changes as the substrate concentration increases. Explain your answer.

[4 marks]

2   A student burned a piece of dry pasta under a boiling tube containing 30 g of water.
     At the start of the experiment, the temperature of the water was 15.2 °C and
     at the end of the experiment the water measured 52.7 °C.

(a)   Calculate the amount of energy, in joules (J), in the piece of pasta.

Use the equation: energy (J) = mass of water (g) × temperature change in water (°C) × 4.2

[2 marks]

(b)   The student repeated the experiment with a different type of pasta.
     One piece of this pasta had a mass of 0.2 g and contained 3050 J of energy.
     Calculate the energy per gram for this piece of pasta.

[1 mark]

Exam Questions

3   **Figure 2** shows the effect of temperature on the action of two different enzymes.

(a)   Estimate the optimum temperature for enzyme **A**.

[1 mark]

(b)   One of these enzymes was extracted from human liver cells. The other was extracted from bacteria living in hot underwater vents.

Suggest which enzyme came from the bacteria. Give a reason for your answer.

[1 mark]

Figure 2

PRACTICAL

4   A student wanted to know which substances were present in a food sample. She prepared a solution containing the food, and added some of the solution to each of three test tubes. She then added iodine solution to test tube **A**, potassium hydroxide solution and copper(II) sulfate solution to test tube **B**, and ethanol to test tube **C**, which was then shaken for one minute and poured into water. Her results are shown in **Figure 3**.

Test tube	Description of solution in test tube
A	Blue-black
B	Blue
C	Milky emulsion

Figure 3

Describe what the student's results show about which substances are present in the food sample.

[3 marks]

PRACTICAL

5   A student was investigating the effect of pH on the rate of amylase activity. He used a syringe to put amylase solution and a buffer solution with a pH of 6 into a test tube. He then used a different syringe to add a starch solution to the boiling tube. He mixed the contents and then started a stop clock. Every 30 seconds he took a sample from the boiling tube and tested it for the presence of starch. When there was no starch present he stopped the stop clock. He repeated the experiment three times.

(a)   Suggest why he used two different syringes when adding substances to the boiling tube.

[1 mark]

(b)   His experiment showed that the average time taken for the starch in the boiling tube to be broken down was 60 seconds. Calculate the rate of the reaction. Give your answer in s^{-1} to 2 significant figures. Use the formula: $rate = \frac{1000}{time}$

[1 mark]

(c)   Suggest what the student needs to do next in his investigation to determine the effect of pH on the rate of amylase activity.

[1 mark]

Diffusion and Active Transport

Substances can move in and out of cells by <u>diffusion</u> and <u>active transport</u>...

Diffusion — Don't be Put Off by the **Fancy Word**

1) <u>Diffusion</u> is simple. It's just the <u>gradual movement</u> of particles from places where there are <u>lots</u> of them to places where there are <u>fewer</u> of them. That's all it is — just the <u>natural tendency</u> for stuff to <u>spread out</u>. Here's the fancy <u>definition</u>:

<u>DIFFUSION</u> is the <u>net (overall) movement</u> of <u>particles</u> from an area of <u>higher concentration</u> to an area of <u>lower concentration</u>.

2) Diffusion happens in both <u>liquids</u> and <u>gases</u> — that's because the particles in these substances are free to <u>move about</u> randomly.

If something moves from an area of higher concentration to an area of lower concentration it is said to have moved down a <u>concentration gradient</u>.

3) Only very <u>small</u> molecules can <u>diffuse</u> through <u>cell membranes</u> — things like <u>glucose</u>, <u>amino acids</u>, <u>water</u> and <u>oxygen</u>. <u>Big</u> molecules like <u>starch</u> and <u>proteins</u> can't fit through the membrane.

Active Transport Works **Against** a **Concentration Gradient**

<u>ACTIVE TRANSPORT</u> is the <u>movement of particles</u> across a membrane against a concentration gradient (i.e. from an area of <u>lower</u> to an area of <u>higher concentration</u>) <u>using energy</u> transferred during respiration.

1) Active transport is a bit <u>different from diffusion</u> because particles are moved <u>up a concentration gradient</u> rather than down, and the process requires <u>energy</u> (unlike diffusion, which is a passive process).

2) Here's an example of active transport at work in the <u>digestive system</u>:

When there's a <u>higher concentration</u> of nutrients in the gut than in the blood, the nutrients <u>diffuse naturally</u> into the blood.
<u>BUT</u> — sometimes there's a <u>lower concentration</u> of nutrients in the gut than in the blood. Active transport allows nutrients to be taken into the blood, despite the fact that the <u>concentration gradient</u> is the wrong way. This is essential to stop us starving.

Both processes involve movement between different concentrations

Make sure you understand the difference — in diffusion, particles passively move <u>down</u> a concentration gradient, whereas in active transport, particles move <u>up</u> a concentration gradient, which requires energy.

Osmosis

If you've got your head round <u>diffusion</u>, osmosis will be a <u>breeze</u>.
If not, have another look at the previous page...

Osmosis is a **Special Case** of **Diffusion**, That's All

<u>OSMOSIS</u> is the <u>net movement of water molecules</u> across a <u>partially permeable membrane</u> from a region of <u>higher water concentration</u> to a region of <u>lower water concentration</u>.

You could also describe osmosis as the net movement of water molecules across a partially permeable membrane from a region of <u>lower solute concentration</u> to a region of <u>higher solute concentration</u>.

1) A <u>partially permeable</u> membrane is just one with very small holes in it. So small, in fact, only tiny <u>molecules</u> (like water) can pass through them, and bigger molecules (e.g. <u>sucrose</u>) can't.

2) The water molecules actually pass <u>both ways</u> through the membrane during osmosis. This happens because water molecules <u>move about randomly</u> all the time.

3) But because there are <u>more</u> water molecules on one side than on the other, there's a steady <u>net flow</u> of water into the region with <u>fewer</u> water molecules, i.e. into the <u>more concentrated</u> solute solution.

4) This means the <u>solute</u> solution gets more <u>dilute</u>. The water acts like it's trying to "<u>even up</u>" the concentration either side of the membrane.

You Can Do an **Experiment** to **Investigate Osmosis**   PRACTICAL

This experiment involves putting <u>potato cylinders</u> into <u>different concentrations</u> of <u>sucrose solution</u> to see what effect different <u>water concentrations</u> have on them.

The higher the concentration of the sucrose solution, the lower the water concentration.

First You Do the Experiment...

1) Prepare <u>sucrose solutions</u> of different concentrations ranging from <u>pure water</u> to a <u>very concentrated sucrose solution</u>.

2) Use a cork borer to cut a <u>potato</u> into the <u>same sized pieces</u>. (The pieces need to be about <u>1 cm</u> in diameter and preferably from the <u>same potato</u>.)

3) Divide the cylinders into <u>groups of three</u> and use a <u>mass balance</u> to measure the <u>mass</u> of each <u>group</u>.

4) Place <u>one group</u> in each solution.

'M' is a unit of concentration (you might also see it written as mol dm⁻³). The solution with a concentration of 0.0 M is pure water.

Osmosis

5) <u>Leave</u> the cylinders in the solution for <u>at least 40 minutes</u> (making sure that they all get the <u>same amount</u> of time).

6) <u>Remove</u> the cylinders and <u>pat dry gently</u> with a paper towel. This removes <u>excess water</u> from the surface of the cylinders, so you get a more <u>accurate</u> measurement of their <u>final masses</u>.

7) <u>Weigh</u> each <u>group</u> again and record your results.

8) The <u>only</u> thing that you should <u>change</u> in this experiment is the <u>sucrose solution concentration</u>. Everything else (e.g. the volume of solution, the size of the potato cylinders, the type of potatoes used, the amount of drying, etc.) must be kept the <u>same</u> or your results <u>won't be valid</u>.

...Then You **Interpret** the **Results**

1) Once you've got all your results, you need to <u>calculate</u> the <u>percentage change in mass</u> for each group of cylinders <u>before</u> and <u>after</u> their time in the sucrose.

Calculating the percentage change allows you to compare the effect of sucrose concentration on cylinders that didn't have the same initial mass.

EXAMPLE: **A group of potato cylinders weighed 13.2 g at the start of the experiment. At the end they weighed 15.1 g. Calculate the percentage change in mass.**

To find the <u>percentage change in mass</u>, use the <u>formula</u> below:

$$\text{percentage change} = \frac{\text{final mass} - \text{initial mass}}{\text{initial mass}} \times 100$$

$$\text{percentage change} = \frac{15.1 - 13.2}{13.2} \times 100 = 14.4\%$$

The positive result tells you the potato cylinders gained mass. If the answer was negative then the potato cylinders lost mass.

2) Then you can plot a <u>graph</u> and <u>analyse your results</u>:

At the points <u>above</u> <u>the x-axis</u>, the water concentration of the <u>sucrose solutions</u> is <u>higher</u> than in the <u>cylinders</u>. The cylinders <u>gain mass</u> as water is <u>drawn in</u> by osmosis.

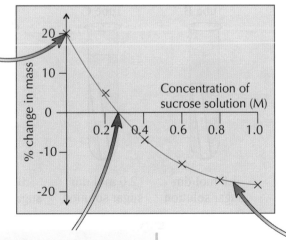

At the points <u>below</u> <u>the x-axis</u>, the water concentration of the <u>sucrose solutions</u> is <u>lower</u> than in the <u>cylinders</u>. This causes the cylinders to <u>lose water</u> so their mass <u>decreases</u>.

Where there is <u>no change</u> in mass (where the curve <u>crosses the x-axis</u>) the fluid <u>inside</u> the cylinders and the <u>sucrose solution</u> are <u>isotonic</u> — they have the <u>same water concentration</u>.

 ## Water always moves into the more concentrated solution

This experiment used <u>sucrose</u> as a <u>solute</u>, but you could do it with <u>different solutes</u> (e.g. salt).

38

Warm-Up and Exam Questions

Question time again — Warm-Up first, then Exam (or the other way round if you want to be different).

Warm-Up Questions

1) Other than diffusion, by what two processes do substances move across cell membranes?
2) Give two differences between diffusion and active transport.
3) Explain what is meant by a partially permeable membrane.
4) What is the definition of osmosis?

Exam Questions

1 A student adds a drop of ink to a glass of cold water.
Describe what you would expect to happen to the drop of ink.
Explain your answer.

[2 marks]

PRACTICAL

2 In an experiment, four 5 cm long cylinders were cut from a fresh potato.
The cylinders were then placed in different sugar solutions, as shown in **Figure 1**.
After 24 hours the potato cylinders were removed and measured.

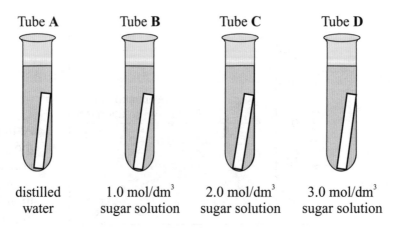

Figure 1

(a) State which potato cylinder you would expect to be shortest after 24 hours.
Explain your answer.

[3 marks]

(b) The potato cylinder in tube **A** increased in length during the 24 hours.
Explain why this happened.

[2 marks]

Topic 1 — Key Concepts in Biology

Revision Summary for Topic 1

Make sure you learn all of Topic 1 — many of the concepts will crop up again in other topics.
- Try these questions and tick off each one when you get it right.
- When you've done all the questions under a heading and are completely happy, tick it off.

Cells and Specialised Cells (p.17-20) ☑

1) What is the function of the cell membrane? ☑
2) Give three structures found in plant cells but not in animal cells. ☑
3) Name the subcellular structures in plant cells where photosynthesis takes place. ☑
4) Name two structures that are found in both prokaryotic cells and eukaryotic cells. ☑
5) What does the term 'haploid' mean? ☑
6) Give three ways in which an egg cell is adapted to its function. ☑
7) What are cilia? ☑
8) What is the purpose of the ciliated epithelial cells that line the airways? ☑

Microscopy (p.21-24) ☑

9) Give an advantage of electron microscopes over light microscopes. ☑
10) Why is it necessary to use thin samples of tissue when viewing cells using a light microscope? ☑
11) Write the equation you would use to find the size of a specimen using
the magnification used and the size of the image seen through a microscope lens. ☑
12) Describe how you would convert a measurement from mm to μm. ☑
13) Which unit can be expressed in standard form as $\times 10^{-12}$ m? ☑

Enzymes (p.26-29) ☑

14) What part of an enzyme makes it specific to a particular substrate? ☑
15) Why can denatured enzymes no longer catalyse chemical reactions? ☑
16) Explain how temperature affects enzyme activity. ☑
17) Describe how you could investigate the effect of pH on the rate of amylase activity. ☑
18) Which two molecules are produced when lipids are broken down? ☑
19) Name a big molecule that's formed from simple sugars. ☑

Testing for Biological Molecules and Energy in Food (p.30-32) ☑

20) Describe the colour change that occurs when Benedict's reagent
is added to a substance containing reducing sugars. ☑
21) How would you test for the presence of lipids in a sample? ☑
22) What chemical reagent is used to test for the presence of starch? ☑
23) Describe briefly how you could use calorimetry to measure the energy content of a peanut. ☑

Diffusion, Osmosis and Active Transport (p.35-37) ☑

24) Define the following terms: a) diffusion, b) active transport. ☑
25) If a potato cylinder is placed in a solution with a very high sucrose concentration,
what will happen to the mass of the potato cylinder over time? Explain why. ☑

Mitosis

In order to survive and grow, our cells have got to be able to <u>divide</u>. And that means our DNA as well...

Chromosomes Contain Genetic Information

1) Most cells in your body have a <u>nucleus</u>. The nucleus contains your <u>genetic material</u> in the form of <u>chromosomes</u>. Chromosomes are <u>coiled up</u> lengths of <u>DNA molecules</u> (see p.59 for more on DNA).

2) <u>Body cells</u> normally have <u>two copies</u> of each <u>chromosome</u> — this makes them 'diploid' cells. One chromosome comes from the organism's 'mother', and one comes from its 'father'.

3) When a cell divides by <u>mitosis</u> (see next page) it makes two cells <u>identical</u> to the original cell — the nucleus of each new cell contains the <u>same number of chromosomes</u> as the original cell.

The Cell Cycle Makes New Cells for Growth and Repair

1) <u>Body cells</u> in <u>multicellular</u> organisms <u>divide</u> to produce new cells during a process called the <u>cell cycle</u>. The stage of the cell cycle when the cell divides is called <u>mitosis</u>.

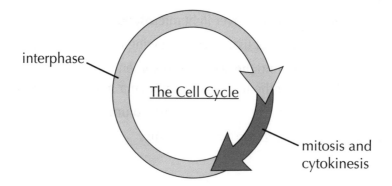

interphase

The Cell Cycle

mitosis and cytokinesis

2) Multicellular organisms use <u>mitosis</u> to <u>grow</u> or to <u>replace cells</u> that have been <u>damaged</u>.

3) Some organisms use mitosis to <u>reproduce</u> — this is called <u>asexual reproduction</u>. E.g. strawberry plants form runners by mitosis, which become new plants.

4) You need to know about the main stages of the <u>cell cycle</u>.

Interphase

In a cell that's not dividing, the DNA is all spread out in <u>long strings</u>.

Before it divides, the cell has to <u>grow</u> and <u>increase</u> the amount of <u>subcellular structures</u> such as <u>mitochondria</u> and <u>ribosomes</u>.

It then <u>duplicates</u> its DNA — so there's one copy for each new cell. The DNA is copied and forms <u>X-shaped</u> chromosomes. Each 'arm' of the chromosome is an <u>exact duplicate</u> of the other.

The left arm has the same DNA as the right arm. Each arm is called a chromatid.

Mitosis

Mitosis and Cytokinesis

Once its contents and DNA have been copied, the cell is ready for <u>mitosis</u>.
Mitosis is divided into <u>four stages</u>:

cell at interphase

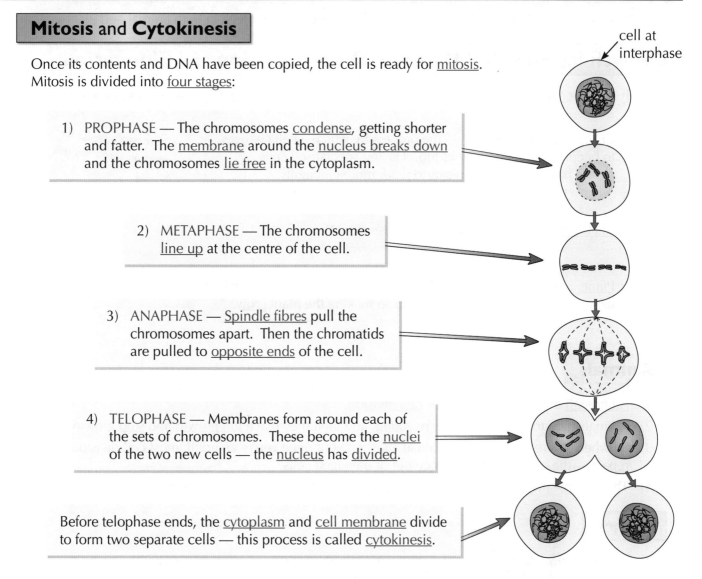

1) PROPHASE — The chromosomes <u>condense</u>, getting shorter and fatter. The <u>membrane</u> around the <u>nucleus breaks down</u> and the chromosomes <u>lie free</u> in the cytoplasm.

2) METAPHASE — The chromosomes <u>line up</u> at the centre of the cell.

3) ANAPHASE — <u>Spindle fibres</u> pull the chromosomes apart. Then the chromatids are pulled to <u>opposite ends</u> of the cell.

4) TELOPHASE — Membranes form around each of the sets of chromosomes. These become the <u>nuclei</u> of the two new cells — the <u>nucleus</u> has <u>divided</u>.

Before telophase ends, the <u>cytoplasm</u> and <u>cell membrane</u> divide to form two separate cells — this process is called <u>cytokinesis</u>.

At the end of mitosis, the cell has produced <u>two new daughter cells</u>. Each daughter cell contains exactly the <u>same sets of chromosomes</u> in its nucleus as the other daughter cell — they're <u>genetically identical diploid cells</u>. They're also genetically identical to the <u>parent cell</u>.

You can Calculate the Final Number of Cells

You can <u>calculate</u> the <u>number of cells</u> there'll be after <u>multiple divisions</u> of a cell by mitosis.
The formula you need is: <u>number of cells = 2^n</u>, where '<u>n</u>' is the <u>number of divisions</u> by mitosis.

EXAMPLE: **A cell divides by mitosis five times. How many cells are present after this process?**

Multiply <u>2</u> by itself for the number of <u>divisions</u> to find the number of <u>cells</u>.

$$2^5 = 2 \times 2 \times 2 \times 2 \times 2 = 32 \text{ cells}$$

Mitosis produces two identical daughter cells

Mitosis can seem tricky at first. But don't worry — just go through it slowly, one step at a time.
This type of division produces <u>identical cells</u>, but there's another type which doesn't... (see page 57).

Cell Division and Growth

Growth — it happens to us all. You need to know the processes involved in both animal and plant growth.

Growth Involves Cell Division, Differentiation and Elongation

Growth is an increase in size or mass. Plants and animals grow and develop due to these processes:

- CELL DIFFERENTIATION — the process by which a cell changes to become specialised for its job. Having specialised cells allows multicellular organisms to work more efficiently.

  See pages 19-20 for more on specialised cells.

- CELL DIVISION — by mitosis (see pages 40-41).

- Plants also grow by CELL ELONGATION. This is where a plant cell expands, making the cell bigger and so making the plant grow.

Animals

1) All growth in animals happens by cell division.
2) Animals tend to grow while they're young, and then they reach full growth and stop growing.
3) So when you're young, cells divide at a fast rate but once you're an adult, most cell division is for repair — the cells divide to replace old or damaged cells.
4) This also means, in most animals, cell differentiation is lost at an early stage.

Plants

1) In plants, growth in height is mainly due to cell elongation — cell division usually just happens in the tips of the roots and shoots (in areas called meristems — see page 44).
2) But plants often grow continuously — even really old trees will keep putting out new branches. So, plants continue to differentiate to develop new parts, e.g. leaves, roots.

Cancer is a Case of Uncontrolled Cell Division

1) The rate at which cells divide by mitosis is controlled by the chemical instructions (genes) in an organism's DNA.
2) If there's a change in one of the genes that controls cell division, the cell may start dividing uncontrollably.
3) This can result in a mass of abnormal cells called a tumour.
4) If the tumour invades and destroys surrounding tissue it is called cancer.

A random change in a gene is called a mutation — see page 62.

Growth is different in plants and animals...

Remember, both plant and animals grow by cell differentiation and cell division, but plants use cell elongation too. Plants continue to grow throughout their lives too, but animals stop growing once they reach full size.

Percentile Charts

It's important to <u>monitor growth</u> in children — there's a certain type of <u>graph</u> that can be used for this...

Percentile Charts are Used to Monitor Growth

1) <u>Growth charts</u> are used to assess a <u>child's growth</u> over time, so that an <u>overall pattern in development</u> can be seen and any <u>problems highlighted</u> (e.g. obesity, malnutrition, dwarfism).

2) For example, a baby's growth is regularly <u>monitored</u> after birth to make sure it's growing <u>normally</u>. Three measurements are taken — <u>length</u>, <u>mass</u> and <u>head circumference</u>.

3) These results are plotted on <u>growth charts</u>, like the one below.

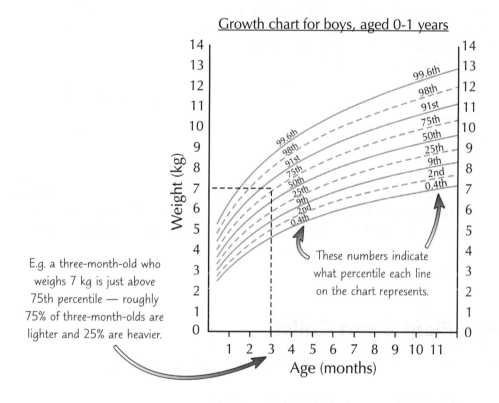

Growth chart for boys, aged 0-1 years

E.g. a three-month-old who weighs 7 kg is just above 75th percentile — roughly 75% of three-month-olds are lighter and 25% are heavier.

These numbers indicate what percentile each line on the chart represents.

4) The chart shows a number of '<u>percentiles</u>'. E.g. the <u>50th percentile</u> shows the mass that <u>50%</u> of babies will have reached at a certain age.

5) Babies <u>vary</u> in size, but doctors are likely to investigate if a baby's size is above the <u>top</u> percentile line or below the <u>bottom</u> percentile line, their size increases or decreases by <u>two or more</u> percentile lines over time, or if there's an <u>inconsistent pattern</u> (e.g. a small baby with a very large head).

Percentile charts show the distribution of sizes in a population

<u>Percentiles</u> tell you <u>where</u> in the data set a data point lies. The <u>value</u> of a percentile tells you what <u>percentage</u> of data has a value <u>equal to or lower than</u> the data points in that percentile.

Stem Cells

Your body is made up of <u>all sorts</u> of cells — this page tells you where they all <u>came from</u>.

Stem Cells can Differentiate into Different Types of Cells

1) As you saw on page 42, cells <u>differentiate</u> to become <u>specialised cells</u>.

2) <u>Undifferentiated</u> cells are called <u>stem cells</u>.

3) Depending on what instructions they're given, stem cells can <u>divide</u> by <u>mitosis</u> to become <u>new cells</u>, which then <u>differentiate</u>.

4) Stem cells are found in early <u>human embryos</u>. These embryonic stem cells have the potential to divide and produce <u>any</u> kind of cell at all. This makes sense — <u>all</u> the <u>different types</u> of cell found in a human have to come from those <u>few cells</u> in the early embryo.

5) This means stem cells are really important for the <u>growth</u> and <u>development</u> of organisms.

6) <u>Adults</u> also have stem cells, but they're only found in certain places, like <u>bone marrow</u>. These aren't as <u>versatile</u> as embryonic stem cells — they can't produce <u>any</u> cell type at all, only certain ones. In animals, adult stem cells are used to <u>replace damaged cells</u>, e.g. to make new skin or blood cells.

undifferentiated
stem cell

differentiated
ciliated
epithelial cell
(see p.20)

Meristems Contain Plant Stem Cells

In plants, the only cells that <u>divide by mitosis</u> are found in plant tissues called <u>meristems</u>.

1) Meristem tissue is found in the areas of a plant that are <u>growing</u>, e.g. the tips of the <u>roots and shoots</u>.

2) Meristems produce <u>unspecialised cells</u> that are able to divide and form <u>any cell type</u> in the plant — they act like <u>embryonic stem cells</u>. But unlike human stem cells, these cells can <u>divide</u> and <u>differentiate</u> to generate any type of cell <u>for as long as the plant lives</u>.

3) The <u>unspecialised cells</u> go on to form <u>specialised tissues</u> like <u>xylem</u> and <u>phloem</u> (see p.125).

Embryonic stem cells can become any type of cell

Unspecialised cells produced by plant meristems can differentiate into <u>any type</u> of cell so that the plant can <u>continue to grow</u>. Because humans <u>stop growing</u>, adult stem cells only differentiate into certain cell types.

Stem Cells

Stem cell research has exciting <u>possibilities</u>, but it's also pretty <u>controversial</u>.

Stem Cells Can be **Used in Medicine**

1) Doctors already use <u>adult stem cells</u> to cure some <u>diseases</u>.
E.g. <u>sickle cell anaemia</u> can sometimes be cured with a <u>bone marrow transplant</u> (containing adult stem cells which produce new blood cells).

2) Scientists have experimented with <u>extracting stem cells</u> from very early <u>human embryos</u> and <u>growing</u> them. Under certain conditions the stem cells can be stimulated to differentiate into <u>specialised cells</u>.

3) It might be possible to use stem cells to create specialised cells to <u>replace</u> those which have been <u>damaged</u> by <u>disease</u> or <u>injury</u>, e.g. new cardiac muscle cells could be <u>transplanted</u> into someone with heart disease. This <u>potential</u> for <u>new cures</u> is the reason for the huge scientific interest in stem cells.

4) Before this can happen, a lot of <u>research</u> needs to be done. There are many <u>potential risks</u> which scientists need to learn more about. For example:

Rejection

If the transplanted cells aren't grown using the patient's own stem cells, the patient's body may recognise the cells as <u>foreign</u> and trigger an <u>immune response</u> to try to get rid of them. The patient can take <u>drugs</u> to <u>suppress</u> this response, but this makes them <u>susceptible</u> to <u>diseases</u>.

Tumour development

Stem cells <u>divide</u> very <u>quickly</u>. If scientists are <u>unable to control the rate</u> at which the transplanted cells divide inside a patient, a <u>tumour</u> may develop (see page 42).

Disease transmission

<u>Viruses</u> live inside cells. If donor stem cells are infected with a virus and this isn't picked up, the virus could be <u>passed on</u> to the recipient and so make them <u>sicker</u>.

5) Research using embryonic stem cells raises <u>ethical issues</u>. E.g. some people argue that human embryos <u>shouldn't</u> be used for experiments because each one is a <u>potential human life</u>. But others think that the aim of <u>curing patients</u> who are <u>suffering</u> should be <u>more important</u> than the potential life of the embryos.

Stem cells could help cure many diseases in the future

Questions on the <u>issues</u> associated with using stem cells in <u>medicine</u> might crop up in the exam, so make sure you know the <u>potential benefits</u> and the <u>risks</u> associated with using them.

Warm-Up and Exam Questions

Here's a page of questions — use them to help you brush up your 'cell division and growth' knowledge.

Warm-Up Questions

1) What does cell 'differentiation' mean?
2) True or false? Plants can grow by cell elongation.
3) What does it mean if the weight of a two-month-old baby is at the 25th percentile on a growth chart?
4) Where in the cell are chromosomes found?

Exam Questions

1   **Figure 1** shows how the amount of DNA per cell changes as a cell undergoes two cell divisions by mitosis. Point **C** is the time when the chromosomes first become visible in the cells.

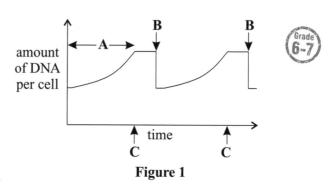

Figure 1

(a) Describe what is happening to the DNA during stage **A**. Suggest why this needs to happen.

[2 marks]

(b) Suggest what happens at time **B**.

[1 mark]

(c) State how many cells there are after the first cell division.

[1 mark]

(d) Cancer is a disease caused by problems in the cell division process. Describe how changes in cells can lead to cancer.

[2 marks]

2   Adult stem cells have already been used to cure disorders, and it is thought that embryonic stem cells have the potential to treat many more disorders.

(a) Describe how embryonic stem cells could be used to treat disorders.

[1 mark]

(b) Explain why embryonic stem cells have the potential to treat more disorders than adult stem cells.

[1 mark]

3   A bacterial cell divides once every 30 minutes. Calculate the number of cells that will be present after 3 hours.

[2 marks]

The Nervous System

The <u>nervous system</u> means that humans can <u>react to their surroundings</u> and <u>coordinate their behaviour</u>.

The **Central Nervous System (CNS) Coordinates** a **Response**

1) The nervous system is made up of <u>neurones</u> (nerve cells) which go to <u>all parts</u> of the body.

2) The body has lots of sensory <u>receptors</u> — groups of <u>cells</u> that can detect a <u>change in your environment</u> (a <u>stimulus</u>). Different receptors detect different stimuli. For example, receptors in your <u>eyes</u> detect <u>light</u>, while receptors in your <u>skin</u> detect <u>touch</u> (pressure) and <u>temperature change</u>.

3) When a <u>stimulus</u> is detected by <u>receptors</u>, the information is <u>converted</u> to a <u>nervous (electrical) impulse</u> and sent along <u>sensory neurones</u> to the <u>CNS</u> (the brain and spinal cord).

4) The CNS <u>coordinates</u> the response (in other words, it <u>decides what to do</u> about the stimulus and tells something to do it). Impulses travel through the CNS along <u>relay neurones</u>.

5) The CNS sends information to an <u>effector</u> (muscle or gland) along a <u>motor neurone</u>. The effector then <u>responds</u> accordingly — e.g. a <u>muscle</u> may <u>contract</u> or a <u>gland</u> may <u>secrete a hormone</u>.

| Stimulus | Receptor | Sensory neurone | CNS | Motor neurone | Effector | Response |

Light receptors in the retina

6) The <u>time</u> it takes you to <u>respond</u> to a stimulus is called your <u>reaction time</u>.

Neurones Transmit Information **Rapidly** as **Electrical Impulses**

1) All neurones have a <u>cell body</u> with a <u>nucleus</u> (plus cytoplasm and other subcellular structures).

2) The cell body has <u>extensions</u> that <u>connect to other neurones</u> — <u>dendrites</u> and <u>dendrons</u> carry nerve impulses <u>towards</u> the cell body, and <u>axons</u> carry nerve impulses <u>away</u> from the cell body.

3) Some axons are surrounded by a <u>myelin sheath</u>. This acts as an <u>electrical insulator</u>, <u>speeding up</u> the electrical impulse.

4) Neurones can be very <u>long</u>, which also <u>speeds up</u> the impulse (<u>connecting</u> with <u>another neurone</u> slows the impulse down, so one long neurone is much <u>quicker</u> than lots of short ones joined together).

There's more on axons and dendrites on the next page.

EXAM TIP

The exam isn't just a test of what you know...

...it's also a test of how well you can <u>apply</u> what you know. For instance, you might have to take what you know about a <u>human's nervous system</u> and apply it to a <u>horse</u>. The key is <u>not to panic</u> — just <u>think carefully</u> about the information that you are given.

The Nervous System

There are **Different Types** of **Neurones**

You need to know the structure and function of sensory, motor and relay neurones.

Sensory Neurone

1) One long dendron carries nerve impulses from receptor cells to the cell body, which is located in the middle of the neurone.
2) One short axon carries nerve impulses from the cell body to the CNS.

receptor cells

dendron   axon

DIRECTION OF IMPULSE

Motor Neurone

1) Many short dendrites carry nerve impulses from the CNS to the cell body.
2) One long axon carries nerve impulses from the cell body to effector cells.

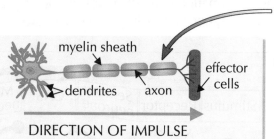

myelin sheath

dendrites   axon   effector cells

DIRECTION OF IMPULSE

The diagram shows a myelinated motor neurone but you can get unmyelinated ones too. Sensory and relay neurones can also be myelinated.

Relay Neurone

1) Many short dendrites carry nerve impulses from sensory neurones to the cell body.
2) An axon carries nerve impulses from the cell body to motor neurones.

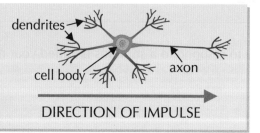

dendrites

cell body   axon

DIRECTION OF IMPULSE

Synapses Connect Neurones

1) The connection between two neurones is called a synapse.
2) The nerve signal is transferred by chemicals called neurotransmitters, which diffuse (move) across the gap.
3) The neurotransmitters then set off a new electrical signal in the next neurone.
4) The transmission of a nervous impulse is very fast, but it is slowed down a bit at the synapse because the diffusion of neurotransmitters across the gap takes time.

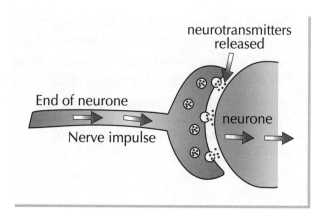

neurotransmitters released

End of neurone

Nerve impulse

neurone

REVISION TIP

Make sure you know the differences between the neurones

You need to know the structures and functions of the different types of neurones — try drawing out the diagrams yourself and putting annotations on them saying what each part does.

Reflexes

Sometimes you respond to a stimulus <u>without thinking</u> about it — this is a <u>reflex</u>.

Reflexes Help **Prevent Injury**

1) <u>Reflexes</u> are <u>automatic</u>, <u>rapid</u> responses to stimuli — they can reduce the chances of being injured.

2) The passage of information in a reflex (from receptor to effector) is called a <u>reflex arc</u>.

3) The neurones in reflex arcs go through the <u>spinal cord</u> or through an <u>unconscious part of the brain</u>.

4) When a <u>stimulus</u> (e.g. a bee sting) is detected by receptors, <u>impulses</u> are sent along a <u>sensory neurone</u> to a <u>relay neurone</u> in the CNS.

5) When the impulses reach a <u>synapse</u> between the sensory neurone and the relay neurone, they trigger <u>neurotransmitters</u> to be released (see previous page). These cause impulses to be sent along the <u>relay neurone</u>.

6) When the impulses reach a <u>synapse</u> between the relay neurone and a motor neurone, the same thing happens. Neurotransmitters are released and cause impulses to be sent along the <u>motor neurone</u>.

7) The impulses then travel along the motor neurone to the <u>effector</u> (in this example it's a muscle, but it could be a gland).

8) The <u>muscle</u> then <u>contracts</u> and moves your hand away from the bee.

9) Because you don't have to spend time thinking about the response, it's <u>quicker</u> than normal responses.

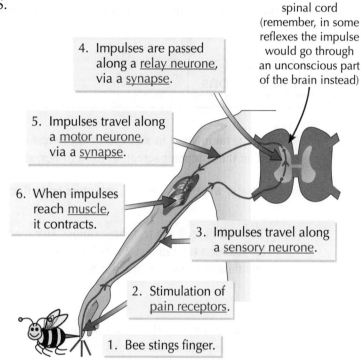

spinal cord (remember, in some reflexes the impulse would go through an unconscious part of the brain instead)

4. Impulses are passed along a <u>relay neurone</u>, via a <u>synapse</u>.

5. Impulses travel along a <u>motor neurone</u>, via a <u>synapse</u>.

6. When impulses reach <u>muscle</u>, it contracts.

3. Impulses travel along a <u>sensory neurone</u>.

2. Stimulation of <u>pain receptors</u>.

1. Bee stings finger.

A **Reflex** Helps to **Protect the Eye**

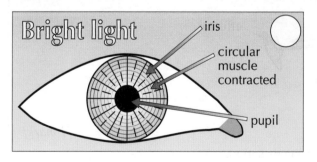

Bright light

iris

circular muscle contracted

pupil

1) <u>Very bright light</u> can <u>damage</u> the eye — so you have a reflex to protect it.

2) <u>Light receptors</u> in the eye detect very bright light and send a message along a <u>sensory neurone</u> to the brain.

3) The message then travels along a <u>relay neurone</u> to a <u>motor neurone</u>, which tells <u>circular muscles</u> in the <u>iris</u> (the coloured part of the eye) to <u>contract</u>, making the pupil smaller.

There's more about the structure of the eye on page 52.

Reflexes are faster than other responses

Reflexes <u>bypass</u> conscious parts of your brain completely when a super <u>quick</u> response is essential — your body just gets on with things. If you had to stop and think first, you'd end up a lot more sore (or worse).

Warm-Up and Exam Questions

Welcome to some questions. There are quite a few of them, but that's because they're pretty important...

Warm-Up Questions

1) What is meant by the term 'stimulus'?
2) What is the function of an axon?
3) How does a myelin sheath speed up electrical impulses?
4) Name the three types of neurone in a reflex arc.
5) What name is given to the connection between two neurones?

Exam Questions

1   A student is taking part in an experiment to test reaction times. Every time a red triangle appears on the computer screen in front of her, she has to click the mouse.

(a)   Suggest what the stimulus, receptors and effectors are in this experiment.

[3 marks]

(b)   The student took the test three times. Her reaction time in test 1 was 328 ms. Her reaction time in test 2 was 346 ms. Her mean reaction time was 343 ms. Calculate her reaction time for test 3.

[2 marks]

2   Young babies have several reflexes not usually present in adults. For example, if an object is placed in the palm of a newborn baby's hand, the baby will move their fingers to grasp the object. The reflex arc for this reflex is shown in **Figure 1**.

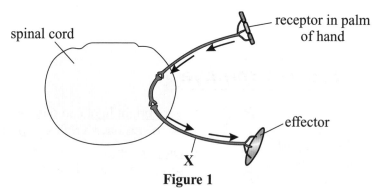

Figure 1

(a)   Name the structure labelled **X** on **Figure 1**.

[1 mark]

(b)   State the type of effector in this response and describe its action.

[2 marks]

(c)   Explain how an electrical impulse in one neurone is able to pass to the next neurone.

[2 marks]

(d)   If an object is placed in the palm of a baby over 6 months old, it can choose whether it wants to grasp hold of the object. Describe **one** way in which the pathway of nervous impulses involved in grasping an object differs between a newborn baby and a baby older than 6 months.

[1 mark]

The Brain and Spinal Cord

Scientists know a bit about the <u>brain</u> but <u>not as much</u> as they'd like. Read on — it's pretty amazing stuff.

The Brain and Spinal Cord make up the Central Nervous System

1) The <u>spinal cord</u> is a long column of <u>neurones</u> (nerve cells) that run from the <u>base of the brain</u> down the spine. At several places down the cord, neurones <u>branch off</u> and <u>connect</u> with other parts of the body. The spinal cord <u>relays information</u> between the <u>brain</u> and the <u>rest of the body</u>.

2) The brain is made up of <u>billions</u> of <u>interconnected neurones</u>. Different brain <u>parts</u> have different <u>functions</u>:

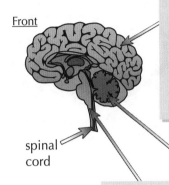

Front

spinal cord

<u>Cerebrum</u> — The <u>largest part</u> of the brain. It's divided into two halves called <u>cerebral hemispheres</u>. The <u>right hemisphere</u> controls <u>muscles</u> on the <u>left side</u> of the body and vice versa. Different parts of the cerebrum are responsible for different things, including <u>movement</u>, <u>intelligence</u>, <u>memory</u>, <u>language</u> and <u>vision</u>.

right
left
Cerebral Hemispheres

<u>Cerebellum</u> — responsible for <u>muscle coordination</u> and <u>balance</u>.

<u>Medulla oblongata</u> — controls <u>unconscious activities</u> like <u>breathing</u> and your <u>heart rate</u>.

Scanners are used to Investigate Brain Function

To investigate the <u>function</u> of the brain you need to look <u>inside</u> it. Brain tissue can be accessed with <u>surgery</u> (by cutting the <u>skull open</u>), but it's pretty <u>risky</u>. The brain can be visualised <u>without surgery</u> using <u>scanners</u>.

CT Scanning

1) A <u>CT scanner</u> uses <u>X-rays</u> to produce an image of the brain.

2) A CT scan shows the <u>main structures</u> in the brain, but it doesn't show the functions of them.

3) However, if a CT scan shows a <u>diseased</u> or <u>damaged</u> brain structure and the patient has <u>lost</u> some <u>function</u>, the function of that part of the brain can be <u>worked out</u>. For example, if an area of the brain is damaged and the patient <u>can't see</u>, then that area is involved in <u>vision</u>.

PET Scanning

1) <u>PET scanners</u> use <u>radioactive chemicals</u> to show which parts of the brain are <u>active</u> when the person is inside the scanner.

2) PET scans are <u>very detailed</u> and can be used to investigate <u>both</u> the <u>structure</u> and the <u>function</u> of the brain in <u>real time</u>.

3) PET scans can show if areas in the brain are <u>unusually inactive or active</u>, so they are useful for <u>studying disorders</u> that change the <u>brain's activity</u>. E.g. in Alzheimer's disease, activity in certain areas of the brain is reduced — PET scans show this reduction when compared to a <u>normal brain</u>.

Treating Problems in the CNS Can be Tricky

There are many things that can <u>go wrong</u> with the <u>central nervous system (CNS)</u>, e.g. <u>injuries</u> to the <u>brain</u> or <u>spinal cord</u>, <u>tumours</u>, <u>diseases</u> (such as Alzheimer's and Parkinson's). These can be <u>difficult</u> to treat:

1) It's <u>hard to repair damage</u> to the nervous system — neurones in the CNS don't readily repair themselves and as of yet scientists <u>haven't</u> developed a way to <u>repair nervous tissue</u> in the <u>CNS</u>.

2) If a problem occurs in a part of the nervous system that's <u>not easy to access</u> it can be hard to treat, e.g. it's not possible to <u>surgically remove</u> tumours growing in certain parts of the brain.

3) Treatment for problems in the nervous system may lead to <u>permanent damage</u>. For example, a person who has injured their <u>spinal cord</u> may need <u>surgery</u> on their <u>spine</u> near to the injury. There is a risk that the spinal cord could be <u>damaged further</u> during the operation, leading to permanent damage.

The Eye

The eye is a sense organ. There's a lot to get your head around, so get focused.

Learn the Eye with All Its Labels

1) The cornea refracts (bends) light into the eye.

2) The iris controls how much light enters the pupil (the hole in the middle).

3) The lens also refracts light, focusing it onto the retina.

4) The retina is the light sensitive part and it's covered in receptor cells called rods and cones, which detect light.

5) Rods are more sensitive in dim light but can't sense colour.

6) Cones are sensitive to different colours but are not so good in dim light.

7) The information from light is converted into electrical impulses. The optic nerve carries these impulses from the receptors to the brain.

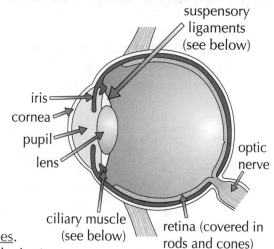

Colour Blindness and Cataracts Cause Vision Problems

1) Colour blind people can't tell the difference between certain colours. The most common form of the disorder is red-green colour blindness — it's caused when red or green cones in the retina are not working properly. There's no cure for colour blindness at the moment because the cone cells can't be replaced.

2) A cataract is a cloudy patch on the lens, which stops light from being able to enter the eye normally. People with cataracts are likely to have blurred vision. They may also experience colours looking less vivid and have difficulty seeing in bright light. A cataract can be treated by replacing the faulty lens with an artificial one.

Focusing on Near and Distant Objects

The lens is elastic, so the eye can focus light onto the retina by changing the shape of the lens.

To Look at Close Objects

1) The ciliary muscle contracts, which slackens the suspensory ligaments.

2) The lens becomes a more rounded shape, so light is refracted more.

The Eye

To Look at **Distant Objects**

1) The <u>ciliary muscle relaxes</u>, which allows the <u>suspensory ligaments</u> to <u>pull tight</u>.
2) This pulls the lens into a <u>less rounded shape</u> so light is refracted <u>less</u>.

Structural Abnormalities Can Cause Long- or Short-sightedness

Long-sightedness

<u>Long-sighted</u> people are <u>unable to focus</u> on <u>near</u> objects:
1) This occurs when the <u>lens</u> is the wrong shape and doesn't <u>bend</u> the light enough, or the <u>eyeball</u> is too <u>short</u>.
2) Light from near objects is brought into focus <u>behind</u> the <u>retina</u>.
3) You can use glasses or contact lenses with a <u>convex lens</u> to correct it.

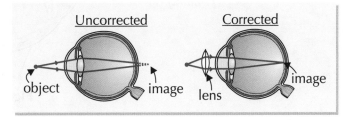

Short-sightedness

<u>Short-sighted</u> people are <u>unable to focus</u> on <u>distant</u> objects:
1) This occurs when the <u>lens</u> is the wrong shape and bends the light <u>too much</u>, or the <u>eyeball</u> is too <u>long</u>.
2) Light from distant objects is brought into focus <u>in front</u> of the <u>retina</u>.
3) You can use glasses or contact lenses with a <u>concave lens</u> to correct it.

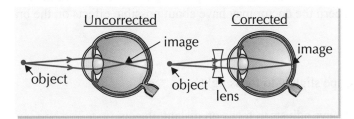

A convex lens increases refraction...

...and a concave lens reduces it. So if the lenses in your eye <u>aren't refracting</u> the light <u>enough</u>, you need a <u>convex lens</u> to correct it. Simple. Well, it will be once you've <u>read</u> through these two pages a few times.

Warm-Up and Exam Questions

Without a good warm-up you're likely to strain a brain cell or two. So take the time to run through these questions and get the facts straight before plunging into the Exam Questions.

Warm-Up Questions

1) Name the region of the brain that controls muscle coordination.
2) What does a CT scan of the brain show?
3) Which type of receptor cells in the retina are more sensitive in dim light?
4) How can glasses help a long-sighted person focus on something nearby?
5) Explain the cause of short-sightedness.

Exam Questions

1   **Figure 1** shows a cross section through the eye.   *Grade 4-6*

   (a)   Name the parts labelled **A** and **B**.

   [2 marks]

   (b)   Describe the function of the iris.

   [1 mark]

Figure 1

2   A patient with a brain tumour is experiencing difficulties with memory and language.   *Grade 6-7*

   (a)   Which of the following areas of the brain is most likely to be affected by the tumour?

   ☐ **A**   medulla   ☐ **C**   cerebellum

   ☐ **B**   cerebrum   ☐ **D**   hypothalamus

   [1 mark]

   (b)   The patient's doctor has concerns about operating to remove the tumour.
         Suggest **one** concern the doctor may have about possible effects on the brain.

   [1 mark]

3   The eye adjusts its shape slightly to focus light.   *Grade 7-9*

   (a)   Describe how the eye adjusts to focus on distant objects.

   [4 marks]

   (b)   Presbyopia is a condition in which the lens of the eye becomes less elastic and isn't easily
         able to form a rounded shape. Suggest how having presbyopia will affect a person's vision.

   [2 marks]

Revision Summary for Topic 2

Well, Topic 2 sure was a brain-tingling, nerve-jangling, eye-popping topic.
Try these questions and tick off each one when you get it right.
When you've done all the questions under a heading and are completely happy, tick it off.

Mitosis and Growth (p.40-43) ☑

1) What is the cell cycle?
2) Give three uses of mitosis in organisms.
3) Name the four stages of mitosis. Describe what happens in each one.
4) Is the following statement true or false?
   "The cells produced at the end of mitosis are identical to each other and the parent cell."
5) Describe how animals grow.
6) What major illness can result from uncontrolled cell division?
7) Describe how a percentile chart is used to monitor growth.

Stem Cells (p.44-45) ☐

8) What is a stem cell?
9) How are embryonic stem cells different to adult stem cells?
10) What are meristems? Where are they found?
11) What are the potential benefits of stem cells being used in medicine?
12) Give three potential risks associated with using stem cells in medicine.

The Nervous System (p.47-49) ☐

13) What effect does a myelin sheath have on the speed of an electrical impulse?
14) Draw and label a motor neurone.
15) What is a synapse?
16) Describe the role of neurotransmitters in the transmission of nervous impulses.
17) What is a reflex arc?
18) Why are reflexes faster than normal nervous responses?

The Brain and The Eye (p.51-53) ☑

19) Produce a sketch of the brain and label the cerebrum, cerebellum and medulla oblongata.
20) Give four things that the cerebrum is responsible for.
21) Describe what a PET scan shows.
22) Give three reasons why it may be tricky to treat problems with the brain and spinal cord.
23) Describe the function of these structures in the eye: a) cornea, b) lens.
24) Which part of the eye controls the amount of light entering the pupil?
25) How are the functions of rods and cones different?
26) Why is there currently no cure for colour blindness?
27) What is a cataract?
28) Describe how short-sightedness can be treated.

Sexual Reproduction

If you've ever wondered why you look <u>like</u> your <u>family members</u>, but <u>not exactly the same</u>, read on...

Sexual Reproduction Produces Genetically Different Cells

1) <u>Sexual reproduction</u> is where genetic information from <u>two</u> organisms (a <u>father</u> and a <u>mother</u>) is combined to produce offspring which are <u>genetically different</u> to either parent.

2) In <u>sexual reproduction</u>, the father and mother produce <u>gametes</u> (reproductive cells). In animals these are <u>sperm</u> and <u>egg cells</u>.

3) Gametes only contain <u>half the number</u> of <u>chromosomes</u> of normal cells — they are <u>haploid</u>. <u>Normal cells</u> (with the full number of chromosomes) are <u>diploid</u> (see p.40).

A human cell nucleus contains 46 chromosomes — so the diploid number for a human is 46 and the haploid number is 23.

4) At <u>fertilisation</u>, a male gamete <u>fuses</u> with a female gamete to produce a <u>fertilised egg</u>, also known as a <u>zygote</u>. The zygote ends up with the <u>full set</u> of chromosomes (so it is diploid).

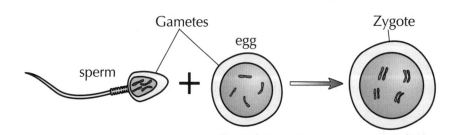

5) The zygote then undergoes <u>cell division</u> (by mitosis — see p.40-41) and develops into an <u>embryo</u>.

In flowering plants, the male gametes are found in the pollen and the female gametes are found in the ovaries at the bottom of the stigma.

6) The embryo <u>inherits characteristics</u> from <u>both parents</u>, as it has received a <u>mixture of chromosomes</u> (and therefore <u>genes</u>) from its mum and its dad.

Sexual reproduction combines genetic information from two parents
Make sure you're confident with this page — it will make learning the next few pages much easier.

Meiosis

This page is all about how gametes end up with <u>half</u> the number of <u>chromosomes</u> of a normal cell.

Gametes are Produced by Meiosis

Meiosis is a type of <u>cell division</u>. It's different to mitosis because it <u>doesn't produce identical cells</u>. In humans, meiosis <u>only</u> happens in the <u>reproductive organs</u> (ovaries and testes).

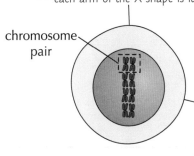

This cell has duplicated each chromosome — each arm of the X-shape is identical.

chromosome pair

Half of the chromosomes in the starting cell were inherited from the organism's father (blue) and half from its mother (red).

DIVISION 1

DIVISION 2

1) Before the cell starts to divide, it <u>duplicates</u> its <u>DNA</u> (so there's enough for each new cell). One arm of each X-shaped chromosome is an <u>exact copy</u> of the other arm.

2) In the <u>first division</u> in meiosis (there are two divisions) the chromosomes <u>line up</u> in pairs in the centre of the cell. One chromosome in each pair came from the organism's mother and one came from its father.

3) The <u>pairs</u> are then <u>pulled apart</u>, so each new cell only has one copy of each chromosome. <u>Some</u> of the father's chromosomes and <u>some</u> of the mother's chromosomes go into each new cell.

4) Each new cell will have a <u>mixture</u> of the mother's and father's chromosomes. Mixing up the genes like this is <u>really important</u> — it creates <u>genetic variation</u> in the offspring.

5) In the <u>second division</u> the chromosomes <u>line up</u> again in the centre of the cell. It's a lot like mitosis. The <u>arms</u> of the chromosomes (called chromatids) are <u>pulled apart</u>.

6) You get <u>four haploid daughter cells</u> — these are the <u>gametes</u>. Each <u>gamete</u> only has a <u>single set</u> of chromosomes. The gametes are all <u>genetically different</u>.

Meiosis is different from Mitosis

REVISION TIP Don't get <u>meiosis</u> mixed up with <u>mitosis</u>. Try remembering m**it**osis has "IT" in it, "IT" for **I**dentical **T**wins, because the cells produced by mitosis are <u>genetically the same</u> — like identical twins. Meiosis doesn't have "IT" so it produces <u>daughter cells</u> which are <u>genetically different</u>.

Asexual and Sexual Reproduction

There Are **Two Types** of **Reproduction**

1) Reproducing is <u>very important</u> to all organisms — it's how they <u>pass on</u> their <u>genes</u>.

2) Some organisms reproduce <u>sexually</u>, some reproduce <u>asexually</u>, and some can do <u>both</u>.

3) When cells reproduce <u>asexually</u>, they divide by <u>mitosis</u> — this results in <u>two diploid daughter cells</u>, which are genetically <u>identical</u> to each other and to the parent cell (see page 40).

4) <u>Sexual reproduction</u> involves <u>meiosis</u> and the production of <u>genetically different</u> haploid gametes, which fuse to form a diploid cell at <u>fertilisation</u> (see page 56).

5) You need to be able to describe some of the <u>advantages</u> and <u>disadvantages</u> of asexual and sexual reproduction. For example:

Asexual Reproduction

Advantages

- Asexual reproduction can produce <u>lots</u> of offspring <u>very quickly</u> because the <u>reproductive cycle</u> (the time it takes to produce independent offspring) is so <u>fast</u>. For example, bacteria, such as *E. coli*, can divide <u>every half an hour</u>. This can allow organisms to <u>colonise a new area</u> very <u>rapidly</u>.

- Only <u>one parent</u> is needed — this means organisms can reproduce whenever conditions are <u>favourable</u>, <u>without</u> having to wait for a <u>mate</u>. For example, aphids reproduce asexually during <u>summer</u> when there is <u>plenty of food</u>.

Disadvantages

- There's <u>no genetic variation</u> between offspring in the population. So, if the <u>environment changes</u> and conditions become <u>unfavourable</u>, the <u>whole population</u> may be affected.

- For example, Black Sigatoka is a disease that affects <u>banana</u> plants, which reproduce <u>asexually</u>. So, if there's an outbreak of the <u>disease</u>, it's likely that <u>all</u> banana plants in the population will be <u>affected</u> as there are <u>none</u> that are <u>resistant</u> to it.

Sexual Reproduction

Advantages

- Sexual reproduction creates <u>genetic variation</u> within the population, which means different individuals have <u>different characteristics</u>. This means that if the environmental conditions <u>change</u>, it's <u>more likely</u> that at least <u>some individuals</u> in the population will have the characteristics to <u>survive</u> the change.

- Over time, this can lead to <u>natural selection</u> and <u>evolution</u> (see p.79) as species become <u>better adapted</u> to their new environment.

Disadvantages

- Sexual reproduction takes more <u>time</u> and <u>energy</u> than asexual reproduction, so organisms produce <u>fewer offspring</u> in their lifetime. Organisms need to <u>find</u> and <u>attract</u> mates, which takes time and energy. E.g. male bowerbirds <u>build</u> structures out of twigs and then <u>dance</u> to impress females.

- <u>Two parents</u> are needed for sexual reproduction. This can be a problem if individuals are <u>isolated</u>. E.g. polar bears often live <u>alone</u>, so male polar bears may walk up to <u>100 miles</u> to find a mate.

DNA

Reproduction is all about <u>passing on your DNA</u> to the next generation. This molecule carries all the <u>instructions</u> for your characteristics — so it's a big part of what makes you <u>you</u>.

DNA is Made Up of Nucleotides

1) DNA strands are <u>polymers</u> made up of lots of repeating units called <u>nucleotides</u>.

2) Each nucleotide consists of a <u>sugar</u>, a <u>phosphate group</u> and <u>one 'base'</u>.

3) The <u>sugar</u> and <u>phosphate</u> groups in the nucleotides form a '<u>backbone</u>' to the DNA strands. The sugar and phosphate groups <u>alternate</u>.

4) One of <u>four</u> different <u>bases</u> joins to each <u>sugar</u>. The bases are: <u>A</u> (adenine), <u>T</u> (thymine), <u>C</u> (cytosine) and <u>G</u> (guanine).

5) A DNA molecule has <u>two strands coiled together</u> in the shape of a <u>double helix</u> (a double stranded spiral).

6) Each base <u>links</u> to a base on the opposite strand in the helix.

7) A <u>always pairs</u> with T, and C <u>always pairs</u> with G. This is called <u>complementary base pairing</u>.

Complementary base pairs:

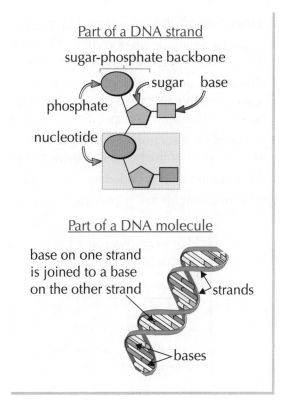

Part of a DNA strand

Part of a DNA molecule

8) The complementary base pairs are joined together by <u>weak hydrogen bonds</u>.

DNA is Stored as Chromosomes and Contains Genes

1) <u>Chromosomes</u> are <u>long</u>, <u>coiled up</u> molecules of <u>DNA</u>. They're found in the <u>nucleus</u> of <u>eukaryotic cells</u>.

2) A <u>gene</u> is a <u>section</u> of DNA on a chromosome that codes for a <u>particular protein</u>.

3) <u>All</u> of an organism's DNA makes up its <u>genome</u>.

You Need to Know How to Extract DNA From Fruit Cells

Don't believe that cells contain DNA?
Well here's a <u>practical</u> you can do to get it out...

1) Mash some strawberries and then put them in a beaker containing a solution of <u>detergent</u> and <u>salt</u>. Mix well.
   - The <u>detergent</u> will <u>break down</u> the <u>cell membranes</u> to release the DNA.
   - The <u>salt</u> will make the <u>DNA stick together</u>.

2) <u>Filter</u> the mixture to get the <u>froth</u> and <u>big, insoluble</u> bits of cell out.

3) Gently add some <u>ice-cold alcohol</u> to the filtered mixture.

4) The DNA will start to come <u>out of solution</u> as it's <u>not soluble</u> in <u>cold alcohol</u>. It will appear as a <u>stringy white precipitate</u> (a solid) that can be carefully fished out with a <u>glass rod</u>.

+ detergent + salt

+ alcohol

Protein Synthesis

So here's how life works — DNA molecules contain a genetic code that determines which proteins are built. The proteins determine how all the cells in the body function.

Proteins are Made by Reading the Code in DNA

1) DNA controls the production of proteins (protein synthesis) in a cell.

2) Proteins are made up of chains of molecules called amino acids. Each different protein has its own particular number and order of amino acids.

3) The amino acid chains fold up to give each protein a different, specific shape — which means each protein can have a different function. This is why enzymes have active sites with a specific shape, and so only catalyse a specific reaction (see page 26).

4) Remember, a section of DNA that codes for a particular protein is called a gene (see previous page). It's the order of the bases in a gene that decides the order of amino acids in a protein.

5) Each amino acid is coded for by a sequence of three bases in the gene — this is called a base triplet.

6) The amino acids are joined together to make proteins, following the order of the bases in the gene.

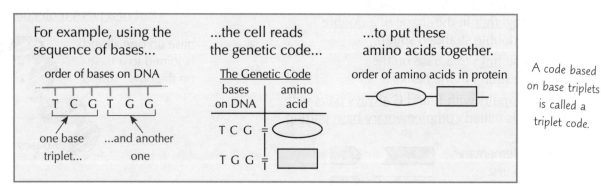

7) Each gene contains a different sequence of bases — which is what allows it to code for a particular protein.

DNA Also Contains Non-Coding Regions

1) Many regions of DNA are non-coding — that means that they don't code for any amino acids.

2) Despite this, some of these regions are still involved in protein synthesis (see next page).

3) All of an organism's DNA (including the non-coding regions) makes up the organism's genome.

DNA decides the order of amino acids in the protein

It's important that you know why the order of bases in a section of DNA affects the function of a protein. If you're unsure don't worry, it's all on the page above — go back and take another look.

Protein Synthesis

This page is all about how you actually <u>use</u> the DNA code to <u>make</u> the proteins that you need.

Proteins are Made in Two Stages

1) Transcription

1) Proteins are made in the <u>cell cytoplasm</u> by subcellular structures called <u>ribosomes</u> (see p.17). DNA is found in the cell <u>nucleus</u> and can't move out of it because it's <u>really big</u>. The cell needs to get the information from the DNA to the ribosome in the cytoplasm.

2) This is done using a molecule called <u>messenger RNA</u> (<u>mRNA</u>). Like DNA, mRNA is a <u>polymer</u> of <u>nucleotides</u>, but it's <u>shorter</u> and only a <u>single strand</u>. It also uses <u>uracil</u> (U) instead of <u>thymine</u> (T) as a <u>base</u>.

   Uracil still pairs with adenine, A-U.

3) <u>RNA polymerase</u> is the <u>enzyme</u> involved in <u>joining together</u> RNA nucleotides to make mRNA. This stage of protein synthesis is called <u>transcription</u>. Here's how it works:

   1) <u>RNA polymerase</u> binds to a region of <u>non-coding DNA</u> in front of a gene.

   2) The two DNA strands <u>unzip</u> and the RNA polymerase <u>moves along</u> one of the strands of the DNA.

   3) It uses the <u>coding DNA</u> in the <u>gene</u> as a <u>template</u> to make the <u>mRNA</u>. <u>Base pairing</u> between the DNA and RNA ensures that the mRNA is <u>complementary</u> to the gene.

   4) Once made, the mRNA molecule moves <u>out</u> of the nucleus and joins with a <u>ribosome</u>.

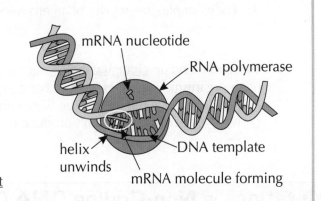

2) Translation

Once the <u>mRNA</u> is bound to a ribosome, the <u>protein</u> can be assembled. This stage is called <u>translation</u>.

1) <u>Amino acids</u> are brought to the <u>ribosome</u> by another RNA molecule called <u>transfer RNA</u> (<u>tRNA</u>).

2) The <u>order</u> in which the amino acids are brought to the ribosome <u>matches</u> the order of the <u>base triplets</u> in mRNA. Base triplets in mRNA are also known as <u>codons</u>.

3) Part of the tRNA's structure is called an <u>anticodon</u> — it is <u>complementary</u> to the <u>codon</u> for the amino acid. The pairing of the codon and anticodon makes sure that the amino acids are brought to the ribosome in the <u>correct order</u>.

4) The amino acids are <u>joined together</u> by the ribosome. This makes a <u>polypeptide</u> (protein).

More on Protein Synthesis

DNA doesn't stay the same for ever. Sometimes the <u>sequence</u> of bases in an organism's DNA <u>randomly changes</u>. This is called <u>mutation</u> and it can have an affect an organism's <u>phenotype</u>.

Genetic Variants Can Arise By Mutations

1) A <u>mutation</u> is a <u>rare</u>, <u>random change</u> to an organism's <u>DNA base sequence</u> that can be <u>inherited</u>.

2) If a mutation happens in a <u>gene</u>, it produces a <u>genetic variant</u> — a different version of the gene.

3) The genetic variant may code for a <u>different sequence</u> of <u>amino acids</u>, which may change the <u>shape</u> of the final <u>protein</u> and so its <u>activity</u>.

Genetic variants are also called alleles — see p.65.

4) For example, the activity of an enzyme might <u>increase</u>, <u>decrease</u> or <u>stop altogether</u>.

5) This could end up <u>changing</u> the <u>characteristics</u> (phenotype, see p.65) of an organism. E.g. XDH is an enzyme. Fruit flies with normal XDH activity have <u>red eyes</u>. Fruit flies with <u>no</u> XDH activity have <u>brown eyes</u> because they can't produce the red eye pigment.

Mutations in Non-Coding DNA Can Also Affect Phenotype

1) Mutations can also happen in <u>non-coding regions</u> of DNA.

2) Before any transcription can happen, <u>RNA polymerase</u> has to bind to a region of non-coding DNA <u>in front</u> of a gene. If a <u>mutation</u> happens in this region of DNA, then it could affect the <u>ability</u> of RNA polymerase to bind to it. It might make it <u>easier</u> to bind to, or <u>more difficult</u>.

3) How well RNA polymerase can bind to this region of DNA will affect <u>how much</u> mRNA is <u>transcribed</u> and therefore how much of the <u>protein</u> is <u>produced</u>. And, depending on the <u>function</u> of the protein, the <u>phenotype</u> of the organism may be affected by <u>how much</u> of it is made.

4) So genetic variants in <u>non-coding regions</u> can still affect the <u>phenotype</u> of an organism, even if they don't <u>code</u> for proteins <u>themselves</u>.

Mutations in coding and non-coding DNA can affect phenotype

Genetic variants in both the <u>coding</u> and <u>non-coding</u> DNA can <u>alter</u> an organism's <u>phenotype</u> — but remember, variants in coding DNA can affect phenotype by changing the <u>activity</u> of a protein and variants in non-coding DNA can affect phenotype by changing <u>how much</u> protein is <u>produced</u>.

Warm-Up and Exam Questions

It's time to see how much you picked up about meiosis, reproduction and DNA.

Warm-Up Questions

1) How many cell divisions take place in meiosis?
2) Which DNA bases pair up according to complementary base pairing?
3) What is a gene?
4) What is a mutation?
5) A mutation affected the activity of a protein. Predict whether the mutation was in a coding or non-coding region of DNA.

Exam Questions

1 A student mashes a small sample of kiwi fruit and then adds detergent and salt. She filters the solution into a test tube and adds liquid X. A stringy white precipitate is formed in the test tube.

Grade 4-6

    (a) Give an identity for liquid X.

[1 mark]

    (b) Name the stringy white precipitate that is formed.

[1 mark]

2 An organism's genetic material is made up of a chemical called DNA.

Grade 4-6

    (a) Which of the following describes the structure of DNA?

      ☐ **A** A protein made up of two strands.   ☐ **C** A polymer made up of two strands.

      ☐ **B** A protein made up of four strands.   ☐ **D** A polymer made up of four strands.

[1 mark]

    (b) Name the type of bond that joins complementary base pairs.

[1 mark]

    (c) Describe the relationship between DNA and the proteins produced by an organism.

[3 marks]

3 A section of an mRNA base sequence is shown in **Figure 1**.

Grade 6-7

U   C   A   G   U   G   A   U   G

Figure 1

    (a) Give the DNA base sequence that would have been used in transcription to produce the mRNA base sequence shown in **Figure 1**.

[2 marks]

    (b) Describe how the base sequence of mRNA ensures that amino acids are brought to the ribosome in the correct order.

[4 marks]

4   Mosquitoes have three pairs of chromosomes in their body cells.
    Figure 2 shows a mosquito cell which is about to divide by meiosis.

Figure 2

   (a) The cell in **Figure 2** undergoes meiosis.
        State how many chromosomes will be present in each new cell produced.

        [1 mark]

   (b) State the number of cells that will be produced in total when the cell in **Figure 2**
        undergoes meiosis.

        [1 mark]

   (c) Explain how the process of sexual reproduction leads to genetic variation
        in the mosquito's offspring.

        [2 marks]

When a mosquito infected with malarial parasites bites a human, parasites present
in the mosquito's saliva pass into the human's bloodstream.

   (d) Malarial parasites reproduce asexually whilst in a human host.
        Give **two** advantages of this method of reproduction compared to sexual reproduction.

        [2 marks]

   (e) Genetic variation within the malarial parasite population increases whilst in the mosquito.
        Suggest why.

        [1 mark]

5   Krabbe disease is a genetic disorder caused by a mutation in the GALC gene.
    The GALC gene codes for an enzyme that is needed for a healthy nervous system.

   (a) One of the mutations that can cause Krabbe disease involves the addition of nucleotides
        to the GALC gene. Describe the structure of a nucleotide.

        [1 mark]

   (b)* Explain how the enzyme coded for by the GALC gene would normally be synthesised
        within a cell.

        [6 marks]

   (c) Explain how a mutation in the GALC gene could alter the activity of the enzyme it codes for.

        [4 marks]

   (d) During protein synthesis, RNA polymerase binds to a non-coding region in front of
        the GALC gene. Suggest how a genetic variant in this non-coding region could affect
        the production of the enzyme the GALC gene codes for.

        [3 marks]

Genes and Alleles

Each pair of <u>chromosomes</u> contain the <u>same genes</u> in the <u>same places</u>. These genes can come in different <u>versions</u>, so the <u>characteristics</u> you have will depend on which versions you <u>inherit</u> from your parents.

Alleles Are Different Versions of the Same Gene

1) What <u>genes</u> you <u>inherit</u> control what <u>characteristics</u> you <u>develop</u>.

2) <u>Different</u> genes control <u>different</u> characteristics. <u>Some</u> characteristics are controlled by a <u>single</u> gene. However, most characteristics are controlled by <u>several genes interacting</u>.

3) All genes exist in different <u>versions</u> called <u>alleles</u> (which are represented by <u>letters</u> in genetic diagrams).

4) You have <u>two</u> versions (alleles) of <u>every gene</u> in your body — <u>one</u> on <u>each chromosome</u> in a pair.

5) If an organism has <u>two alleles</u> for a particular gene that are <u>the same</u>, then it's <u>homozygous</u> for that trait. If its two alleles for a particular gene are <u>different</u>, then it's <u>heterozygous</u>.

6) Some alleles are <u>dominant</u> (shown with a <u>capital letter</u>, e.g. '<u>C</u>') and some are <u>recessive</u> (shown by a <u>small letter</u>, e.g. '<u>c</u>'). Dominant alleles <u>overrule</u> recessive alleles, so if an organism has <u>one dominant</u> and <u>one recessive</u> allele for a gene (e.g. '<u>Cc</u>'), then the <u>dominant allele</u> will determine what <u>characteristic</u> is present.

7) To display a <u>dominant characteristic</u>, an organism can have either <u>two dominant alleles</u> for a particular gene or <u>one dominant</u> and <u>one recessive</u> allele for that gene. But for an organism to display a <u>recessive</u> characteristic, <u>both</u> its alleles must be <u>recessive</u>.

8) Your <u>genotype</u> is the combination of <u>alleles</u> you have. Your alleles determine what characteristics you have — your <u>phenotype</u>. So <u>different</u> combinations of alleles give rise to <u>different</u> phenotypes.

There are lots of fancy words to learn on this page...

Make sure you fully understand what all the <u>different terms</u> on this page mean (i.e. genes, alleles, homozygous, heterozygous, dominant, recessive, genotype and phenotype). You'll feel much more comfortable going into the exam knowing that these words aren't going to trip you up.

Genetic Diagrams

Genetic Diagrams Can Show Inheritance of a Single Characteristic

The inheritance of a <u>single</u> characteristic is called <u>monohybrid inheritance</u>. You can use a <u>monohybrid cross</u> to show how <u>recessive</u> and <u>dominant</u> traits for a <u>single characteristic</u> are inherited.

For example, let's say an allele that causes hamsters to have superpowers is <u>recessive</u> ("b"), and that <u>normal</u> (boring) hamsters don't have superpowers due to a <u>dominant</u> allele ("B"). Here's how you could use a monohybrid cross to show the <u>probability</u> of either the <u>dominant</u> or <u>recessive</u> trait being <u>inherited</u>:

1) The first step is to cross two <u>homozygous</u> hamsters (BB and bb):   *'Cross' just means 'breed together'.*

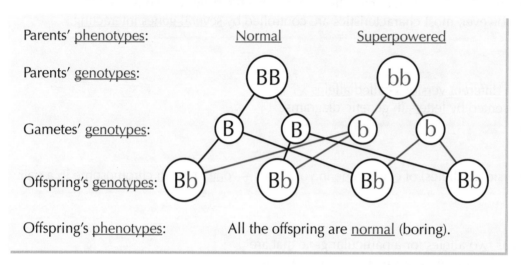

If a hamster has the genotype BB or Bb, its phenotype will be normal and boring. If a hamster has the genotype bb, it will have superpowers.

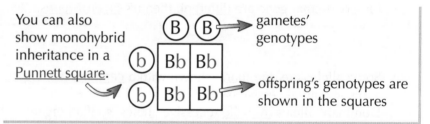

You can also show monohybrid inheritance in a <u>Punnett square</u>.

gametes' genotypes

offspring's genotypes are shown in the squares

2) If two of these <u>offspring</u> now <u>breed</u>, you'll get the next generation:

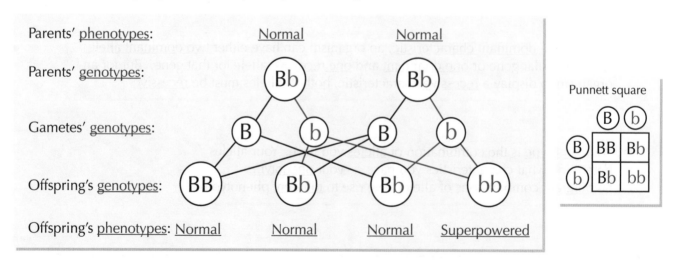

Punnett square

3) In this generation, there's a <u>3:1 ratio</u> of normal to superpowered offspring. In other words, there's a <u>3 in 4</u> (<u>75%</u>) probability of <u>normal hamsters</u> and a <u>1 in 4</u> (<u>25%</u>) probability of <u>superpowers</u>.

Genetic Diagrams

You can work out the probability of offspring being male or female by using a genetic diagram.

A Genetic Diagram Can Show How Sex is Determined in Humans

1) There are 23 matched pairs of chromosomes in every human body cell. The 23rd pair is labelled XX or XY. They're the two chromosomes that decide whether you turn out male or female.

2) Males have an X and a Y chromosome (XY). The Y chromosome causes male characteristics.

3) Females have two X chromosomes (XX). The XX combination allows female characteristics to develop.

4) Because of this, there's an equal chance of having either a boy or a girl. Here's a genetic diagram to prove it:

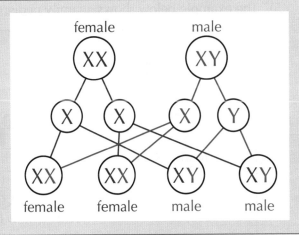

1) Even though we're talking about inheriting chromosomes here and not single genes, the genetic diagram still works the same way.

2) When you plug the letters into the diagram, it shows that there are two XX results and two XY results, so there's the same probability of getting a boy or a girl.

3) Don't forget that this 50 : 50 ratio is only a probability. If you had four kids they could all be boys — or all girls.

5) All eggs have one X chromosome, but a sperm can have either an X chromosome or a Y chromosome. So sex determination in humans depends on whether the sperm that fertilises an egg carries an X or a Y.

There are lots of diagrams on these pages...

There's a good chance you'll be asked to draw or interpret a genetic diagram or punnet square in the exam. Whether this is for sex determination, the inheritance of an allele you've looked at in class or one you've never heard of, the principle is always the same — so make sure you know how to use them.

Genetic Diagrams

Family Pedigrees Can Also Show Monohybrid Inheritance

Knowing how inheritance works helps you to interpret a <u>family pedigree</u> (a family tree of genetic disorders). Here's an example using <u>cystic fibrosis</u> — a genetic disorder of the cell membranes.

Cystic Fibrosis is a Recessive Genetic Disorder

1) The allele which causes cystic fibrosis (CF) is a <u>recessive allele</u>, 'f', carried by about <u>1 person in 30</u>.
2) Because it's recessive, people with only <u>one copy</u> of the allele <u>won't</u> have the disorder — they're known as <u>carriers</u>.
3) For a child to inherit the disorder, <u>both parents</u> must either have the disorder themselves or be <u>carriers</u>.

This diagram shows a <u>monohybrid cross</u> between two people who are <u>carriers</u> of the cystic fibrosis allele.

You can see from the diagram that there's a <u>1 in 4 chance</u> of a child having the disorder if <u>both</u> parents are <u>carriers</u>.

The probability of each outcome can also be expressed as a ratio — 1 : 2 : 1 for unaffected : carrier : disorder.

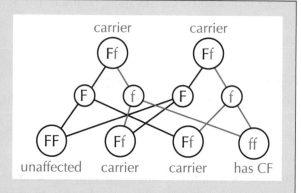

4) You can show information about how <u>alleles</u> are passed through families on a <u>family pedigree</u> diagram. The <u>lines</u> on the pedigree link the <u>parents</u> to <u>each other</u> (<u>horizontal</u>) and to their <u>children</u> (<u>vertical</u>).
5) The example below shows a <u>family pedigree</u> for a family that includes <u>carriers</u> of <u>cystic fibrosis</u>:

- You can tell from the pedigree that the <u>allele</u> for cystic fibrosis <u>isn't</u> dominant because plenty of family members <u>carry</u> the allele but don't have the disorder.
- There is a 1 in 4 (<u>25%</u>) chance that the new baby will have <u>cystic fibrosis</u> and a 1 in 2 (<u>50%</u>) chance that it will be a <u>carrier</u> (because <u>both</u> of its parents are carriers).
- In fact, the case of the new baby is the same as in the monohybrid cross diagram above — they could be <u>unaffected</u> (FF), be a <u>carrier</u> (Ff) or have the <u>disorder</u> (ff).

It's enough to make you go cross-eyed...

If you're struggling to interpret a family pedigree in the exam, try writing the <u>genotype</u> of each person on to it. You might get a family tree showing the inheritance of a <u>dominant</u> allele instead — in this case, there <u>won't be any carriers</u> (because everyone with the allele has that phenotype).

Warm-Up and Exam Questions

Take a deep breath and go through these Warm-Up Questions one by one. Then on to the Exam Questions. Don't panic if you get something wrong — as they say, practice makes perfect...

Warm-Up Questions

1) What are alleles?
2) What does phenotype mean?
3) For a certain type of mouse, having the genotype bb results in white fur. Having the genotype Bb or BB, results in brown fur. Which characteristic, white fur or brown fur is recessive? Explain your answer.
4) What combination of sex chromosomes do human females have?

Exam Questions

1   Cystic fibrosis is a genetic disorder caused by a recessive allele.

F = normal allele   **f** = faulty allele that leads to cystic fibrosis

Figure 1 is an incomplete Punnett square showing the possible inheritance of cystic fibrosis from one couple.

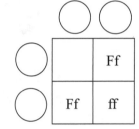

Figure 1

   (a)   Complete the Punnett square to show the genotype of the missing offspring and the genotypes of the gametes.

[2 marks]

   (b)   Give the proportion of the possible offspring that are homozygous.

[1 mark]

   (c)   State the phenotype of the possible offspring with the genotype ff.

[1 mark]

2   Albinism is a condition characterised by the lack of pigment in the hair and skin. It is caused by the recessive allele **a**. The dominant allele **A** results in normal pigmentation.

   (a)   State the possible genotypes of a rabbit that shows no symptoms of albinism.

[1 mark]

A rabbit with albinism mated with a rabbit that showed no symptoms of the condition. 56% of the offspring had albinism.

   (b)   Deduce the genotypes of the parent rabbits and the possible genotypes of their offspring. Use a genetic diagram to explain your answer.

[3 marks]

   (c)   Using your genetic diagram, give the percentage of offspring that are likely to have albinism.

[1 mark]

   (d)   Suggest why the percentage of offspring which were born with albinism was not exactly the same as that suggested by your genetic diagram.

[1 mark]

The Work of Mendel

Gregor Mendel's discoveries about <u>inheritance</u> were really important. So here's a whole page on him...

Mendel Did Genetic Experiments with Pea Plants

1) <u>Gregor Mendel</u> was an Austrian monk who trained in <u>mathematics</u> and <u>natural history</u>. On his garden plot at the monastery in the <u>mid 19th century</u>, Mendel noted how <u>characteristics</u> in <u>plants</u> were <u>passed on</u> from one generation to the next.

2) The results of his research were published in <u>1866</u> and eventually became the <u>foundation</u> of modern <u>genetics</u>. Here's an example of one of his experiments:

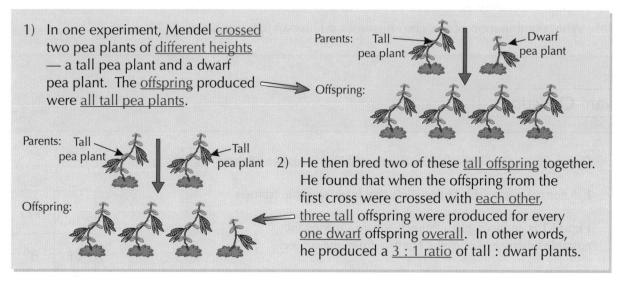

1) In one experiment, Mendel <u>crossed</u> two pea plants of <u>different heights</u> — a tall pea plant and a dwarf pea plant. The <u>offspring</u> produced were <u>all tall pea plants</u>.

2) He then bred two of these <u>tall offspring</u> together. He found that when the offspring from the first cross were crossed with <u>each other</u>, <u>three tall</u> offspring were produced for every <u>one dwarf</u> offspring <u>overall</u>. In other words, he produced a <u>3 : 1 ratio</u> of tall : dwarf plants.

3) Mendel had shown that the height characteristic in pea plants was determined by separately inherited "<u>hereditary units</u>" passed on from each parent. The <u>ratios</u> of tall and dwarf plants in the offspring showed that the unit for tall plants, <u>T</u>, was <u>dominant</u> over the unit for dwarf plants, <u>t</u>.

4) As well as height, Mendel also showed that <u>other characteristics</u> of pea plants were inherited in the <u>same way</u>, e.g. he found that a purple flower colour was <u>dominant</u> over a white colour.

We now know that the pea plants in the first cross were each <u>homozygous</u> for their trait and that their tall offspring were <u>heterozygous</u> for their trait.

Mendel Reached Three Important Conclusions

Mendel reached these three important conclusions about <u>heredity in plants</u>:

1) Characteristics in plants are determined by "<u>hereditary units</u>".

2) Hereditary units are passed on to offspring <u>unchanged</u> from both parents, <u>one unit</u> from <u>each parent</u>.

3) Hereditary units can be <u>dominant</u> or <u>recessive</u> — if an individual has <u>both</u> the dominant and the recessive unit for a characteristic, the <u>dominant</u> characteristic will be expressed.

Although Mendel didn't investigate heredity in animals, similar experiments have since shown that heredity in animals works the same way.

It Took a While For People to Understand His Work

1) Mendel's work was <u>cutting edge</u> and <u>new</u> to the scientists of the day.

2) We now know that his "hereditary units" are of course <u>genes</u>. But at the time, scientists didn't have the background knowledge to <u>properly understand</u> Mendel's findings — they had <u>no idea</u> about <u>genes</u>, <u>DNA</u> and <u>chromosomes</u>.

3) It wasn't until <u>after his death</u> that people realised how <u>significant</u> his work was and that the <u>mechanism</u> of <u>inheritance</u> could be fully explained.

Sex-Linked Genetic Disorders

There are some genetic disorders that you're more likely to end up with if you're male. This is because these disorders are linked to the sex chromosomes, which are different in males and females.

Some Genetic Characteristics Are Sex-Linked

X chromosome

Gene that men have two alleles for.

Y chromosome

Gene that men have only one allele for.

1) A characteristic is sex-linked if the allele that codes for it is located on a sex chromosome (X or Y).

2) The Y chromosome is smaller than the X chromosome and carries fewer genes. So most genes on the sex chromosomes are only carried on the X chromosome.

3) As men only have one X chromosome they often only have one allele for sex-linked genes.

4) Because men only have one allele, the characteristic of this allele is shown even if it is recessive. This makes men more likely than women to show recessive characteristics for genes that are sex-linked.

5) Disorders caused by faulty alleles located on sex chromosomes are called sex-linked genetic disorders.

Colour Blindness is a Sex-Linked Disorder

1) Colour blindness is caused by a faulty allele carried on the X chromosome.

2) As it's sex-linked, both the chromosome and the allele are written in the genetic diagram, e.g. X^n, where X represents the X chromosome and n the faulty allele for colour vision. The Y chromosome doesn't have an allele for colour vision so is just represented by Y.

3) Women need two copies of the recessive allele to be colour blind, while men only need one copy. This means colour blindness is much rarer in women than men.

4) A woman with only one copy of the recessive allele is a carrier of colour blindness. This means that she isn't colour blind herself, but she can pass the allele on to her offspring.

5) Here's a genetic cross between a carrier female and an unaffected (non-colour blind) male:

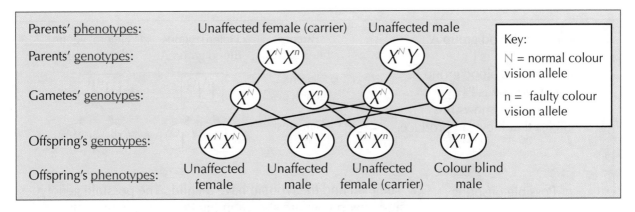

Parents' phenotypes: Unaffected female (carrier)   Unaffected male

Parents' genotypes: $X^N X^n$ $X^N Y$

Gametes' genotypes: X^N X^n X^N Y

Offspring's genotypes: $X^N X^N$ $X^N Y$ $X^N X^n$ $X^n Y$

Offspring's phenotypes: Unaffected female   Unaffected male   Unaffected female (carrier)   Colour blind male

Key:
N = normal colour vision allele
n = faulty colour vision allele

6) In the example above, the ratio of unaffected : colour blind offspring is 3 : 1. Be careful with this one, it may be disguised as a 2 : 1 : 1 ratio (unaffected : carrier : colour blind), but it means the same thing.

7) In other words, there's a 1 in 4 (25%) chance of a child being colour blind. This rises to 1 in 2 (50%) if you know that the child will be a boy.

Haemophilia is another sex-linked disorder. It's also caused by a faulty allele that's carried on the X chromosome, so it's inherited in the same way as colour blindness. A genetic diagram for the inheritance of haemophilia will look the same as the one for colour blindness, shown above.

Haemophilia is a disease where the blood doesn't clot properly.

Inheritance of Blood Groups

This is a bit more <u>complicated</u> than the examples on previous pages, but don't worry, just go through slowly.

There Are **Multiple Alleles** That Determine **Blood Group**

1) So far you've probably only come across cases where there are <u>two</u> <u>possible alleles</u> for a gene — one that's <u>recessive</u> and one that's <u>dominant</u>.

2) Well, sometimes you'll get <u>more than two</u> (multiple) <u>alleles</u> for a <u>single gene</u>. This makes studying the inheritance of characteristics controlled by these genes a little more <u>complicated</u>.

3) For example, humans have <u>four</u> potential <u>blood types</u> — <u>O</u>, <u>A</u>, <u>B</u> and <u>AB</u>. The <u>gene</u> for blood type in humans has <u>three different alleles</u> — I^O, I^A and I^B.

4) I^A and I^B are <u>codominant</u> with each other. That means that when an individual has <u>both</u> of these alleles (genotype $I^A I^B$), then they'll have the blood type <u>AB</u> — one allele <u>isn't</u> dominant over the other one.

5) However, I^O is <u>recessive</u>. So when you get I^O with I^A (genotype $I^A I^O$) you only see the effect of I^A — giving blood type <u>A</u>. In the same way, I^O with I^B (genotype $I^B I^O$) only gives the effect of I^B, making you blood type <u>B</u>.

6) You only get <u>blood type O</u> when you have <u>two of the recessive alleles</u> ($I^O I^O$).

Recessive blood groups are normally rare, but it just so happens that lots of people in Britain are descended from people who were $I^O I^O$, so O's really common.

You Can Predict **Blood Groups** Using **Genetic Diagrams**

1) You can draw <u>genetic diagrams</u> for <u>codominant</u> alleles in the same way that you would for alleles that are <u>recessive</u> and <u>dominant</u>.

2) The tricky bit is predicting the potential <u>phenotypes</u> in the offspring once you've worked out what the potential <u>genotypes</u> are. You need to remember how the different alleles <u>interact with each other</u> to produce a phenotype.

3) Here's an example showing how you can use <u>genetic diagrams</u> to predict the <u>blood type</u> inherited by the offspring:

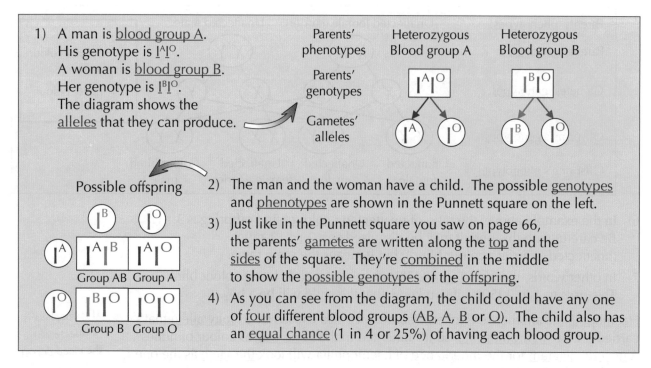

1) A man is <u>blood group A</u>. His genotype is $I^A I^O$. A woman is <u>blood group B</u>. Her genotype is $I^B I^O$. The diagram shows the <u>alleles</u> that they can produce.

Parents' phenotypes — Heterozygous Blood group A — Heterozygous Blood group B

Parents' genotypes — $I^A I^O$ — $I^B I^O$

Gametes' alleles — I^A I^O — I^B I^O

Possible offspring

	I^B	I^O
I^A	$I^A I^B$ Group AB	$I^A I^O$ Group A
I^O	$I^B I^O$ Group B	$I^O I^O$ Group O

2) The man and the woman have a child. The possible <u>genotypes</u> and <u>phenotypes</u> are shown in the Punnett square on the left.

3) Just like in the Punnett square you saw on page 66, the parents' <u>gametes</u> are written along the <u>top</u> and the <u>sides</u> of the square. They're <u>combined</u> in the middle to show the <u>possible genotypes</u> of the <u>offspring</u>.

4) As you can see from the diagram, the child could have any one of <u>four</u> different blood groups (<u>AB</u>, <u>A</u>, <u>B</u> or <u>O</u>). The child also has an <u>equal chance</u> (1 in 4 or 25%) of having each blood group.

Warm-Up and Exam Questions

You need to test your knowledge with a few Warm-Up Questions, followed by some Exam Questions...

Warm-Up Questions

1) What do we now know Mendel's "hereditary units" to be?
2) Suggest why the importance of Mendel's work wasn't realised straight away.
3) Where is an allele that codes for a sex-linked characteristic located?
4) True or False? In humans the O, A, B and AB blood types are determined by monohybrid inheritance.

Exam Questions

1 Mendel carried out genetic experiments in pea plants to investigate the inheritance of flower colour. He found that a purple flower colour was dominant over a white flower colour.

A pea plant with white flowers is crossed with another which is homozygous for purple flowers. Explain why all offspring of the cross will have purple flowers.

[2 marks]

2 Colour blindness in humans is caused by a recessive allele, X^n, found on the X chromosome. It is more common in men because men have only one X chromosome. The dominant version of the allele, which gives normal colour vision, is X^N.

A colour blind man with the genotype X^nY has a child with a woman who has the genotype X^NX^N.

(a) Draw a genetic diagram to show the possible genotypes of their offspring.

[2 marks]

(b) The child is a boy. Explain why the boy will not be colour blind.

[1 mark]

(c) State the probability that a daughter of this couple would be colour blind.

[1 mark]

3 Humans have four potential blood types (O, A, B and AB). The gene for blood type in humans has three different alleles (I^O, I^A and I^B). A man has blood type A and is heterozygous for the allele.

(a) Give the genotype of the man.

[1 mark]

(b) The man has a child with a homozygous woman who has blood group B.
(i) Draw a punnet square to show the possible genotypes for the blood group of the child.

[2 marks]

(ii) State the probability that the child will have B blood type.

[1 mark]

(iii) State and explain the phenotype of a child that inherits an I^A allele and an I^B allele.

[2 marks]

Variation

You'll probably have noticed that not all people are <u>identical</u>. There are reasons for this.

Organisms of the **Same Species** Have **Differences**

1) Different species <u>look different</u>.

2) But even organisms of the <u>same species</u> will usually look at least slightly <u>different</u>. E.g. all dogs are the <u>same species</u>, but a <u>Dalmatian</u> looks quite different to a <u>Pug</u>.

3) These differences are called the <u>variation</u> within a species. It can be <u>genetic</u> or <u>environmental</u>.

4) <u>Genetic variation</u> within a species is caused by organisms having <u>different alleles</u> (versions of genes) which can lead to differences in <u>phenotype</u> (the <u>characteristics</u> an organism displays).

5) Genetic variation can be caused by <u>new alleles</u> arising through <u>mutations</u> (see next page). <u>Sexual reproduction</u> also causes genetic variation since it results in alleles being <u>combined</u> in lots of <u>different ways</u> in offspring.

Sexual reproduction means no two members of a species are genetically identical (apart from identical twins).

6) There tends to be <u>a lot</u> of genetic variation <u>within a population</u> of a species. This is mostly due to <u>neutral mutations</u> (see next page).

7) <u>Variation</u> within a species can also be caused by the <u>environment</u> (the conditions in which organisms live). For example:

A plant grown on a nice sunny windowsill could grow <u>luscious</u> and <u>green</u>.

The same plant grown in darkness would grow <u>tall</u> and <u>spindly</u> and its leaves would turn <u>yellow</u>.

These <u>environmental variations</u> in phenotype are also known as <u>acquired characteristics</u>. They're characteristics that organisms acquire (get) during their lifetimes.

8) Most variation in phenotype is determined by a <u>mixture</u> of <u>genetic</u> and <u>environmental</u> factors.

For example, the <u>maximum height</u> that an animal or plant could grow to is determined by its <u>genes</u>. But whether it actually grows that tall depends on its <u>environment</u> (e.g. how much food it gets).

You can't blame all of your faults on your parents...

Although the <u>genes</u> that you <u>inherit</u> from your parents are really important at determining what <u>characteristics</u> you have, the <u>conditions</u> in which you live usually <u>play a role too</u>.

Variation and the Human Genome Project

Alleles Arise Due to Genetic Mutations

1) Mutations are changes to the base sequence of DNA.

2) When they occur within a gene they result in an allele, or a different version of the gene.

3) They don't always have a big effect on the phenotype of an organism. In fact, most mutations don't have any effect — in other words they are neutral.

4) But some mutations do have a small effect on the phenotype — they alter an individual's characteristics, but only very slightly. E.g. a mutation might give a hamster long hair instead of short hair.

There's more about the structure of DNA and mutations on pages 59 and 62.

5) Very rarely, a single mutation will have a big effect on phenotype. For example, it might result in the production of a protein that is so different that it can no longer carry out its function.

> This is what happens in cystic fibrosis (see page 68). A mutation causes a protein that controls the movement of salt and water into and out of cells to stop working properly. This leads to the production of thick, sticky mucus in the lungs and the digestive system, which can make it difficult to breathe and digest food.

6) New combinations of alleles may also interact with each other to produce new phenotypes.

Over 20 000 Genes Were Mapped in the Human Genome Project

1) Thousands of scientists from all over the world collaborated (worked together) on the Human Genome Project. The big idea was to find every single human gene.

2) The project officially started in 1990 and a complete map of the human genome, including the locations of around 20 500 genes, was completed in 2003.

3) Now that the genes have all been found, scientists are trying to figure out what they all do.

4) So far, the project has helped to identify about 1800 genes related to disease, which has huge potential benefits for medicine (see next page).

The Human Genome Project

Here's a bit more about the Human Genome Project — including how we might use the data it produced.

There are Lots of **Medical Applications** for the Project's **Research**

Prediction and prevention of diseases

Many common diseases like cancers and heart disease are caused by the interaction of different genes, as well as lifestyle factors. If doctors knew what genes predisposed people to what diseases, we could all get individually tailored advice on the best diet and lifestyle to avoid our likely problems. Doctors could also check us regularly to ensure early treatment if we do develop the diseases we're susceptible to.

Testing and treatment for inherited disorders

1) Inherited disorders (e.g. cystic fibrosis) are caused by the presence of one or more faulty alleles in a person's genome.

2) Thanks to the Human Genome Project, scientists are now able to identify the genes and alleles that are suspected of causing an inherited disorder much more quickly than they could do in the past.

3) Once an allele that causes an inherited disorder has been identified, people can be tested for it and it may be possible to develop better treatments or even (eventually) a cure for the disease.

New and better medicines

1) Genome research has highlighted some common genetic variations between people. Some variations affect how our individual bodies will react to certain diseases and to the possible treatments for them.

2) Scientists can use this knowledge to design new drugs that are specifically tailored to people with a particular genetic variation. They can also determine how well an existing drug will work for an individual. Tests can already identify whether or not someone with breast cancer will respond to a particular drug, and what dosage is most appropriate for certain drugs in different patients.

3) More generally, knowing how a disease affects us on a molecular level should make it possible to design more effective treatments with fewer side-effects.

But There Could Also be **Drawbacks**

1) Increased stress — for example, if someone knew from an early age that they're susceptible to a nasty brain disease, they could panic every time they get a headache (even if they never get the disease).

2) Gene-ism — people with genetic problems could come under pressure not to have children.

3) Discrimination by employers and insurers — life insurance could become impossible to get (or expensive at least) if you have any genetic likelihood of serious disease. And employers might discriminate against people who are genetically likely to get a disease.

Scientists can learn a lot about diseases from the human genome

Working out the human genome was a massive project — it involved scientists from many different parts of the world and took more than ten years to complete. Still, if scientists can use the information to help us understand more about diseases and how to fight them, then I reckon it was well worth all the effort.

Warm-Up and Exam Questions

By doing these questions, you'll soon find out if you've got the basic facts straight.

Warm-Up Questions

1) Explain what is meant by environmental variation.

2) Amy and Beth are sisters. Amy's hair is curly and Beth's hair is straight. Suggest one way that this difference could be caused by a) a genetic factor, b) an environmental factor.

3) True or False? Genetic mutations in an organism's DNA always have an effect on the organism's phenotype.

Exam Questions

1 Helen and Stephanie are identical twins. This means they have identical DNA. **(Grade 4-6)**

(a) Which of the following characteristics can you be certain that Helen and Stephanie will share?

☐ A They will speak the same language.

☐ B They will be the same height.

☐ C They will both be fast runners.

☐ D They will have the same blood group.

[1 mark]

(b) Helen weighs 7 kg more than Stephanie.
Explain whether this is due to genes, environmental factors or both.

[2 marks]

(c) Stephanie has a birthmark on her shoulder. Helen doesn't.
State whether this type of birthmark is caused by genes and explain your answer.

[1 mark]

2 A group of scientists used data from the Human Genome Project to identify an allele that puts people who carry it at high risk of developing colorectal cancer. Eshan has a family history of colorectal cancer. He is offered a genetic test that will tell him if he is carries the allele or not. **(Grade 6-7)**

(a) Suggest **one** advantage to Eshan of having this genetic test.

[1 marks]

(b) Suggest **one** disadvantage to Eshan of having this genetic test.

[1 mark]

3 Genetic variation in a population arises partly due to mutations. **(Grade 6-7)**

(a) Explain how mutations can increase variation in a species.

[3 marks]

(b) Some mutations are neutral, having no effect on an organism, but some do have an impact.
Suggest how a single mutation could have a large impact on phenotype.

[2 marks]

Revision Summary for Topic 3

That's Topic 3 done with — make sure you can answer these questions before moving on.
Try these questions and tick off each one when you get it right.
When you've done all the questions under a heading and are completely happy with it, tick it off..

Reproduction and Meiosis (p.56-58) ☑

1) Name the gametes in humans.
2) What happens to the DNA in a cell before the first division in meiosis?
3) What is the advantage of having genetic variation in a population?
4) Give a reason why sexual reproduction can take more time than asexual reproduction.

DNA and Protein Synthesis (p.59-62) ☑

5) What are the repeating units that make up DNA?
6) What is meant by the term 'double helix'?
7) When extracting DNA from a fruit, what is the purpose of mixing the fruit with detergent?
8) What effect does ice-cold alcohol have on a solution containing free DNA molecules?
9) Fill in the blank: Proteins are made up of _____ joined together in a chain.
10) How do DNA bases code for specific amino acids?
11) Name the enzyme that joins together RNA nucleotides to make mRNA.
12) True or False? A mutation in non-coding DNA can affect the phenotype of an organism.

Genes, Alleles and Genetic Diagrams (p.65-68) ☑

13) What does it mean if an organism is
    a) homozygous for a gene?
    b) heterozygous for a gene?
14) What is monohybrid inheritance?
15) A couple have a child.
    What's the probability that the child will have the XX combination of sex chromosomes?
16) How are carriers shown on a family pedigree?

Mendel, Sex-Linked Genetic Disorders and Inheritance of Blood Groups (p.70-72) ☑

17) Describe the experiment that Mendel used to study the inheritance of height in pea plants.
18) Give three conclusions that Mendel reached by performing his experiments.
19) Why are men more likely to show recessive characteristics that are sex-linked?
20) What is meant by the term 'codominance'?
21) What blood group does an individual have if they have the genotype $I^A I^O$?

Variation and The Human Genome Project (p.74-76) ☑

22) What causes genetic variation in a species?
23) What is an acquired characteristic?
24) Write down three applications of the knowledge gained from the Human Genome Project.
25) Describe three potential drawbacks of being able to read a person's genome.

Natural Selection and Evidence for Evolution

Evolution is the <u>slow and continuous change</u> of organisms from one generation to the next.
<u>Charles Darwin</u> came up with the theory of <u>natural selection</u> to explain how <u>evolution</u> occurs.

Natural Selection Means "Survival of the Fittest"

1) Individuals in a population show <u>genetic variation</u> because of differences in their <u>alleles</u> (see page 74). New alleles arise through <u>mutations</u>.

Alleles are versions of genes — see page 65.

2) Things like <u>predation</u>, <u>competition</u> for resources (e.g. food, water, mates, etc.) and <u>disease</u> act as <u>selection pressures</u>. This means they affect an organism's chance of <u>surviving</u> and <u>reproducing</u>.

3) Those individuals with <u>characteristics</u> that make them <u>better adapted</u> to the selection pressures in their environment have a <u>better chance of survival</u> and so are more likely to <u>breed</u> successfully.

4) This means the <u>alleles</u> that are responsible for the useful characteristics are more likely to be <u>passed on</u> to the <u>next generation</u>.

5) However, some individuals will be <u>less well adapted</u> to the selection pressures in their environment and may be less able to <u>compete</u>. These individuals are <u>less likely</u> to survive and reproduce.

A species that can't compete is likely to go extinct.

6) The <u>beneficial characteristics</u> become more <u>common</u> in the population over time.

Fossils Provide Evidence for Evolution

1) A fossil is <u>any trace</u> of an animal or plant that lived <u>a long time ago</u> (e.g. over a thousand years). They are most commonly found in <u>rocks</u>. Generally, the <u>deeper</u> the rock, the <u>older</u> the fossil.

2) By arranging fossils in <u>chronological</u> (date) order, <u>gradual changes</u> in organisms can be observed. This provides <u>evidence</u> for evolution, because it shows how species have <u>changed</u> and <u>developed</u> over billions of years. Fossils that provide evidence for <u>human evolution</u> are covered on page 82.

Natural selection — the fittest pass on their alleles...

Natural selection's all about the organisms with the <u>best characteristics</u> surviving to <u>pass on</u> their <u>alleles</u>, so that the whole species ends up adapted to its environment. It doesn't happen overnight though.

Natural Selection and Evidence for Evolution

It's not just fossils from many, many years ago that provide <u>evidence for evolution</u> — we can observe the process of <u>natural selection</u> happening in real-time in <u>bacteria</u>...

Bacteria Provide Evidence for Evolution

1) Like all organisms, bacteria sometimes develop <u>random mutations</u> in their DNA. These can create <u>new alleles</u>, which can <u>change</u> the bacteria's <u>characteristics</u> — e.g. a bacterium could become <u>less affected</u> by a particular <u>antibiotic</u> (a drug designed to kill bacteria or prevent them from reproducing).

2) For the bacterium, the ability to <u>resist</u> this antibiotic is a big <u>advantage</u>. In a host who's being treated to get rid of the infection, a resistant bacterium is <u>better able to survive</u> than a non-resistant bacterium — and so it lives for longer and <u>reproduces</u> many more times.

3) This leads to the allele for antibiotic resistance being <u>passed on</u> to lots of offspring — it's just <u>natural selection</u>. This is how it spreads and becomes <u>more common</u> in a population of bacteria over time.

It's easy to see evolution happening in bacteria because they reproduce so rapidly.

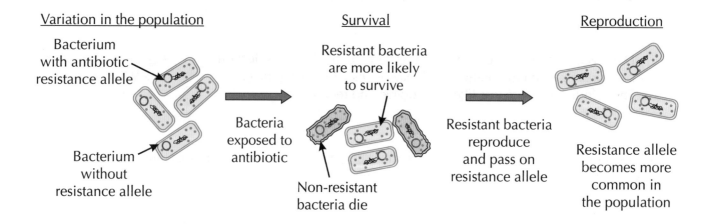

Variation in the population

Bacterium with antibiotic resistance allele

Bacterium without resistance allele

Bacteria exposed to antibiotic

Survival

Resistant bacteria are more likely to survive

Non-resistant bacteria die

Resistant bacteria reproduce and pass on resistance allele

Reproduction

Resistance allele becomes more common in the population

4) Antibiotic resistance provides <u>evidence</u> for evolution because it makes the bacteria <u>better adapted</u> to an <u>environment</u> in which <u>antibiotics</u> (a <u>selection pressure</u>) are <u>present</u>. And as a result, antibiotic resistance becomes <u>more common</u> in the population over time.

5) The emergence of <u>other</u> resistant organisms (e.g. <u>rats</u> resistant to the poison <u>warfarin</u>) <u>also</u> provides evidence for evolution.

WORKING SCIENTIFICALLY

Don't become resistant to revision...

Evolution by natural selection is a <u>theory</u> — an <u>accepted hypothesis</u>. <u>Evidence</u> is really important when it comes to accepting or rejecting scientific hypotheses — if there's no evidence to support a hypothesis, it won't become a theory.

Darwin and Wallace

It was two clever chaps — <u>Darwin</u> and <u>Wallace</u> — who first developed the <u>theory of evolution by natural selection</u>. Little did they know we'd still be harping on about them <u>150 years later</u>...

Darwin Proposed The **Theory of Evolution by Natural Selection**...

1) <u>Charles Darwin</u> was the guy that came up with the <u>theory of evolution by natural selection</u>.
2) He spent 5 years on a <u>voyage</u> around the world <u>studying</u> <u>plants</u> and <u>animals</u> on a ship called <u>HMS Beagle</u>.
3) He noticed that there was <u>variation</u> in members of the <u>same species</u> and that those with characteristics <u>most suited</u> to the <u>environment</u> were more likely to <u>survive</u>.
4) He also noticed that characteristics could be <u>passed on</u> to offspring.
5) He wrote his <u>theory of evolution by natural selection</u> to explain his observations.

DNA and genes hadn't been discovered when Darwin was doing his work, so he didn't know exactly how characteristics were passed on — these details were added to the theory much later on.

...and **Wallace** Contributed **Too**

1) <u>Alfred Russel Wallace</u> was a scientist working at the <u>same time</u> as Darwin.
2) He also came up with the idea of natural selection, <u>independently</u> of Darwin.
3) He and Darwin <u>published</u> their papers on evolution <u>together</u> and <u>acknowledged</u> each other's work — although they didn't always <u>agree</u> on the <u>mechanisms</u> involved in <u>natural selection</u>.
4) Wallace's <u>observations</u> provided lots of <u>evidence</u> to help support the theory of evolution by natural selection.

> E.g. he realised that <u>warning colours</u> are used by some species (e.g. butterflies) to <u>deter predators</u> from eating them — an example of a <u>beneficial characteristic</u> that had <u>evolved</u> by natural selection.

5) But it was <u>Darwin's famous book</u> 'On the Origin of Species' (published in 1859) that made other scientists pay attention to the theory. In this book Darwin gave lots of <u>evidence</u> to support the theory and <u>expanded on it</u>. This book is partly why <u>Darwin</u> is usually <u>better remembered</u> than Wallace.

Ideas About **Evolution** have **Influenced Modern Biology**

1) The theory of evolution by natural selection is still <u>relevant today</u> — it helps us to <u>understand</u> many areas of <u>biology</u>.
2) We now understand that all life <u>changes</u> through the process of evolution, and that the evidence suggests we have <u>all descended</u> from a <u>common ancestor</u>.
3) This has affected lots of <u>different areas</u> of biology, including:

Classification
If all living organisms have descended from a common ancestor, then we're all <u>related</u> in some way. We now <u>classify</u> organisms (arrange them into groups) based on how <u>closely related</u> they are (see page 85).

Antibiotic Resistance
We now understand the importance of <u>finishing</u> the course of drugs to <u>prevent</u> resistant bacteria <u>spreading</u> and we know we need to <u>constantly</u> develop <u>new antibiotics</u> to fight <u>newly evolved</u> resistant bacteria (see previous page).

Conservation
We now understand the importance of <u>genetic diversity</u> and how it helps populations <u>adapt to changing environments</u>. This has led to <u>conservation projects</u> to protect species.

Evidence for Human Evolution

There's a lot of <u>fossil evidence</u> that suggests that humans evolved from a <u>common ancestor</u> with other <u>apes</u>.

Fossils Give Us Clues About What Human Ancestors Were Like

1) Evidence from <u>fossils</u> suggests that humans and chimpanzees evolved from a <u>common ancestor</u> that existed around 6 million years ago.

2) Human beings and their ancestors are known as <u>hominids</u>. Fossils of several different <u>hominid species</u> have been found.

3) These fossils have characteristics that are <u>between</u> apes and humans — by looking at <u>hominid fossils</u> you can see how humans have <u>evolved</u> over time.

'Ardi' is a Fossil Hominid 4.4 Million Years Old

<u>Ardi</u> is a <u>fossil</u> of the species <u>*Ardipithecus ramidus*</u>. She was found in Ethiopia and is <u>4.4 million years old</u>. Ardi's features are a <u>mixture</u> of those found in humans and in apes:

1) The structure of her <u>feet</u> suggests she <u>climbed trees</u> — she had an <u>ape-like big toe</u> to grasp branches.
2) She also had <u>long arms</u> and <u>short legs</u> (more like an ape than a human).
3) Her <u>brain size</u> was about the same as a <u>chimpanzee's</u>.
4) But the structure of her legs suggests that she <u>walked upright</u>. Her <u>hand bone</u> structure also suggests she didn't use her <u>hands</u> to help her <u>walk</u> (like <u>apes</u> do).

Brain size is found by working out 'cranial capacity' — the space taken up by the brain in the skull.

'Lucy' is a Fossil Hominid 3.2 Million Years Old

<u>Lucy</u> is a fossil of the species <u>*Australopithecus afarensis*</u>. She was found in Ethiopia and is <u>3.2 million years old</u>. Lucy also has a <u>mixture</u> of human and ape features, but she is <u>more human-like</u> than Ardi.

1) Lucy had <u>arched feet</u>, more adapted to walking than climbing, and no ape-like big toe.
2) The size of her <u>arms</u> and <u>legs</u> was <u>between</u> what you would expect to find in apes and humans.
3) Her <u>brain</u> was <u>slightly larger</u> than Ardi's but still similar in size to a <u>chimp's brain</u>.
4) The structure of Lucy's leg bones and feet suggest she <u>walked upright</u>, but more <u>efficiently</u> than Ardi.

Leakey and His Team Found Fossil Hominids 1.6 Million Years Old

In 1984 scientist <u>Richard Leakey</u> organised an expedition to Kenya to look for <u>hominid fossils</u>. He and his team discovered <u>many important fossils</u> of different <u>*Australopithecus*</u> and <u>*Homo*</u> species.

1) One find was <u>Turkana Boy</u> — a <u>1.6 million year old</u> fossil skeleton of the species <u>*Homo erectus*</u>. He has a <u>mixture</u> of human and ape-like features, but is <u>more human-like</u> than Lucy.
2) His <u>short arms</u> and <u>long legs</u> are much more like a <u>human</u> than an <u>ape</u>, and his <u>brain size</u> was <u>much larger</u> than Lucy's — similar to <u>human</u> brain size.
3) The structure of his legs and feet suggest he was even better adapted to <u>walking upright</u> than Lucy.

Evidence for Human Evolution

You Can Show **Human Evolution on a Timeline**

So you know that the _Ardipithecus_ and _Australopithecus_ species were more <u>ape-like</u>, compared to the _Homo_ species, which are <u>human-like</u>. They can all be put on a timeline, showing how <u>humans</u> have <u>evolved</u>:

Stone Tools Provide More **Evidence** for **Human Evolution**

The different _Homo_ species continued to <u>evolve</u>. You can tell this because they started using <u>stone tools</u> and these gradually became more <u>complex</u> (so their brains must have been getting <u>larger</u>):

Homo species	Tool use	
Homo habilis (2.5-1.5 million years ago)	Made simple stone tools called pebble tools by hitting rocks together to make sharp flakes. These could be used to scrape meat from bones or crack bones open.	
Homo erectus (2-0.3 million years ago)	Sculpted rocks into shapes to produce more complex tools like simple hand-axes. These could be used to hunt, dig, chop and scrape meat from bones.	
Homo neanderthalensis (300 000-25 000 years ago)	More complex tools. Evidence of flint tools, pointed tools and wooden spears.	
Homo sapiens (200 000 years ago-present)	Flint tools widely used. Pointed tools including arrowheads, fish hooks and needles appeared around 50 000 years ago.	

Stone Tools and **Fossils** Can be **Dated**

When an ancient stone tool or hominid fossil (see previous page) is found, there are several <u>different ways</u> scientists can work out <u>how old it is</u>. These include:

Dating tools and fossils isn't always very accurate, e.g. rock layers can move over time.

1) Looking at the <u>structural features</u> of the tool or fossil. For example, <u>simpler tools</u> are likely to be <u>older</u> than more complex tools.

2) Using <u>stratigraphy</u> — the study of <u>rock layers</u>. <u>Older</u> rock layers are normally found <u>below</u> younger layers, so tools or fossils in <u>deeper</u> layers are usually <u>older</u>.

3) Stone tools are sometimes found with <u>carbon-containing material</u>, for instance a wooden handle. <u>Carbon-14 dating</u> can be used to date this material.

Don't get bogged down by all this information...

It's a bit mind-boggling really how <u>fossils</u> can still exist even <u>millions of years</u> after the organism died. They really are fascinating things, and scientists have learned a whole lot from studying them in detail.

The Pentadactyl Limb

The <u>pentadactyl limb</u> not only provides evidence for the <u>evolution of humans</u>, but for a wide range of <u>species</u>.

The **Pentadactyl Limb** Also Provides **Evidence** for **Evolution**

1) A <u>pentadactyl limb</u> is a limb with <u>five digits</u>.

2) You can see the pentadactyl limb in <u>many species</u>, e.g. mammals, reptiles, amphibians.

3) In each of these species the pentadactyl limb has a <u>similar bone structure</u>, but usually a <u>different function</u>.

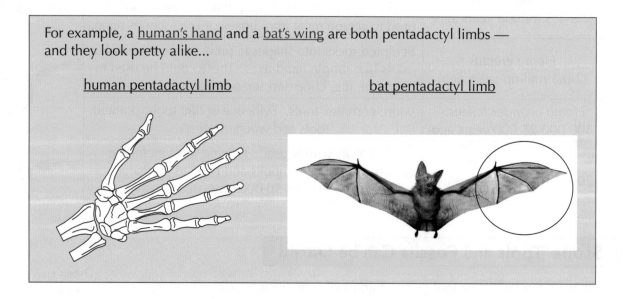

For example, a <u>human's hand</u> and a <u>bat's wing</u> are both pentadactyl limbs — and they look pretty alike...

<u>human pentadactyl limb</u>

<u>bat pentadactyl limb</u>

4) The <u>similarity</u> in bone structure provides <u>evidence</u> that species with a pentadactyl limb have all <u>evolved</u> from a <u>common ancestor</u> (that had a pentadactyl limb). If they'd all evolved from different ancestors, it'd be <u>highly unlikely</u> that they'd share a similar bone structure.

One basic structure, many different functions...

Some modern organisms with a pentadactyl limb, e.g. birds and horses, have actually <u>lost</u> some of their five digits through further evolution, but fossils of their ancestors show how they <u>originally</u> had <u>five digits</u>.

Classification

It seems to be a basic human urge to want to <u>classify</u> things — that's the case in biology anyway...

Classification is Organising **Living Organisms** into Groups

1) Traditionally, organisms were <u>classified</u> according to similarities and differences in their <u>observable</u> <u>characteristics</u>, i.e. things you can see (like how many legs something has). As <u>technology</u> <u>improved</u>, this included things you can see with a <u>microscope</u>, e.g. <u>cell structure</u>.

2) These characteristics were used to classify organisms in the <u>five kingdom classification system</u>. In this system, living things are first divided into <u>five groups</u> called <u>kingdoms</u>. These are:

- <u>Animals</u> — fish, mammals, reptiles, etc.
- <u>Plants</u> — grasses, trees, etc.
- <u>Fungi</u> — mushrooms and toadstools, yeasts, mould.
- <u>Prokaryotes</u> — all <u>single-celled</u> organisms <u>without</u> a nucleus.
- <u>Protists</u> — <u>eukaryotic single-celled</u> organisms, e.g. algae.

There's more on prokaryotes and eukaryotes on p.17.

3) The <u>kingdoms</u> are then subdivided into smaller and smaller groups that have common features — <u>phylum</u>, <u>class</u>, <u>order</u>, <u>family</u>, <u>genus</u>, <u>species</u>.

Classification Systems **Change** Over Time

1) The <u>five kingdom</u> classification system is still used, but it's now a bit <u>out of date</u>.

2) Over time, <u>technology</u> has developed further and our understanding of things like <u>biochemical processes</u> and <u>genetics</u> has increased. For example, we are now able to determine the <u>sequence of DNA bases</u> in different organisms' <u>genes</u> and <u>compare them</u> — the more <u>similar</u> the sequence of a gene, the more <u>closely related</u> the organisms. Scientists are also able to compare <u>RNA sequences</u> in a similar way.

There's more on DNA and RNA on pages 59-62.

3) This led to a bit of a rethink about the way organisms are <u>classified</u> and to the proposal of the <u>three domain system</u> of classification by a scientist called Carl Woese.

4) Using <u>RNA sequencing</u>, Woese found that some members of the <u>Prokaryote kingdom</u> were not as closely related as first thought. He proposed that this kingdom should be split into two groups called <u>Archaea</u> and <u>Bacteria</u>.

5) In fact, Woese suggested that all organisms should first be divided into <u>three</u> <u>large groups</u> called <u>domains</u>. Archaea and Bacteria are <u>two</u> of these domains, and the third domain is <u>Eukarya</u>.

> ARCHAEA — Organisms in this domain <u>look similar</u> to <u>bacteria</u> but are actually quite <u>different</u> — as differences in their <u>DNA and RNA sequences</u> show. They were first found in <u>extreme places</u> such as hot springs and salt lakes.
>
> BACTERIA — This domain contains <u>true bacteria</u> like *E. coli* and *Staphylococcus*.
>
> EUKARYA — This domain includes a <u>broad range</u> of organisms including <u>fungi</u>, <u>plants</u>, <u>animals</u> and <u>protists</u>.

6) The three domains are then <u>subdivided</u> into <u>smaller groups</u> used in the <u>five kingdom system</u> (beginning with kingdom and finishing with species).

Warm-Up and Exam Questions

There's only one way to do well in the exam — learn the facts and practise, practise, practise.
We couldn't have made it much easier for you — so have a go.

Warm-Up Questions

1) Why is a beneficial characteristic likely to become more common in a population over time?
2) What is a fossil?
3) Name two scientists who contributed to the theory of evolution by natural selection.
4) How does the pentadactyl limb show evidence for evolution?
5) Give one example of how advances in technology allowed scientists to distinguish between Archaea and Bacteria.

Exam Questions

1   Most populations of organisms show a lot of variation due to differences in their alleles.

    (a)   State how new alleles arise in a population.

[1 mark]

A selection pressure is a change in an environment which can affect the
chance of an organism surviving and reproducing.

    (b)   (i)   Give **two** examples of a selection pressure in an environment.

[2 marks]

         (ii) Explain why some organisms may not be able to survive if a new
            selection pressure is introduced to the environment.

[2 marks]

2   During an expedition to Kenya, Richard Leakey and his team discovered a
1.6 million year old fossil of the species *Homo erectus*, known as Turkana Boy.

    (a)   Describe how fossils of human ancestors provide evidence for the evolution of humans.

[2 marks]

Stone tools have been found which are believed to have been used by *Homo erectus*.

    (b)   Give **two** methods that could have been used by scientists to determine the age of the stone tools.

[2 marks]

    (c)   Suggest how a stone tool that was used by *Homo erectus* would compare to a stone tool
that was used by *Homo sapiens*, a later *Homo* species.

[1 mark]

    (d)   Describe how the difference in the stone tools used by the different *Homo* species
provide evidence for human evolution.

[1 mark]

Exam Questions

3 Scientists can carry out genetic analysis of DNA and RNA to determine the evolutionary relationships between organisms.

Figure 1 shows the percentage similarities between the DNA sequences of humans and four other organisms.

Organism	A	B	C	D
% DNA sequence similarity to humans	18	44	92	54

Figure 1

(a) Suggest which of the organisms, A-D, is most closely related to humans. Explain your answer.

[2 marks]

(b) Genetic analysis led the scientist Carl Woese to propose the three domain classification system. Name the three domains in this system.

[3 marks]

4 *Clostridium difficile* is a bacterium that causes diarrhoea when it infects the bowel.

Infections by *Clostridium difficile* are becoming increasingly difficult to treat as some strains of the bacterium have developed resistance to a number of antibiotics.

Explain how a population of *Clostridium difficile* bacteria could have developed resistance to an antibiotic.

[4 marks]

5* Figure 2 shows a type of stingray. The stingray's appearance mimics a flat rock. It spends most of its time on a rocky sea bed.

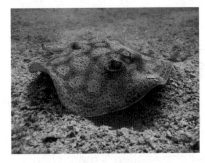

Figure 2

Explain how the stingray might have evolved to look like this.

[6 marks]

Topic 4 — Natural Selection and Genetic Modification

88

Selective Breeding

'Selective breeding' sounds like it has the potential to be a tricky topic, but it's not too bad really.
You just take the best plants or animals and breed them together to get the best possible offspring. That's it.

Selective Breeding is Very Simple

Selective breeding is when humans artificially select the plants or animals that are going
to breed so that the genes for particular characteristics remain in the population.
Organisms are selectively bred to develop features that are useful or attractive. For example:

- Animals that produce more meat or milk.
- Crops with disease resistance.
- Dogs with a good, gentle temperament.
- Plants that produce bigger fruit.

This is the basic process involved in selective breeding:

1) From your existing stock, select the ones which have the characteristics you're after.
2) Breed them with each other.
3) Select the best of the offspring, and breed them together.
4) Continue this process over several generations, and the desirable trait gets
   stronger and stronger. Eventually, all the offspring will have the characteristic.

Selective breeding
is also known as
'artificial selection'.

Selective breeding is nothing new — people have been doing it for thousands of years. It's how we
ended up with edible crops from wild plants and how we got domesticated animals like cows and dogs.

Selective Breeding is Useful...

Selective breeding is important in agriculture and medical research. For example:

In agriculture

Genetic variation means some cattle will have
better characteristics for producing meat than
others (e.g. a larger size). To improve meat
yields, a farmer could select cows and bulls with
these characteristics and breed them together.
After doing this, and selecting the best of the
offspring for several generations, the farmer
would get cows with a very high meat yield.

In medical research

In several studies investigating the reasons
behind alcoholism, rats have been bred with
either a strong preference for alcohol or a
weak preference for alcohol.
This has allowed researchers to compare the
differences between the two different types of
rats, including differences in their behaviour
and in the way that their brains work.

...but Also Has Disadvantages

1) The main problem with selective breeding is that it reduces the gene pool — the number of
   different alleles (forms of a gene) in a population. This is because the "best" animals or plants
   are always used for breeding — and they are all closely related. This is known as inbreeding.
2) Inbreeding can cause health problems because there's more chance of the organisms inheriting harmful
   genetic defects when the gene pool is limited. Some dog breeds are susceptible to certain defects
   because of inbreeding, e.g. pugs often have breathing problems. This leads to ethical considerations —
   particularly if animals are deliberately bred to have negative characteristics for medical research.
3) There can also be serious problems if a new disease appears. There's not much variation in the
   population, so there's less chance of resistance alleles being present. All the stock are closely related to
   each other, so if one is going to be killed by a new disease, the others are also likely to succumb to it.

Topic 4 — Natural Selection and Genetic Modification

Tissue Culture

By taking little bits of tissues and <u>growing them</u>, scientists are able to reproduce tissue from a <u>single individual</u> — so they don't have to go through the lengthy process of selective breeding.

Plants Can be Grown Using Tissue Culture

1) Tissue culture involves growing cells on an <u>artificial growth medium</u>.

2) <u>Whole plants</u> can be grown via tissue culture — it's really <u>easy</u> and really <u>useful</u> too.
   Plants grown this way can be made very <u>quickly</u>, in <u>very little space</u> and can be grown <u>all year</u>.

3) The plants produced via tissue culture are also <u>clones</u> — <u>genetically identical</u> organisms.
   This means you can use tissue culture to create <u>lines</u> of clones all with the <u>same beneficial</u>
   <u>features</u>, e.g. <u>pesticide resistance</u>, <u>tasty fruit</u>, etc. Here's how it works:

   1) First you choose the plant you want to clone based on its <u>characteristics</u> —
      e.g. a beautiful flower, a good fruit crop.

   2) You <u>remove</u> several <u>small pieces</u> of <u>tissue</u> from the <u>parent plant</u>.
      You get the best results if you take tissue from <u>fast-growing root or shoot tips</u>.

   3) You grow the tissue in a <u>growth medium</u> containing <u>nutrients</u> and <u>growth hormones</u>. This is done
      under <u>aseptic</u> (sterile) conditions to prevent growth of <u>microbes</u> that could harm the plants.

   4) As the tissues produce shoots and roots they can be moved to <u>potting compost</u> to carry on growing.

Parent plant

Tissue removed from
the tip of the plant

Tissue placed on a medium
containing growth hormones

Hundreds of
clones can be
made from
just one
parent plant

Animal Tissue Culture is Useful for Medical Research

1) <u>Animal</u> tissue culture is often used in <u>medical research</u> because it means that you can
   carry out all kinds of <u>experiments</u> on tissues in <u>isolation</u>. E.g. you can investigate the
   effect of <u>glucose</u> on cells in the <u>pancreas</u> by growing pancreatic cells in culture.

   Whole animals aren't grown via tissue culture.

2) It means that you can look at the effects of a <u>particular substance</u> or <u>environmental change</u> on
   the cells of a <u>single tissue</u>, without <u>complications</u> from other processes in the <u>whole</u> organism.

3) Tissue culture of <u>animal cells</u> is carried out as follows:

   1) First, a <u>sample</u> of the <u>tissue</u> you want to study, e.g. tissue from the
      pancreas, is <u>extracted from</u> the animal.

   2) The cells in the sample are <u>separated</u> from each other using <u>enzymes</u>.

   3) Then they are placed in a <u>culture vessel</u> and bathed
      in a <u>growth medium</u> containing all the <u>nutrients</u> that
      they need. This allows them to <u>grow</u> and <u>multiply</u>.

   4) After several rounds of <u>cell division</u>, the cells can be <u>split up</u> again
      and placed into <u>separate vessels</u> to encourage <u>further growth</u>.

   5) Once the tissue culture has been grown, it can be <u>stored</u> for future use.

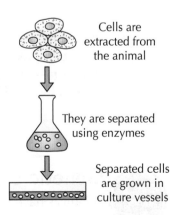

Cells are
extracted from
the animal

They are separated
using enzymes

Separated cells
are grown in
culture vessels

Genetic Engineering

Genetic engineering is a relatively new area of science (well, it began in the 1970s). We've already put the technology to good use and it has many more exciting possibilities too...

Genetic Engineering is Useful in Agriculture and Medicine

Genetic engineering involves modifying an organism's genome (its DNA) to introduce desirable characteristics. For example:

In agriculture, crops can be genetically modified to be resistant to herbicides (chemicals that kill plants). Making crops herbicide-resistant means farmers can spray their crops to kill weeds, without affecting the crop itself. This can also increase crop yield.

In medicine, bacteria can be genetically engineered to produce human insulin, (see next page).

Researchers have managed to transfer human genes that produce useful proteins into sheep and cows. E.g. human antibodies used in therapy for illnesses like arthritis, some types of cancer and multiple sclerosis. These proteins can then be extracted from the animal, e.g. from their milk.

It's possible that animals with organs suitable for organ transplantation into humans might also be produced in the future.

Genetic Engineering Comes With Risks

1) Genetic engineering has risks as well as benefits.

2) There are concerns about growing genetically modified crops. One is that transplanted genes may get out into the environment. E.g. a herbicide resistance gene may be picked up by weeds, creating a new 'superweed' variety. Another concern is that genetically modified crops could adversely affect food chains — or even human health.

3) There are also concerns about the genetic engineering of animals. It can be hard to predict what effect modifying its genome will have on the organism — many genetically modified embryos don't survive and some genetically modified animals suffer from health problems later in life.

Genetic engineering has huge potential benefits...

Scientists have used genetic engineering to produce organisms that benefit humans in all sorts of ways — from bacteria that can make medicines for us, to food crops that contain extra vitamins. But, as with any new technology, we need to be aware of the risks that it carries too.

Genetic Engineering

The process of transferring a new gene into another organism's genome requires enzymes and vectors.

Enzymes Can Cut Up DNA or Join DNA Pieces Together

1) Restriction enzymes recognise specific sequences of DNA and cut the DNA at these points — the pieces of DNA are left with sticky ends where they have been cut.

2) Ligase enzymes are used to join two pieces of DNA together at their sticky ends.

3) Two different bits of DNA stuck together are known as recombinant DNA.

Vectors Can Be Used To Insert DNA Into Other Organisms

A vector is something that's used to transfer DNA into a cell. There are two sorts — plasmids and viruses:

1) Plasmids are small, circular molecules of DNA that can be transferred between bacteria.

2) Viruses insert DNA into the organisms they infect.

Here's how genetic engineering works:

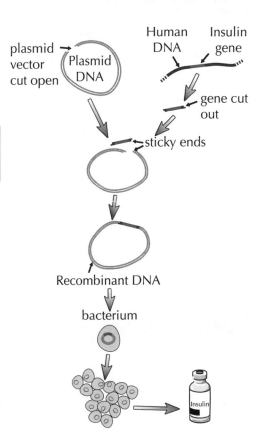

1) The DNA you want to insert (e.g. the gene for human insulin) is cut out with a restriction enzyme. The vector DNA is then cut open using the same restriction enzyme.

2) The vector DNA and the DNA you're inserting are left with sticky ends. They are mixed together with ligase enzymes.

3) The ligases join the pieces of DNA together to make recombinant DNA.

4) The recombinant DNA (i.e. the vector containing new DNA) is inserted into other cells, e.g. bacteria.

5) These cells can now use the gene you inserted to make the protein you want. E.g. bacteria containing the gene for human insulin can be grown in huge numbers in a fermenter to produce insulin for people with diabetes.

It looks hard, but it's a fancy cut and paste...

The process of genetic engineering uses two key types of enzyme. Make sure you know the names of both types of enzyme for the exam and what they're used for in genetic engineering.

GMOs and Human Population Growth

Genetically modified organisms are also known as GM organisms or GMOs.
GMOs are being used to help provide food for many people in the world that suffer from hunger.

Crops can be Genetically Modified to be Resistant to Insects

1) One reason why people might want to genetically engineer crops is to make them resistant to insect pests. This can improve crop yields and reduce the need for chemical pesticides.

2) There's a bacterium called *Bacillus thuringiensis* (Bt) which produces a toxin (poison) that kills many of the insect larvae that are harmful to crops.

3) The gene for the Bt toxin is inserted into crops, such as corn and cotton, which then produce the toxin in their stems and leaves — making them resistant to the insect pests.

4) The toxin is specific to insect pests — it's harmless to humans, animals and other insects. However, the long-term effects of exposure to Bt crops aren't yet known.

5) The insects that feed on the crops are constantly exposed to the toxin, so there's a danger they'll develop resistance and no longer be killed by it. Farmers try to avoid this happening by using other insecticides too.

GMOs Can Be Used to Provide More Food for People

1) The world's population is rising very quickly — and it's not slowing down.

2) This means that global food production must increase too so that we all have access to enough food that is safe for us to eat and has the right balance of nutrition — this is known as 'food security'.

3) GM crops can be used to help increase food production — e.g. crops that are genetically engineered to be resistant to pests or to grow better in drought conditions can help to improve crop yields.

4) Some crops can be engineered to combat certain deficiency diseases, e.g. Golden Rice has been genetically engineered to produce a chemical that's converted in the body to vitamin A.

5) Unfortunately, not everyone thinks this is a good idea:

- Many people argue that people go hungry because they can't afford to buy food, not because there isn't any food about. So they argue that you need to tackle poverty first.
- There are fears that countries may become dependent on companies who sell GM seeds.
- Sometimes poor soil is the main reason why crops fail, and even GM crops won't survive.

Other Techniques Can Also be Used to Increase Food Production

1) Using GMOs is a relatively new way of improving crop yields — and it might not always be helpful.

2) For example, if soils are poor, applying fertilisers is likely to be the best way to increase yields. Fertilisers contain minerals that are essential for plant growth, e.g. nitrates and phosphates. They replace the nutrients that have been lost from the soils to previous crops. However, excess fertilisers can cause problems in rivers and lakes through the process of eutrophication — see p.177.

3) Pests can also be controlled without the use of GM crops or chemical pesticides. Biological control methods use other organisms (including predators and parasites) to reduce pest numbers. For example, cane toads were introduced into Australia to eat beetles that were damaging crops.

4) Biological control can have longer-lasting effects than chemical pesticides and be less harmful to wildlife, but introducing new organisms can cause problems, e.g. cane toads are now a pest themselves in Australia because they poison the native species that eat them.

Warm-Up and Exam Questions

The end of Topic 4 is in sight — hurrah. There are just a few questions to get through first, to make sure you've been paying close enough attention.

Warm-Up Questions

1) Why might a plant nursery use selective breeding?
2) What potential issues can selective breeding cause?
3) Name two types of enzyme needed for the process of genetic engineering.

Exam Questions

1 Organisms can be genetically modified.
This means an organism's genes can be altered to alter its characteristics.

   (a) Give **one** function of the enzymes used in genetic engineering.

   [1 mark]

   (b) Suggest **one** useful way that plants can be genetically modified.

   [1 mark]

   (c) Some people think that it is wrong to genetically modify crop plants.
   Give **two** objections that people might have.

   [2 marks]

2 In medical research, investigations are often carried out using isolated animal tissue, rather than whole organisms.

   Describe the process of animal tissue culture.

   [4 marks]

3 The characteristics of two varieties of wheat plants are shown in **Figure 1**.

Variety	Grain yield	Resistance to bad weather
Tall stems	High	Low
Dwarf stems	Low	High

Figure 1

   (a) Describe how selective breeding could be used to create a wheat plant with a high grain yield and high resistance to bad weather.

   [3 marks]

   (b) Explain why selectively breeding the wheat plants could cause problems if the selectively bred wheat plants are exposed to a new wheat disease.

   [3 marks]

Revision Summary for Topic 4

Well, it's all over for Topic 4 folks — but I know how much you'll miss it, so here are some questions on it...
Try these questions and tick off each one when you get it right.
When you've done all the questions under a heading and are completely happy, tick it off.

Natural Selection and Evolution (p.79-84) ☑

1) Describe how organisms evolve by the process of natural selection. ☑
2) How do antibiotic-resistant bacteria provide evidence for evolution? ☑
3) Name three important areas of modern biology that have been influenced by
   Darwin and Wallace's theory of evolution by natural selection. ☑
4) What are hominids? ☑
5) Which fossil is older — "Ardi" or "Lucy"? ☑
6) Who was Richard Leakey? What important discoveries
   did he make in relation to human evolution? ☑
7) What is stratigraphy? How might it be used to date stone tools? ☑

Classification (p.85) ☑

8) Describe how organisms were classified using the five kingdom classification system. ☑
9) What classification system was proposed by Carl Woese and what led him to propose it? ☑

Selective Breeding (p.88) ☑

10) What is artificial selection? ☑
11) How can selective breeding be used to improve yields in the meat industry? ☑
12) Describe one way in which selective breeding can be useful outside of agriculture. ☑
13) What is a gene pool? ☑
14) Why does selective breeding reduce gene pools? ☑

Tissue Culture (p.89) ☑

15) What is a clone? ☑
16) Why is it useful to be able to make many clones of a single plant? ☑
17) What are the benefits of using animal tissue culture for medical research? ☑

Genetic Engineering and Human Population Growth (p.90-92) ☑

18) What are restriction enzymes used for in genetic engineering? ☑
19) In genetic engineering, what is a vector? ☑
20) What are the concerns over creating genetically modified organisms? ☑
21) Complete the sentence:
    A gene from Bacillus thuringiensis is used to make crops more resistant to _____. ☑
22) How can poor soils be improved to increase crop yields? ☑
23) Give an example of a biological pest control method. ☑

Health and Disease

Try as we might, it's unlikely that we'll be in tip-top condition for all of our lives — disease tends to get us all at some point. There are lots of different types of diseases we could get...

You Need to Know How 'Health' is Defined

1) It might surprise you to know that being healthy is about more than just not being sick.

2) The World Health Organisation (the WHO) defines health as "a state of complete physical, mental and social well-being, and not merely the absence of disease or infirmity".

3) This means that even if someone is very physically fit, they still might be unhealthy if, e.g. they have mental health issues or are socially isolated.

Infirmity means weakness or frailness, commonly due to old age.

Diseases Can be Communicable or Non-Communicable

1) A disease is a condition where part of an organism doesn't function properly. There are two sorts of disease — communicable and non-communicable.

2) Communicable diseases are diseases that can be spread between individuals.

3) Non-communicable diseases can't be transmitted between individuals. They include things like cancer and heart disease. There's more on these on pages 114-115.

4) If you are affected by one disease, it could make you more susceptible to others — your body may become weakened by the disease, so it's less able to fight off others.

Being susceptible to a disease, means that you have an increased chance of getting it.

Communicable Diseases are Caused by Pathogens

Pathogens are organisms such as viruses, bacteria, fungi and protists (see p.85) that cause communicable diseases. Here are some examples of communicable diseases that you need to know about for your exam:

Ebola is a Viral Disease

1) Ebola is a virus.
2) It causes haemorrhagic fever (a fever with bleeding).
3) It is spread via bodily fluids.
4) Transmission can be reduced by isolating infected individuals and sterilising any areas where the virus may be present.

Chalara Ash Dieback is a Fungal Disease

1) Chalara ash dieback is caused by a fungus that infects ash trees.
2) Symptoms include leaf loss and bark lesions (wounds).
3) The fungus is carried through the air by the wind. (It also spreads when diseased ash trees are moved between areas.)
4) Transmission can be reduced by removing young, infected ash trees and replanting with different species or by restricting the import or movement of ash trees.

Health and Disease

Malaria is a Disease Caused by a Protist

1) The pathogen that causes malaria is a protist.
2) The effects of malaria include damage to red blood cells and, in severe cases, to the liver.
3) Mosquitoes act as animal vectors (carriers) — they pass on the protist to humans but don't get the disease themselves.
4) Mosquito nets and insect repellent can be used to prevent mosquitoes carrying the pathogen from biting people.

Cholera, Tuberculosis and Some Stomach Ulcers are Bacterial Diseases

1) Cholera is a disease caused by a bacterium called *Vibrio cholerae*.
2) It causes diarrhoea.
3) Cholera spreads via contaminated water sources.
4) Transmission can be reduced by making sure that people have access to clean water supplies.

1) Tuberculosis is caused by a bacterium called *Mycobacterium tuberculosis*.
2) It causes coughing and lung damage.
3) The bacteria are spread through the air when infected individuals cough.
4) Infected people should avoid crowded public spaces, practise good hygiene and sleep alone. Their homes should also be well-ventilated.

1) Some stomach ulcers are caused by a bacterium called *Helicobacter pylori*.
2) Symptoms include stomach pain, nausea and vomiting.
3) The bacteria are spread through oral transmission, e.g. swallowing contaminated water or food.
4) Transmission can be reduced by having clean water supplies and hygienic living conditions.

Communicable diseases spread from one individual to another

EXAM TIP You could be asked how to prevent the transmission of a disease. Remember, preventing the spread of a disease is linked to how it spreads. If a disease is transmitted via bodily fluids, then its spread can be prevented by avoiding contact with the bodily fluids of an infected individual.

Sexually Transmitted Infections

Some communicable diseases are transmitted <u>sexually</u>.

STIs are **Sexually Transmitted Infections**

STIs are infections that are spread through <u>sexual contact</u>, including <u>sexual intercourse</u>.
Here are <u>two</u> STIs that you need to know about:

Some STIs, including Chlamydia, are spread by genital contact, not just sexual intercourse.

Chlamydia

1) *Chlamydia* is a kind of <u>bacterium</u>, but it behaves in a similar way to a <u>virus</u> (see next page) because it can only reproduce <u>inside host cells</u>.

2) Although it doesn't always cause <u>symptoms</u>, it can result in <u>infertility</u> in men and women.

3) The <u>spread</u> of *Chlamydia* can be <u>reduced</u> by wearing a <u>condom</u> when having sex, <u>screening</u> individuals so they can be <u>treated</u> for the infection or <u>avoiding sexual contact</u>.

HIV

1) HIV is the <u>Human Immunodeficiency Virus</u> — it kills <u>white blood cells</u>, which are really important in the <u>immune response</u>.

2) HIV infection eventually leads to <u>AIDS</u> (Acquired Immune Deficiency Syndrome).

3) This is when the infected person's immune system <u>deteriorates</u> and eventually <u>fails</u> — because of this, the person becomes very <u>vulnerable</u> to opportunistic infections by <u>other pathogens</u>.

4) HIV is spread via infected <u>bodily fluids</u> (e.g. blood, semen, vaginal fluids). One of the main ways to prevent its spread is to use a <u>condom</u> when having sex. <u>Drug users</u> should also avoid <u>sharing needles</u>. <u>Medication</u> can <u>reduce the risk</u> of an infected individual passing the virus on to others during sex (or of a mother passing the virus to her baby during pregnancy) so <u>screening</u> and <u>proper treatment</u> are also important.

Watch yourself, there are a lot of nasties out there...

Try drawing out a <u>table</u> with columns for 'disease', 'pathogen', 'symptom / effects', 'how it's spread' and 'how to reduce/prevent transmission', then fill it in for all the diseases on the previous three pages. See how much you can write down <u>without</u> looking back at the pages.

Viruses

Viruses, such as <u>Ebola</u> (see p.95) and <u>HIV</u> (see p.97) can cause serious problems.

Viruses Can Only Reproduce Inside Living Cells

1) Viruses <u>aren't cells</u>. They're usually no more than a <u>protein coat</u> around a strand of <u>genetic material</u>.

2) They have to <u>infect living cells</u> (called host cells) in order to <u>reproduce</u>. <u>Specific</u> types of viruses will only infect <u>specific cells</u>.

3) The <u>life cycle</u> of a virus starts with when it infects a <u>new host cell</u>. Many will then reproduce by the <u>lytic pathway</u>, but some can enter the <u>lysogenic</u> pathway <u>first</u>:

genetic material

protein coat

A typical virus

The lytic pathway

1) The virus attaches itself to a <u>specific host cell</u> and <u>injects</u> its <u>genetic material</u> into the cell.

2) The virus uses <u>proteins</u> and <u>enzymes</u> in the host cell to <u>replicate</u> its <u>genetic material</u> and produce the <u>components</u> of new viruses.

3) The viral components <u>assemble</u>.

4) The host cell <u>splits open</u>, releasing the new viruses, which infect <u>more cells</u>.

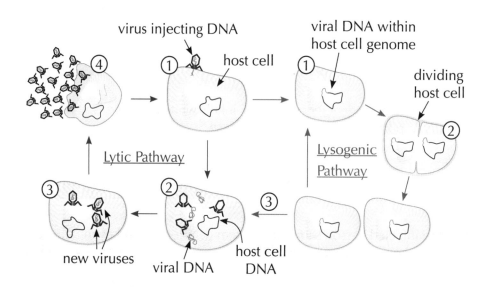

virus injecting DNA

viral DNA within host cell genome

host cell

dividing host cell

Lytic Pathway

Lysogenic Pathway

new viruses

viral DNA

host cell DNA

The lysogenic pathway

1) The injected <u>genetic material</u> is <u>incorporated</u> into the <u>genome</u> (DNA) of the host cell.

2) The viral <u>genetic material</u> gets <u>replicated</u> along with the <u>host DNA</u> every time the host cell <u>divides</u> — but the virus is <u>dormant</u> (inactive) and <u>no new viruses</u> are made.

3) Eventually a <u>trigger</u> (e.g. the presence of a <u>chemical</u>) causes the viral genetic material to <u>leave</u> the genome and enter the <u>lytic pathway</u>.

REVISION TIP

Viruses are much smaller than cells

Make sure you know which pathway in a viral life cycle is which. Remember, the <u>lysogenic</u> pathway incorporates the viral genetic material into the host's <u>genome</u>.

Plant Diseases

Plants have some pretty nifty ways of <u>defending</u> themselves against <u>disease</u> — in fact we use many of their <u>chemical defences</u> to make our <u>medicines</u>.

Plants Have **Physical Defences** Against **Pathogens** and **Pests...**

1) Most plant <u>leaves</u> and <u>stems</u> have a <u>waxy cuticle</u>, which provides a <u>barrier</u> to stop pathogens <u>entering</u> them or pests from <u>damaging</u> them. It may also stop <u>water collecting</u> on the leaf, which could reduce the risk of infection by pathogens that are <u>transferred</u> between plants <u>in water</u>.

2) Plant cells themselves are surrounded by <u>cell walls</u> made from <u>cellulose</u>. These form a <u>physical barrier</u> against pathogens that make it past the waxy cuticle.

...as Well as **Chemical** Ones

1) Plants don't just rely on <u>physical defences</u>. They also produce <u>chemicals</u> that help prevent <u>damage</u> to the plant. For example, they produce chemicals called <u>antiseptics</u>, which <u>kill</u> bacterial and fungal <u>pathogens</u>. They also produce <u>chemicals</u> to <u>deter pests</u> (e.g. insects) from <u>feeding</u> on their leaves.

2) Some of these chemicals can be used as <u>drugs</u> to <u>treat human diseases</u> or <u>relieve symptoms</u>. E.g.

   - <u>Quinine</u> comes from the <u>bark</u> of the cinchona tree. For years it was the main <u>treatment</u> for <u>malaria</u>.
   - <u>Aspirin</u> is used to relieve <u>pain</u> and <u>fever</u>. It was developed from a chemical found in the <u>bark</u> and <u>leaves</u> of <u>willow trees</u>.

Plant Diseases Can be **Detected** in the **Field** and in the **Lab**

1) In the <u>field</u>, plant diseases are usually detected by <u>observations</u>. Plant <u>pathologists</u> (experts in plant disease) recognise the <u>symptoms</u>. E.g. <u>galls</u> (abnormal growths) might indicate <u>crown gall disease</u> in many different types of plant, including <u>apple</u> and other <u>fruit trees</u>.

2) Sometimes plants may show <u>symptoms</u> of a <u>disease</u> (e.g. yellow leaves) which are actually due to <u>environmental causes</u>, such as a <u>nutrient deficiency</u>. By changing the <u>environmental conditions</u> (e.g. adding nutrients to the soil) and observing any <u>change</u> in the plant's symptoms, it can be possible to determine whether a plant is <u>diseased</u> or if the symptoms were due to something else.

3) Different pathogens are spread in <u>different ways</u> — so plant pathologists can analyse the <u>distribution</u> of <u>diseased plants</u> to identify the kind of pathogen involved. E.g. <u>patches</u> of diseased plants may suggest that the disease is spread through the <u>soil</u> and a <u>random distribution</u> may suggest an airborne pathogen.

4) Laboratory-based <u>diagnostic testing</u> allows accurate <u>identification</u> of specific pathogens. It might involve:

Detecting Antigens

- <u>Pathogens</u> have unique <u>molecules</u> on their surface called <u>antigens</u> (see page 102).
- Antigens from a particular <u>pathogen</u> will be <u>present</u> in a plant <u>infected</u> with that pathogen and can be <u>detected</u> in a sample of plant tissue (using <u>monoclonal antibodies</u>, see p.105).
- The detection of an <u>antigen</u> unique to a particular pathogen allows that <u>pathogen</u> to be <u>identified</u> and the <u>disease diagnosed</u>.

Detecting DNA

- If a plant is <u>infected</u> with a pathogen, the pathogen's <u>DNA</u> will be present in the plant's <u>tissues</u>.
- Scientists have techniques that allow them to detect even <u>small amounts</u> of <u>pathogen DNA</u> in a sample of plant tissue, allowing them to <u>identify</u> the particular pathogen that is present.

Warm-Up and Exam Questions

Have a go at these questions to test what you've picked up about diseases — their symptoms, how they are transmitted and how their spread can be limited. You can go back over anything you struggle with.

Warm-Up Questions

1) How does the World Health Organisation (WHO) define the term 'health'?
2) What does it mean if a disease is 'communicable'?
3) Name two diseases caused by bacteria.
4) How is HIV spread through sexual contact?
5) Give one way to reduce the spread of *Chlamydia*.

Exam Questions

1   Chalara ash dieback is caused by a pathogen that infects ash trees. *(Grade 4-6)*

(a)   Give the definition of the term 'pathogen'.

[1 mark]

(b)   What type of pathogen causes Chalara ash dieback?

☐ **A**   A bacterium

☐ **B**   A virus

☐ **C**   A protist

☐ **D**   A fungus

[1 mark]

(c)   Outline **one** way that Chalara ash dieback spreads.

[1 mark]

2   The methods used to prevent the spread of a disease depend on how the disease is transmitted. *(Grade 6-7)*

(a)   Explain why hand washing may not be helpful in limiting the spread of malaria.

[2 marks]

(b)   Suggest and explain **one** reason why efforts to limit the spread of malaria often focus on the mosquito.

[1 mark]

Typhoid fever is a bacterial disease that infects humans. Typhoid fever is spread by eating or drinking food or water contaminated with the faeces of an infected person.

(c)   Suggest **one** way that the spread of typhoid fever could be reduced.

[1 mark]

Exam Questions

3 The health of plants can be affected by pathogens, pests and environmental factors.

Plants have many methods to protect themselves against pests and pathogens.

(a) Give **two** methods of physical defence used by plants to stop pathogens entering.

[2 marks]

(b) Give **two** ways in which plants use chemicals to defend themselves against pests and/or pathogens.

[2 marks]

(c) State **one** way that some of the defence chemicals produced by plants can benefit humans.

[1 mark]

Fusarium wilt is a fungal disease caused by *Fusarium oxysporum*. It affects a wide variety of crops, including tomato, sweet potato and banana plants. When infected with this fungus, crops show signs of wilting, such as dried out and drooping leaves.

(d) Outline how a scientist could eliminate possible environmental causes of plant wilting.

[2 marks]

(e) Give **one** reason why a scientist might want to analyse the distribution of wilting crops.

[1 mark]

(f) Outline **one** way that laboratory-based diagnostic testing could be used to confirm that wilting crops are infected with *Fusarium oxysporum*.

[1 mark]

4 Viruses can reproduce using the lytic or lysogenic pathways. Enterobacteria phage T4 is a virus that infects *Escherichia coli* bacteria. It reproduces via the lytic pathway. **Figure 1** shows the four stages of the lytic pathway.

Figure 1

(a) At stage 1 of the cycle, the Enterobacteria phage T4 virus attaches itself to a host cell and injects its genetic material into the cell.
Describe what is happening at **stage 2** of the cycle, as shown in **Figure 1**.

[2 marks]

HIV is a virus that reproduces inside humans using both the lytic the lysogenic pathways.

(b)* Explain how the life cycle of HIV differs from the life cycle of Enterobacteria phage T4.

[6 marks]

Fighting Disease

The human body has some pretty neat features when it comes to <u>fighting disease</u>.

Physical and Chemical Barriers Stop Pathogens Entering the Body

Like plants (see page 99) the <u>human body</u> has <u>physical</u> and <u>chemical</u> defences against pathogen entry.

Physical barriers

1) The skin acts as a <u>barrier</u> to pathogens, and, if it gets <u>damaged</u>, <u>blood clots</u> quickly <u>seal cuts</u> and keep microorganisms <u>out</u>.
2) <u>Hairs</u> and <u>mucus</u> in your nose <u>trap</u> particles that could contain <u>pathogens</u>.
3) <u>Cells</u> in your <u>trachea</u> and <u>bronchi</u> (airways in the lungs) also produce <u>mucus</u>, which traps pathogens. <u>Other cells</u> that line the trachea and bronchi have <u>cilia</u>. These are <u>hair-like structures</u> which waft the mucus up to the <u>back of the throat</u> where it can be <u>swallowed</u>.

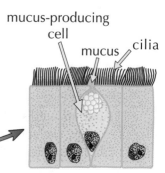

Chemical barriers

1) The <u>stomach</u> produces <u>hydrochloric acid</u>. This <u>kills</u> most pathogens that are swallowed.
2) The <u>eyes</u> produce a chemical called <u>lysozyme</u> (in tears) which <u>kills bacteria</u> on the <u>surface</u> of the eye.

These physical and chemical barriers are non-specific — they work against many different types of pathogens.

Your Immune System Can Attack Pathogens

1) If pathogens do make it into your body, your <u>immune system</u> kicks in to <u>destroy</u> them.
2) The most important part of your immune system is the <u>white blood cells</u>. They travel around in your <u>blood</u> and crawl into every part of you, patrolling for <u>pathogens</u>.
3) <u>B-lymphocytes</u> are a type of white blood cell that are involved in the <u>specific immune response</u> — this is the immune response to a <u>specific pathogen</u>. Here's how it works:

   1) Every pathogen has <u>unique molecules</u> (e.g. proteins) on its surface called <u>antigens</u>.
   2) When your B-lymphocytes come across an antigen on a <u>pathogen</u>, they start to produce <u>proteins</u> called <u>antibodies</u>. Antibodies <u>bind</u> (lock on) to the new invading <u>pathogen</u>, so it can be <u>found</u> and <u>destroyed</u> by other white blood cells. The antibodies produced are <u>specific</u> to that pathogen — they won't lock on to any <u>other</u> pathogens.
   3) The <u>antibodies</u> are then produced <u>rapidly</u> and flow all round the body to find all similar <u>pathogens</u>.

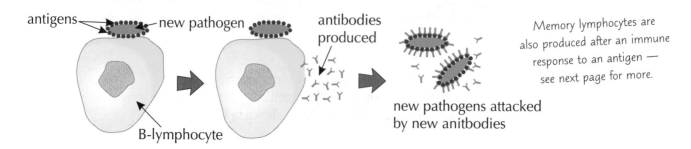

Memory lymphocytes are also produced after an immune response to an antigen — see next page for more.

Antigens on the surfaces of pathogens trigger an immune response

If you have a low level of <u>white blood cells</u>, you'll be more susceptible to <u>infections</u>. HIV attacks white blood cells and <u>weakens</u> the immune system, making it easier for other pathogens to invade.

Memory Lymphocytes and Immunisation

Immunisation has changed the way we fight disease. We don't always have to deal with the problem once it's happened — we can <u>prevent</u> it happening in the first place.

Memory Lymphocytes Give Immunity To Later Infection

1) When a pathogen enters the body for the <u>first time</u> the response is <u>slow</u> because there aren't many <u>B-lymphocytes</u> that can make the <u>antibody</u> needed to <u>lock on to the antigen</u>.

2) <u>Eventually</u> the body will produce <u>enough</u> of the right antibody to <u>overcome</u> the infection. Meanwhile the infected person will show <u>symptoms</u> of the disease.

3) As well as antibodies, <u>memory lymphocytes</u> are also produced in response to a foreign antigen. Memory lymphocytes remain in the body for a <u>long time</u>, and 'remember' a <u>specific</u> antigen.

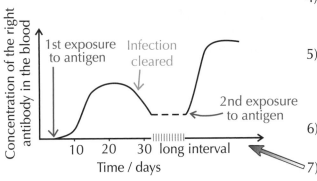

4) The person is now <u>immune</u> — their immune system has the ability to <u>respond quickly</u> to a <u>second</u> infection.

5) If the <u>same pathogen</u> enters the body again, there are more cells that will recognise it and produce antibodies against it. This <u>secondary immune response</u> is <u>faster</u> and <u>stronger</u>.

6) The <u>secondary response</u> often <u>gets rid</u> of the pathogen <u>before</u> you begin to show any symptoms.

7) This can all be shown in a <u>graph</u> like the one here.

Immunisation Stops You Getting Infections

1) To avoid getting ill, you can be <u>immunised</u> against some diseases, e.g. measles.

2) <u>Immunisation</u> usually involves injecting <u>dead</u> or <u>inactive</u> pathogens into the body. These are <u>antigenic</u> (they carry antigens), so even though they're <u>harmless</u> your body makes <u>antibodies</u> to help destroy them.

3) The antigens also trigger the production of <u>memory lymphocytes.</u>

4) So, if <u>live</u> pathogens of the <u>same type</u> get into the body, there will already be <u>memory lymphocytes</u> that can cause a fast <u>secondary immune response</u>. This means that you're less likely to get the disease.

...there are memory lymphocytes around to recognise them and produce antibodies against them...

Memory lymphocytes speed up the next response to the pathogen
<u>Immunisation</u> has helped to save millions of lives — and it's all because of <u>antibodies</u> and <u>memory cells</u>.

Immunisation

Getting <u>immunised</u> against a whole range of diseases is pretty much standard now, so children today are <u>much less likely</u> to catch the kinds of diseases that they might have done in the past. That doesn't mean that immunisation is without its problems though...

There are **Pros** and **Cons** of Immunisation

Pros:

1) Big outbreaks of diseases, called <u>epidemics</u>, can be prevented if a <u>large percentage</u> of the population are <u>immunised</u>. Even the people who <u>aren't immunised</u> are unlikely to catch the disease because there are fewer people able to <u>pass it on</u> — this is known as '<u>herd immunity</u>'. But if a <u>significant number</u> of people aren't immunised, the disease can spread <u>quickly</u> through them and <u>lots</u> of people will be ill at the same time.

2) Some diseases, e.g. <u>smallpox</u>, have been virtually <u>wiped out</u> by <u>immunisation programmes</u>.

Cons:

1) Immunisation <u>doesn't always</u> work — sometimes it doesn't give you <u>immunity</u>.

2) You can sometimes have a <u>bad reaction</u> to a vaccine (e.g. <u>swelling</u>, or maybe something <u>more serious</u> like a fever or seizures). But bad reactions are very <u>rare</u>.

Prevention is better than cure...

Deciding whether to be immunised means <u>balancing risks</u> — the risk of catching the disease if you don't have a vaccine, against the risk of having a bad reaction if you do. As always, you need to look at the <u>evidence</u>. For example, if you get measles (the disease), there's about a 1 in 15 chance that you'll get complications (e.g. pneumonia) — and about 1 in 500 people who get measles actually die. However, the number of people who have a problem with the vaccine is more like 1 in 1 000 000.

Monoclonal Antibodies

Antibodies aren't only used by the immune system — scientists have engineered them for lots of new uses.

Monoclonal Antibodies are Identical Antibodies

1) Antibodies are produced by B-lymphocytes — a type of white blood cell (see page 102).

2) Monoclonal antibodies are produced from lots of clones of a single B-lymphocyte. This means all the antibodies are identical and will only target one specific protein antigen.

3) However, you can't just grab the lymphocyte that made the antibody and grow more — lymphocytes don't divide very easily.

4) Tumour cells, on the other hand, don't produce antibodies but divide lots — so they can be grown really easily.

5) It's possible to fuse a mouse B-lymphocyte with a type of tumour cell called a myeloma cell, to create a cell called a hybridoma.

6) Hybridomas can be cloned to get lots of identical cells. These can all divide really quickly to produce the same antibodies (monoclonal antibodies). These can be collected and purified.

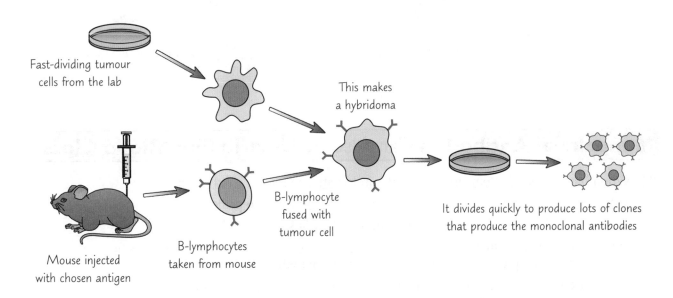

Fast-dividing tumour cells from the lab

This makes a hybridoma

Mouse injected with chosen antigen

B-lymphocytes taken from mouse

B-lymphocyte fused with tumour cell

It divides quickly to produce lots of clones that produce the monoclonal antibodies

7) You can make monoclonal antibodies that bind to anything you want, e.g. an antigen that's only found on the surface of one type of cell. Monoclonal antibodies are really useful because they will only bind to (target) this molecule — this means you can use them to target a specific cell or chemical in the body.

Monoclonal Antibodies

Monoclonal Antibodies Are Used In Pregnancy Tests

A hormone called HCG is found in the urine of women only when they are pregnant.
Pregnancy testing sticks detect this hormone. Here's how they work:

1) The bit of the stick you wee on has some antibodies to the hormone, with blue beads attached.

2) The test strip (the bit of the stick that turns blue if you're pregnant) has some more antibodies to the hormone stuck onto it (so that they can't move).

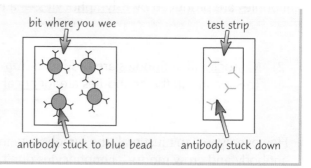

bit where you wee   test strip

antibody stuck to blue bead   antibody stuck down

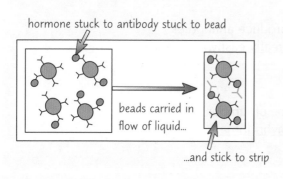

hormone stuck to antibody stuck to bead

beads carried in flow of liquid...

...and stick to strip

3) If you're pregnant and you wee on the stick:
- The hormone binds to the antibodies on the blue beads.
- The urine moves up the stick, carrying the hormone and the beads.
- The beads and hormone bind to the antibodies on the strip.
- So the blue beads get stuck on the strip, turning it blue.

4) If you're not pregnant and you wee on the stick:
- The urine still moves up the stick, carrying the blue beads.
- But there's nothing to stick the blue beads onto the test strip, so it doesn't go blue.

beads carried in flow of liquid...

...but don't stick

Monoclonal Antibodies Can Also Be Used To Find Blood Clots

1) When blood clots, proteins in the blood join together to form a solid mesh.
2) Monoclonal antibodies have been developed that bind to these proteins.
3) You can attach a radioactive element to these antibodies.
4) Then, if you inject them into the body and take a picture using a camera that picks up the radiation, that picture will have a really bright spot where there is a blood clot.
5) This is useful because you can easily find a potentially harmful blood clot (and get rid of it before it harms the patient).

Handy little things, these monoclonal antibodies...

Monoclonal antibodies have lots more uses in medicine, e.g. a test similar to a pregnancy test can be used to detect the antigens of pathogens in a blood sample. There's more about their uses on the next page.

Monoclonal Antibodies

Because monoclonal antibodies can be produced to <u>target</u> a <u>specific</u> chemical or cell, they can help with the diagnosis and treatment of <u>cancer</u>.

You Can Make **Monoclonal Antibodies** That **Target Cancer Cells**

1) <u>Cancer cells</u> have <u>proteins</u> on their cell membranes that <u>aren't</u> found on <u>normal</u> body cells. They're called <u>tumour markers</u>.
2) In the <u>lab</u>, you can make monoclonal antibodies that will <u>bind</u> to these tumour markers. They can be used to help <u>diagnose</u> and <u>treat cancer</u>.

Monoclonal Antibodies Can Be Used To **Diagnose Cancer...**

1) First, the antibodies are labelled with a <u>radioactive element</u>.
2) Then, the <u>labelled antibodies</u> are given to a patient through a <u>drip</u>. They go into the <u>blood</u> and are <u>carried around</u> the body.
3) When the antibodies come into <u>contact</u> with the cancer cells they <u>bind</u> to the <u>tumour markers</u>.
4) A <u>picture</u> of the patient's body is taken using a special camera that detects <u>radioactivity</u>. Anywhere there are <u>cancer cells</u> will show up as a <u>bright spot</u>.
5) Doctors can see <u>exactly</u> where the cancer is, what <u>size</u> it is, and find out if it is <u>spreading</u>.

...and to Target Drugs to Cancer Cells

1) An <u>anti-cancer drug</u> is attached to <u>monoclonal antibodies</u>.
2) The antibodies are given to the patient through a <u>drip</u>.
3) The antibodies <u>target specific cells</u> (the cancer cells) because they <u>only bind</u> to the tumour markers.
4) The drug <u>kills</u> the cancer cells but <u>doesn't kill</u> any <u>normal body cells</u> near the tumour.
5) Other cancer treatments (like other <u>drugs</u> and <u>radiotherapy</u>) can affect <u>normal</u> body cells <u>as well as</u> killing cancer cells.
6) So the <u>side effects</u> of an <u>antibody-based</u> drug are <u>lower</u> than for other drugs or radiotherapy.

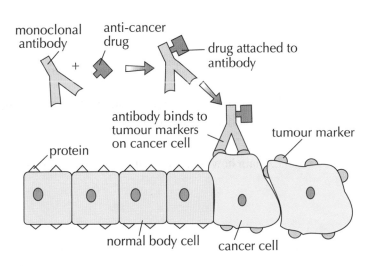

Radiotherapy involves firing high-energy beams (like X-rays) straight at a tumour.

Monoclonal antibodies have got lots of uses in research and medicine

As you've just found out, monoclonal antibodies are really useful for <u>finding stuff</u>. Imagine having a horde of trained <u>fireflies</u> to search for your lost keys. Instead of you having to search under everything, you just release the fireflies and wait for them to cluster around your lost stuff, in a big <u>glowing mass</u>. Genius.

Warm-Up and Exam Questions

It's easy to think you've learnt everything until you try some questions. Don't panic if there's a bit you've forgotten, just go back over that bit until it's firmly fixed in your brain.

Exam Questions

1   There are many different lines of defence in the human body that help to prevent pathogens from entering the blood.

   (a)   Give the role of mucus in the nose.

   [1 mark]

   (b)   Describe how the cilia in the trachea and bronchi help to defend the body.

   [1 mark]

   (c)   Name the substance produced by the stomach to kill pathogens.

   [1 mark]

   (d)   Name the chemical produced to kill bacteria on the surface of the eyes.

   [1 mark]

2   Monoclonal antibodies have many uses in medicine.

   (a)   Explain **one** advantage of using monoclonal antibodies to treat cancer instead of using normal treatment methods.

   [2 marks]

   (b)   Explain how mononclonal antibodies can be used to find blood clots.

   [3 marks]

3   Rubella is a communicable viral disease. The rubella virus is spread in droplets through the air when an infected person coughs, sneezes or talks. The virus causes several symptoms including fever and painful joints. Fortunately, the spread of the disease can be reduced by immunisation.

   (a)* Explain how being immunised against rubella can prevent a person from catching the disease and suggest why immunising a large proportion of the population reduces the risk of someone who hasn't been immunised from catching rubella.

   [6 marks]

   (b)   Suggest **one** reason why some individuals may choose not to receive an immunisation against a disease.

   [1 mark]

Antibiotics and Other Medicines

New medicines are constantly being <u>developed</u>. This page tells you all about how that happens.

Antibiotics Are Used to Treat **Bacterial Infections**

1) Antibiotics work by <u>inhibiting processes</u> in <u>bacterial cells</u>, but <u>not</u> in the <u>host organism</u>. For example, some antibiotics inhibit the <u>building</u> of bacterial <u>cell walls</u> — this <u>prevents</u> the bacteria from <u>dividing</u>, and eventually <u>kills them</u>, but has <u>no effect</u> on cells in the <u>human host</u> (which <u>don't</u> have cell walls).

2) <u>Different antibiotics</u> kill <u>different types</u> of bacteria, so it's important to be treated with the <u>right one</u>.

3) But antibiotics <u>don't destroy viruses</u> (e.g. <u>flu</u> or <u>cold</u> viruses). Viruses reproduce <u>using your body cells</u>, which makes it <u>very difficult</u> to develop drugs that destroy just the virus <u>without</u> killing the body's cells.

There Are Several **Stages** in the **Development** of **New Drugs**

1) First a drug has to be <u>discovered</u>. This can happen in lots of different ways — for example:

> <u>Penicillin</u> is an <u>antibiotic</u>. It was discovered by Alexander Fleming when he was clearing out Petri dishes containing <u>bacteria</u>. He noticed that one of the dishes had <u>mould</u> on it and that the area around the mould was <u>free</u> of bacteria. The mould was producing <u>penicillin</u>, which was <u>killing</u> the bacteria.

2) Nowadays, most scientists use their knowledge of how a disease <u>works</u> to try and identify <u>molecules</u> that could be used as drugs to <u>fight</u> the disease.

3) Once a new potential drug has been <u>discovered</u>, it needs to be <u>developed</u>. This involves <u>preclinical</u> and <u>clinical testing</u>.

Preclinical testing

1) In preclinical testing, drugs are <u>first</u> tested on <u>human cells and tissues</u> in the lab. However, you can't use human cells and tissues to test drugs that affect whole or multiple body systems, e.g. a drug for blood pressure must be tested on a whole animal.

2) The next step is to test the drug on <u>live animals</u>. This is to <u>test</u> that the drug <u>works</u> (produces the <u>effect</u> you're looking for), to find out how <u>toxic</u> (<u>harmful</u>) it is and to find the best <u>dosage</u>.

Clinical testing

1) If the drug <u>passes</u> the tests on animals then it's tested on <u>human volunteers</u> in a <u>clinical trial</u>.

2) First, the drug is tested on <u>healthy volunteers</u> to make sure that it doesn't have any <u>harmful side effects</u> when the body is working <u>normally</u>.

3) If the results of the tests on healthy volunteers are good, the drugs can be tested on people suffering from the <u>illness</u>. The <u>optimum dose</u> is found — this is the dose of drug that is the <u>most effective</u> and has the <u>fewest side effects</u>.

4) Patients are <u>randomly</u> put into <u>two groups</u>. One is given the <u>new drug</u>, the other is given a <u>placebo</u> (a substance that <u>looks like</u> the drug being tested but <u>doesn't do anything</u>, e.g. a sugar pill). This is to allow for the <u>placebo effect</u> (when the patient expects the treatment to work and so <u>feels better</u>, even though the treatment isn't doing anything).

5) Clinical trials are <u>blind</u> — the patient in the study <u>doesn't know</u> whether they're getting the <u>drug</u> or the <u>placebo</u>. In fact, they're often <u>double-blind</u> — neither the <u>patient</u> nor the <u>doctor</u> knows until all the <u>results</u> have been gathered. This is so the doctors <u>monitoring</u> the patients and <u>analysing</u> the results aren't <u>subconsciously influenced</u> by their knowledge.

4) When a drug has finally passed all of these tests, it still needs to be <u>approved</u> by a <u>medical agency</u> before it can be used to <u>treat</u> patients. All of this means that drugs are as <u>effective</u> and <u>safe</u> as possible.

PRACTICAL Investigating Antibiotics and Antiseptics

And now for some hands-on stuff. You can grow your own microorganisms and test how effective different antibiotics, antiseptics or plant extracts are at killing them...

You Can **Grow Bacteria** in the Lab

1) Bacteria (and some other microorganisms) are cultured (grown) in a growth medium, which contains the carbohydrates, minerals, proteins and vitamins they need to grow.

2) The growth medium used can be a nutrient broth solution or solid agar jelly.

3) Bacteria grown on agar 'plates' will form visible colonies on the surface of the jelly, or will spread out to give an even covering.

- To make an agar plate, hot agar jelly is poured into shallow round plastic dishes called Petri dishes.
- When the jelly's cooled and set, inoculating loops (wire loops) can be used to transfer microorganisms to the agar jelly. Alternatively, a sterile dropping pipette and spreader can be used to get an even covering of bacteria.
- The microorganisms then multiply.

4) In the lab at school, cultures of microorganisms are kept at about 25 °C because harmful pathogens are less likely to grow at this temperature. Outside of schools, scientists may culture microorganisms at higher temperatures to provide optimum conditions for growth.

Pathogens are microorganisms that cause disease (see p.95).

You Can Investigate the **Effect** of **Substances** on **Bacterial Growth**

Antibiotics kill bacteria inside the body. Antiseptics kill bacteria outside the body (e.g. on the skin). You can investigate the effect of antibiotics and antiseptics on cultures of bacteria. Since many plants produce antiseptics in self-defence (see p.99) you can also test the effects of different plant extracts in a similar way. Here's how it can be done, using antibiotics as an example:

1) Place paper discs soaked in different types of antibiotics on an agar plate that has an even covering of bacteria. Leave some space between the discs.

2) The antibiotic should diffuse (soak) into the agar jelly. Antibiotic-resistant bacteria (i.e. bacteria that aren't affected by the antibiotic — see p.80) will continue to grow on the agar around the paper discs, but non-resistant strains will die. A clear area will be left where the bacteria have died — this is called an inhibition zone.

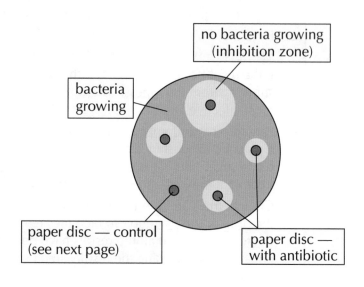

Investigating Antibiotics and Antiseptics

3) Make sure you use a <u>control</u>. This is a paper disc that has <u>not been soaked</u> in an antibiotic. You can then be sure that any <u>difference</u> between the <u>growth</u> of the bacteria around the <u>control</u> disc and around one of the <u>antibiotic</u> discs is due to the <u>effect</u> of the antibiotic <u>alone</u> (and not something weird in the paper, for example).

4) Leave the plate for 48 hours at 25 °C.

5) The <u>more effective</u> the antibiotic is against the bacteria, the <u>larger</u> the <u>inhibition zone</u> will be (see next page).

You Need to Use **Aseptic Techniques**

<u>Contamination</u> by <u>unwanted</u> microorganisms will <u>affect your results</u> and can potentially result in the growth of <u>pathogens</u>. To <u>avoid</u> this, the following <u>aseptic techniques</u> should be used:

1) The Petri dishes and growth medium must be <u>sterilised</u> before use. This can be done by placing them in a machine called an <u>autoclave</u>, which uses <u>steam</u> at a <u>high pressure</u> and <u>temperature</u> to <u>kill</u> any microorganisms present.

2) Before being used to transfer bacteria, an <u>inoculating loop</u> should be <u>sterilised</u> by <u>passing it through a hot flame</u>, so that any <u>unwanted microorganisms</u> are killed.

inoculating loop

3) Liquid bacterial cultures should be kept in a <u>culture vial</u> with a <u>lid</u>. The lid should only be removed <u>briefly</u> when transferring the bacteria, to prevent <u>other microbes</u> getting in.

4) After transferring bacteria to it, a <u>Petri dish</u> should be <u>covered</u> with a lid, which should be <u>lightly taped on</u>. This is to stop microorganisms from the <u>air</u> getting in.

storing a Petri dish

5) The Petri dish should be stored <u>upside down</u> to <u>stop</u> drops of <u>condensation</u> falling onto the agar.

PRACTICAL | Investigating Antibiotics and Antiseptics

Once you've done the experiment on the previous pages, there's a little <u>maths</u> you can do with your results.

Calculate the Sizes of the Inhibition Zones to Compare Results

You can <u>compare</u> the <u>effectiveness</u> of different <u>antibiotics</u> (or <u>antiseptics</u> or <u>plant extracts</u>) on bacteria by looking at the <u>relative sizes</u> of the <u>inhibition zones</u>. The <u>larger</u> the inhibition zone around a disc, the <u>more bacteria killed</u> and so the <u>more effective</u> the antibiotic is against the bacteria.

> You can do this <u>by eye</u> if there are large differences in size. But to get more accurate results it's a good idea to calculate the <u>areas</u> of the inhibition zones using their <u>diameter</u> (the distance <u>across</u>).

Don't open the Petri dish to measure the inhibition zones — they should be visible through the bottom of the dish.

To calculate the area of an inhibition zone, you need to use <u>this equation</u>:

This is the equation for the area of a circle. You're likely to use the units cm^2 or mm^2.

$$\text{Area} = \pi r^2$$

r is the radius of the inhibition zone — it's equal to half the diameter.

π is just a number. You should have a button for it on your calculator. If not, just use the value 3.14.

EXAMPLE:

The diagram below shows the inhibition zones produced by antibiotics A and B. Use the areas of the inhibition zones to compare the effectiveness of the antibiotics.

1) Divide the diameter of zone A by <u>two</u> to find the <u>radius</u>.

   Radius of A = 14 ÷ 2 = 7 mm

2) Stick the radius value into the <u>equation</u> area = πr^2.

   Area of A = $\pi \times 7^2$ = 154 mm^2

3) <u>Repeat</u> steps 1 and 2 for zone B.

   Radius of B = 20 ÷ 2 = 10 mm
   Area of B = $\pi \times 10^2$ = 314 mm^2

4) <u>Compare</u> the <u>sizes</u> of the <u>areas</u>. 314 mm^2 is just over twice 154 mm^2, so you could say that:

   The inhibition zone of antibiotic B is roughly twice the size of the inhibition zone of antibiotic A.

You Can Also Find the Area of a Colony

The equation above can also be used to calculate the <u>area</u> of a bacterial <u>colony</u>. You just need to measure the <u>diameter</u> of the colony you are interested in first.

One colony

Agar

The greater the area, the more effective the antibiotic

PRACTICAL TIP If the inhibition zones aren't perfect circles, you'll need to measure the diameter in <u>more than one</u> direction and work out a <u>mean</u>. Don't be tempted to measure the radius — it's not as accurate.

Warm-Up and Exam Questions

It's that time again — time to test just how much of the previous pages you really remember...

Warm-Up Questions

1) True or false? Antibiotics kill viruses.
2) What is a placebo?
3) When culturing bacteria, why is it important to sterilise the Petri dishes and growth medium before use?
4) How can inhibition zones on agar plates be used to compare the effectiveness of different antibiotics?

Exam Questions

1   A scientist is carrying out a clinical trial.

(a) What is a drug tested on in a clinical trial?

☐ **A** human cells

☐ **B** human volunteers

☐ **C** live animals

☐ **D** human tissue

[1 mark]

(b) The clinical trial is double blind. Explain what this means.

[2 marks]

When testing the drug on living organisms, the scientist has to find out how toxic the drug is by seeing whether it causes any harm.

(c) Apart from the toxicity of the drug, suggest **two** other factors that scientists research during drug testing.

[2 marks]

PRACTICAL

2   A student was investigating the effectiveness of different antibiotics on a strain of bacteria.
    The student placed paper discs soaked in the different antibiotics on an agar plate
    that had an even covering of the bacteria. The results are shown in **Figure 1**.

Antibiotic	X	Y	Z
Diameter of inhibition zone (mm)	15	9	0

Figure 1

(a) Calculate the area of the inhibition zone for antibiotic **X**. Give your answer in mm^2.
     Use the equation: area $= \pi r^2$

[2 marks]

(b) No inhibition zone was formed around the disc soaked in antibiotic **Z**.
     Suggest a reason why.

[1 mark]

Non-Communicable Diseases

Non-communicable diseases <u>aren't caused by pathogens</u>. Instead, there are <u>risk factors</u> associated with them.

Lifestyle Factors May Increase the Risk of Disease

1) <u>Risk factors</u> are things that are linked to an <u>increase</u> in the <u>likelihood</u> that a person will develop a certain disease during their lifetime. They <u>don't guarantee</u> that someone <u>will</u> get the disease.

2) Risk factors can be <u>unavoidable</u>, e.g. a person's <u>age</u> or <u>gender</u> may make them <u>more likely</u> to get a disease. But some are <u>lifestyle factors</u> that people <u>can change</u>. For example:

Smoking is a <u>major risk factor</u> associated with <u>cardiovascular disease</u> — any disease associated with the heart or blood vessels, e.g. a <u>heart attack</u> or <u>stroke</u> (see p.117). This is because:
- <u>Nicotine</u> in cigarette smoke <u>increases heart rate</u>, which <u>increases blood pressure</u>.
- High blood pressure <u>damages artery walls</u>, which contributes to the build up of <u>fatty deposits</u> in the arteries. These deposits restrict blood flow and increase the risk of a <u>heart attack</u> or <u>stroke</u>.
- Smoking increases the risk of <u>blood clots</u> forming in arteries, which can <u>restrict</u> or <u>block</u> blood flow, leading to a <u>heart attack</u> or <u>stroke</u>.

3) Other lifestyle factors are associated with different <u>diseases</u>. E.g.

A diet with <u>too many</u> or <u>too few nutrients</u> can lead to <u>malnutrition</u> (and diseases associated with <u>malnutrition</u>, e.g. <u>scurvy</u> — a <u>vitamin C deficiency</u> disease.)

Malnutrition doesn't just mean not getting enough nutrients. Getting too many nutrients is also a form of malnutrition, and it can lead to obesity.

Not getting enough <u>exercise</u> and having a diet <u>high</u> in <u>fat</u> and <u>sugar</u> are risk factors for <u>obesity</u>.

Drinking too much <u>alcohol</u> is a major risk factor for the development of <u>liver disease</u>, e.g. <u>cirrhosis</u> (scarring of the liver). This is because alcohol is <u>broken down</u> by enzymes in the liver and some of the <u>products</u> are <u>toxic</u>. Drinking too much over a long period of time can cause <u>permanent liver damage</u>.

Non-communicable diseases don't spread between people

In the exam, you might need to <u>read data</u> related to disease risk factors from a table, graph or chart, or <u>explain</u> what the data is showing. Remember to always check any <u>units</u> or <u>graph scales</u> carefully before answering any questions.

Non-Communicable Diseases

You need to know about the effect of <u>lifestyle factors</u> on non-communicable diseases at different <u>levels</u>.

Non-Communicable Diseases Have Many **Risk Factors**

1) As well as <u>smoking</u>, there are lots of other risk factors associated with <u>cardiovascular disease</u>, including: drinking too much <u>alcohol</u>, <u>lack of exercise</u>, and a diet <u>high</u> in saturated <u>fat</u>.

2) In fact, many <u>non-communicable</u> diseases are caused by <u>several different</u> risk factors <u>interacting</u> with each other, rather than <u>one factor alone</u>, including <u>cancer</u>, <u>liver</u> and <u>lung diseases</u> and <u>obesity</u>. <u>Obesity</u> is also a risk factor for <u>other</u> non-communicable diseases, e.g. <u>type 2 diabetes</u> (see p.147) and <u>cardiovascular disease</u>.

Non-Communicable Diseases Can Have **Wide-Ranging Effects**

1) Non-communicable diseases can have <u>knock-on effects</u> for local areas. For example, in areas where there are <u>high levels</u> of <u>obesity</u>, <u>smoking</u> or <u>excess alcohol consumption</u>, there's likely to be a <u>high occurrence</u> of certain <u>non-communicable diseases</u>, e.g. cardiovascular or liver disease. This can put <u>pressure</u> on the <u>resources</u> (money, beds, staff, etc.) of <u>local hospitals</u>.

2) Non-communicable diseases are also costly at a <u>national level</u> because the <u>National Health Service</u> provides the <u>resources</u> for the treatment of patients all over the UK. And sometimes, people <u>suffering</u> from a non-communicable disease may not be able to <u>work</u>. A <u>reduction</u> in the number of people able to work can affect a country's <u>economy</u>.

3) As well as being costly, non-communicable diseases are <u>very common</u>, e.g. <u>cardiovascular disease</u> is the <u>number one</u> cause of death <u>worldwide</u>. In <u>developing countries</u>, <u>malnutrition</u> is also a big problem because people are not able to access <u>enough food</u>. The high cost and occurrence of these diseases can hold back the <u>development</u> of a <u>country</u> — so they have an effect at a <u>global</u> level.

It's hard to avoid all risk factors of disease...

...but risk factors don't mean you'll <u>definitely</u> get the disease — they just increase the chance of getting it.

Measures of Obesity

People come in all sorts of <u>shapes</u> and <u>sizes</u>, so you can't just say that anyone <u>over a particular weight</u> is <u>obese</u>. You have to use <u>indices</u> and <u>ratios</u> to figure this out instead — which is what this page is all about.

A **Body Mass Index** Indicates If You're **Under-** or **Overweight**

1) The <u>Body Mass Index</u> (<u>BMI</u>) is used as a guide to help decide whether someone is <u>underweight</u>, <u>normal</u>, <u>overweight</u> or <u>obese</u>. It's calculated from their <u>height</u> and <u>mass</u>:

$$BMI = \frac{mass\ (kg)}{(height\ (m))^2}$$

Body Mass Index	Weight Description
below 18.5	underweight
18.5 - 24.9	normal
25 - 29.9	overweight
30 - 40	moderately obese
above 40	severely obese

2) Once you have a <u>value</u> for a person's BMI, you can refer to a <u>table</u> that shows how the different values are <u>classified</u>.

EXAMPLE: **Calculate the BMI of a person who has a mass of 63.0 kg and is 1.70 m tall. Is this person overweight?**

$BMI = \frac{mass\ (kg)}{(height\ (m))^2}$ = 63.0 kg ÷ 1.70 m² = 21.8 kg m⁻² This person is not overweight — their BMI lies between 18.5 and 24.9 (the normal mass range).

3) If you eat a <u>high fat</u>, <u>high sugar diet</u> and you <u>don't do</u> enough <u>exercise</u>, you're likely to <u>take in</u> more energy than you <u>use</u>. The <u>excess</u> energy is <u>stored</u> as <u>fat</u>, so you're more likely to have a <u>high BMI</u> and be obese.

4) BMI <u>isn't</u> always a <u>reliable</u> measure of obesity. For example, athletes have lots of <u>muscle</u>, which has a <u>higher mass</u> than fat, so they can come out with a <u>high BMI</u> even though they're <u>not overweight</u>.

A **Waist-to-Hip Ratio** Can Also Be Used

1) By measuring the <u>circumference</u> of a person's <u>waist</u> and <u>hips</u>, you can use the following formula to figure out their <u>waist-to-hip ratio</u>.

$$waist\text{-}to\text{-}hip\ ratio = \frac{waist\ circumference}{hip\ circumference}$$

(e.g. in cm)

The <u>circumference</u> of a person's waist or hips is the distance the whole way around their body at that point.

2) The <u>higher</u> your waist-to-hip ratio, the <u>more weight</u> you're likely to be carrying around your middle.

3) A ratio <u>above 1.0</u> for <u>males</u> and <u>above 0.85</u> for <u>females</u> indicates you're carrying <u>too much weight</u> around your middle — this is known as <u>abdominal obesity</u>. It puts you at a <u>greater risk</u> of developing obesity-related <u>health problems</u>, such as type 2 diabetes (see p.147).

EXAMPLE: **A woman has a waist measurement of 29 cm and a hip measurement of 36 cm. Find her waist-to-hip ratio.**

$waist\text{-}to\text{-}hip\ ratio = \frac{waist\ circumference\ (cm)}{hip\ circumference\ (cm)}$ = 29 ÷ 36 = 0.81

These measures of obesity aren't perfect...

However, they do provide a good guide for helping people know when it's time to <u>lose weight</u>.

Treatments for Cardiovascular Disease

Cardiovascular disease is a big, big problem in the UK. The good news is there are lots of ways to treat it.

Cardiovascular Disease Affects Your Heart and Blood Vessels

Cardiovascular disease (CVD) is any disease associated with your heart and blood vessels.

1) Arteries are blood vessels that carry blood away from the heart.

See p.164-165 for more on blood vessels and the heart.

2) Cholesterol is a fatty substance that the body needs to make things like cell membranes. But too much cholesterol in the blood can cause fatty deposits to build up in arteries, restricting blood flow.

artery wall

cholesterol builds up to form a plaque

3) Deposits occur in areas where the artery wall has been damaged, e.g. by high blood pressure.

4) The fatty deposits can also trigger blood clots to form, which can block blood flow completely. If this happens in an artery supplying the heart muscle, the heart muscle will be deprived of oxygen. This causes a heart attack. A blockage in the brain deprives the brain of oxygen and can cause a stroke.

Lifestyle Changes Can be Used to Treat CVD

1) Making changes to your lifestyle can reduce your risk of developing CVD. If you already have CVD, these changes can form part of the treatment, helping to reduce the risk of a further heart attack or stroke.

2) People with (or at risk of) CVD may be encouraged to eat a healthy, balanced diet, which is low in saturated fat (as saturated fat can increase blood cholesterol level). They may also be encouraged to exercise regularly, lose weight if necessary and stop smoking.

3) Lifestyle changes are often recommended first because they don't really have any downsides.

Cardiovascular disease is associated with blood flow

Other factors, such as age, gender and family history can also increase the risk of developing CVD. These factors can't be changed, but it is possible to control and modify lifestyle-related risk factors.

Treatments for Cardiovascular Disease

Lifestyle changes aren't always enough to treat CVD. Sometimes medicine or surgery is needed too.

Some **Drugs** Can **Reduce** the **Risk** of a **Heart Attack** or **Stroke**

Lifestyle changes aren't always <u>enough</u> to treat CVD. Sometimes <u>medicines</u> are needed too. <u>Some people</u> may need to take these medicines for the <u>rest of their lives</u>.

1) <u>Statins reduce</u> the amount of <u>cholesterol</u> in the <u>bloodstream</u>. This <u>slows down</u> the rate at which fatty deposits form — <u>reducing</u> the risk of <u>heart attacks</u> and <u>strokes</u>. However, they can sometimes cause <u>negative side effects</u>, e.g. aching muscles. Some of these side effects can be <u>serious</u>, e.g. liver damage.

2) <u>Anticoagulants</u> (e.g. Warfarin™) are drugs which make <u>blood clots less likely to form</u>. However, this can cause excessive <u>bleeding</u> if the person is hurt in an <u>accident</u>.

3) <u>Antihypertensives</u> reduce <u>blood pressure</u>. This helps to <u>prevent damage</u> to <u>blood vessels</u> and so reduces the risk of <u>fatty deposits</u> forming. However, they can cause <u>side effects</u>, e.g. headaches and fainting.

Surgical Procedures are Sometimes **Necessary** to **Repair Damage**

1) Stents are <u>tubes</u> that are inserted <u>inside arteries</u>. They keep them <u>open</u>, making sure <u>blood can pass through</u> to the heart muscles, <u>lowering</u> the <u>risk</u> of a <u>heart attack</u>. But <u>over time</u>, the artery can <u>narrow</u> again as stents can <u>irritate</u> the artery and make <u>scar tissue</u> grow. The patient also has to take <u>drugs</u> to stop <u>blood clotting</u> on the stent.

2) If part of a blood vessel is <u>blocked</u>, a piece of <u>healthy vessel</u> taken from elsewhere can be used to <u>bypass</u> the blocked section. This is known as <u>coronary bypass surgery</u>.

3) The whole heart can be replaced with a <u>donor heart</u>. However, the new heart does not always start <u>pumping</u> properly and <u>drugs</u> have to be taken to stop the body <u>rejecting</u> it. These drugs can have <u>side effects</u>, e.g. making you more vulnerable to infections.

Any heart surgery is a <u>major procedure</u> and there is risk of <u>bleeding</u>, <u>clots</u> and <u>infection</u>.

Don't lose heart...

You could be asked to <u>evaluate</u> treatments for <u>cardiovascular disease</u>. Don't panic — just use any information you're given and your own knowledge to weigh up the <u>advantages</u> and <u>disadvantages</u>. Make sure your answer doesn't just focus on <u>one side</u> — e.g. don't just talk about the advantages and ignore the disadvantages — and don't forget to include a justified <u>conclusion</u>.

Warm-Up and Exam Questions

It's time for some more questions — don't just assume that you've remembered everything you read on the past few pages. Give these a go, and then go back over anything that you struggled with.

Warm-Up Questions

1) Give an example of a national cost associated with non-communicable diseases in the UK.
2) Give one disadvantage of the body mass index (BMI) as a measure of obesity.
3) Give one advantage of making lifestyle changes as treatment for CVD.

Exam Questions

1 Many non-communicable diseases are associated with certain lifestyle factors. Grade 4-6

   (a) Give **one** lifestyle factor associated with liver disease.

   [1 mark]

   (b) Give **one** example of a cost to the local area associated with liver disease.

   [1 mark]

2 Cardiovascular disease is non-communicable. Grade 6-7

   (a) Describe what is meant by the term 'non-communicable disease'.

   [1 mark]

   (b) Explain how smoking increases a person's risk of cardiovascular disease.

   [4 marks]

3 Before beginning a new diet and exercise routine, a person has a mass of 76.0 kg and has a height of 1.58 m. Three weeks later their mass has dropped to 73.0 kg. Grade 6-7

   (a) Calculate the person's BMI at:

   (i) The beginning of the three week period.

   [1 mark]

   (ii) The end of the three week period.

   [1 mark]

   (b) Use **Figure 1** to determine the weight description of the person before and after the three week period.

Body Mass Index	Weight Description
below 18.5	underweight
18.5 - 24.9	normal
25 - 29.9	overweight
30 - 40	moderately obese
above 40	severely obese

Figure 1

[2 marks]

Revision Summary for Topic 5

Well, that's Topic 5 finished. Now it's time to test how much you've taken in...
- Try these questions and tick off each one when you get it right.
- When you've done all the questions under a heading and are completely happy, tick it off.

Health, Disease, Viruses and STIs (p.95-99) ☑

1) Explain why being healthy doesn't just mean not being sick. ☑
2) True or False? Non-communicable diseases are caused by pathogens. ☑
3) How can the transmission of malaria be prevented? ☑
4) What bacterium can cause stomach ulcers? ☑
5) Name a sexually transmitted infection (STI) caused by a bacterium. ☑
6) Why does HIV eventually lead to AIDS? ☑
7) True of False? All viruses reproduce using the lysogenic pathway. ☑
8) Why do plants produce antiseptic chemicals? ☑
9) Give an example of a drug used in medicine which is extracted from plants. ☑
10) Give four ways in which a plant disease can be identified. ☑

Fighting Disease, Immunisation and Monoclonal Antibodies (p.102-107) ☑

11) Give two types of chemical defence that prevent pathogens from infecting humans. ☑
12) What is an antigen? ☑
13) What does a B-lymphocyte do when it recognises a pathogen? ☑
14) How do vaccines prepare the immune system against infection by a particular pathogen? ☑
15) What is 'herd immunity'? ☑
16) What are monoclonal antibodies? ☑
17) Why are tumour cells used to make hybridoma cells in the production of monoclonal antibodies? ☑
18) Explain how a positive result in a pregnancy test is detected using antibodies. ☑
19) How can you use monoclonal antibodies to identify cancer cells? ☑

Antibiotics and Other Medicines (p.109-112) ☑

20) Which type of pathogen can antibiotics be used to kill? ☑
21) What is the placebo effect? ☑
22) Describe how you could test the effect of an antibiotic on a particular strain of bacteria. ☑
23) What is the purpose of using aseptic techniques when studying the effect of substances on the growth of microorganisms? ☑
24) How would you calculate the size of an inhibition zone around an antibiotic disc in a culture of bacteria? ☑

Non-Communicable Diseases (p.114-118) ☑

25) Give two risk factors related to lifestyle associated with obesity. ☑
26) Write the equation for finding the body mass index of an individual. ☑
27) Give three examples of lifestyle changes that can help to prevent cardiovascular disease. ☑

Photosynthesis

Photosynthesis is where energy enters most of the food chains on Earth. Organisms that can carry out photosynthesis have crucial positions at the start of those food chains.

Plants are Able to Make Their Own Food by Photosynthesis

1) During photosynthesis, photosynthetic organisms, such as green plants and algae, use energy from the Sun to make glucose.

2) Some of the glucose is used to make larger, complex molecules that the plants or algae need to grow. These make up the organism's biomass — the mass of living material.

3) The energy stored in the organisms' biomass then works its way through the food chain as animals eat them and each other. So photosynthetic organisms are the main producers of food for nearly all life on Earth.

4) Photosynthesis happens inside chloroplasts — they contain chlorophyll which absorbs light. Energy is transferred to the chloroplasts by light. This is the equation for photosynthesis:

$$\text{carbon dioxide} + \text{water} \xrightarrow[\text{chlorophyll}]{\text{light}} \text{glucose} + \text{oxygen}$$
$$6CO_2 + 6H_2O \xrightarrow[\text{chlorophyll}]{\text{light}} C_6H_{12}O_6 + 6O_2$$

5) Photosynthesis is an endothermic reaction — energy is taken in during the reaction.

6) The rate of photosynthesis is affected by the light intensity, the concentration of CO_2 and the temperature. Any of these three factors can become the limiting factor. This just means that it's stopping photosynthesis from happening any faster.

The TEMPERATURE has to be Just Right for Photosynthesis

Temperature affects the rate of photosynthesis because it affects the enzymes involved.

1) Usually, if the temperature is the limiting factor it's because it's too low — the enzymes needed for photosynthesis work more slowly at low temperatures.

2) But if the plant gets too hot, the enzymes it needs for photosynthesis and its other reactions will be denatured (see page 27).

3) This happens at about 45 °C (which is pretty hot for outdoors, although greenhouses can get that hot if you're not careful).

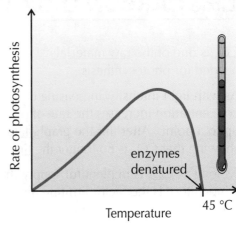

Photosynthesis

Not Enough **LIGHT** Slows Down the Rate of **Photosynthesis**

1) Light transfers the <u>energy</u> needed for photosynthesis.

2) At first, as the <u>light level</u> is raised, the rate of photosynthesis <u>increases steadily</u> (the rate is <u>directly proportional</u> to light intensity). But this is only true up to a <u>certain point</u>.

3) Beyond that, it <u>won't</u> make any difference — it'll be either the <u>temperature</u> or the <u>CO_2 level</u> which is the limiting factor.

4) In the lab you can investigate light intensity by <u>moving</u> a <u>lamp</u> closer to or further away from your plant (see next page).

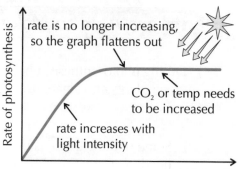

rate is no longer increasing, so the graph flattens out

CO_2 or temp needs to be increased

rate increases with light intensity

Rate of photosynthesis

Light intensity

5) But if you just plot the rate of photosynthesis against "distance of lamp from the plant", you get a <u>weird-shaped graph</u>. To get a graph like the one above you either need to <u>measure</u> the light intensity at the plant using a <u>light meter</u> or do a bit of maths with your results. Here's why:

> The square of the distance from the lamp and the light intensity are <u>inversely proportional</u> to each other — this means as the <u>distance increases</u>, the <u>light intensity decreases</u>. However, light intensity decreases in proportion to the <u>square</u> of the distance. This is called the <u>inverse square law</u> and is written like this:

$\propto$ is the 'proportional to' symbol.

$$\text{light intensity} \propto \frac{1}{\text{distance (d)}^2}$$

6) The inverse square law means that if you <u>halve</u> the <u>distance</u>, the <u>light intensity</u> will be <u>four times greater</u>. And if you <u>double</u> the distance, the light intensity will be <u>four times smaller</u>. (<u>Trebling</u> the distance would make it <u>nine times smaller</u>.) You can use $1/d^2$ as a measure of light intensity:

EXAMPLE: **Using the inverse square law, calculate the light intensity at both 20 cm and 10 cm from a lamp.**

1) Use the <u>formula</u> for calculating light intensity.

$$\text{light intensity} = \frac{1}{d^2}$$

'a.u.' stands for 'arbitrary units'.

2) For each of the distances, put the value into the formula, then <u>calculate the answer</u>.

At 20 cm: light intensity $= \dfrac{1}{20^2} = \dfrac{1}{400} = 0.0025$ a.u

At 10 cm: light intensity $= \dfrac{1}{10^2} = \dfrac{1}{100} = 0.0100$ a.u.

<u>Halving</u> the distance has made the light intensity <u>four times</u> greater.

Too Little **CARBON DIOXIDE** Slows **Photosynthesis** Down

1) CO_2 is one of the <u>raw materials</u> needed for photosynthesis.

2) As with light intensity, increasing the <u>CO_2</u> concentration <u>increases</u> the rate of photosynthesis up to a point. After this the graph <u>flattens out</u>, showing that CO_2 is no longer the <u>limiting factor</u>.

3) As long as <u>CO_2</u> is in plentiful supply then light or temperature is the factor limiting photosynthesis.

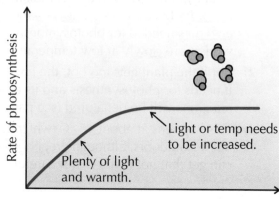

Rate of photosynthesis

Light or temp needs to be increased.

Plenty of light and warmth.

% level of CO_2

Investigating Photosynthesis

It's practical time again. This one lets you see how changing <u>light intensity</u> affects the <u>rate of photosynthesis</u>.

You Can Investigate the Rate of Photosynthesis

<u>Canadian pondweed</u> (an aquatic plant) can be used to measure the effect of <u>light intensity</u> on the <u>rate of photosynthesis</u>. The rate at which the pondweed produces <u>oxygen</u> corresponds to the rate at which it's photosynthesising — the <u>faster</u> the rate of oxygen production, the <u>faster</u> the rate of photosynthesis. Here's how the experiment works:

1) The <u>apparatus</u> is <u>set up</u> as shown in the <u>diagram</u> below. The gas syringe should be empty to start with. <u>Sodium hydrogencarbonate</u> may be added to the water to make sure the plant has enough <u>carbon dioxide</u> (sodium hydrogencarbonate releases CO_2 in solution).

2) A source of <u>white light</u> is placed at a <u>specific distance</u> from the pondweed.

3) The pondweed is left to photosynthesise for a <u>set amount of time</u>.

This experiment can be modified to test the effect of temperature or carbon dioxide concentration too — just remember to only change one variable at a time.

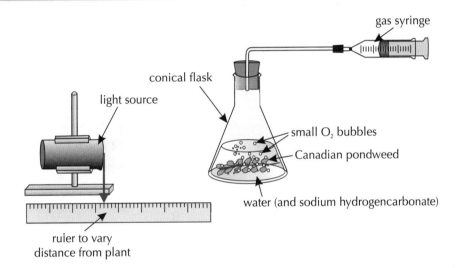

light source

conical flask

gas syringe

small O_2 bubbles

Canadian pondweed

water (and sodium hydrogencarbonate)

ruler to vary distance from plant

You can also investigate the rate of photosynthesis using algal balls, instead of pondweed. These are little balls of jelly which contain algae.

4) As it photosynthesises, the oxygen released will collect in the <u>gas syringe</u>. This allows you to <u>accurately measure</u> the <u>volume</u> of oxygen produced.

You could measure how much oxygen is produced by counting the number of bubbles given off in a certain time instead — but this is less accurate.

5) The whole experiment is repeated with the <u>light source</u> at <u>different distances</u> from the pondweed. The <u>rate of oxygen production</u> at each distance can then be calculated (volume produced ÷ time taken).

6) For this experiment, any <u>variables</u> that could affect the results should be <u>controlled</u>, e.g. the <u>temperature</u> (which can be controlled by putting the conical flask in a <u>water bath</u>) and the <u>carbon dioxide concentration</u> (which can be controlled by adding a <u>set amount</u> of sodium hydrogencarbonate to a <u>set volume</u> of water).

The faster photosynthesis happens, the faster oxygen is produced

You can <u>compare</u> the <u>rate of photosynthesis</u> at different light intensities by comparing the <u>rate of oxygen production</u> (the volume of O_2 produced per unit time e.g. in $cm^3 \ min^{-1}$). Increasing light intensity <u>increases</u> the rate of oxygen production (but only until temperature or CO_2 become the limiting factor instead).

Warm-Up & Exam Questions

Time for a break in the topic and some questions. Do them now, whilst all that learning is fresh in your mind. Using that knowledge will help you to remember it all, and that's what this game is all about.

Warm-Up Questions

1) True or false? Photosynthesis is an exothermic reaction.
2) What is meant by a limiting factor for the rate of photosynthesis?
3) Explain why the rate of photosynthesis decreases if the temperature is too high.
4) Write down the inverse square law for light intensity.

Exam Questions

PRACTICAL

1 A student did an experiment to see how the rate of photosynthesis depends on light intensity. **Figure 1** shows some of her apparatus.

(Grade 4-6)

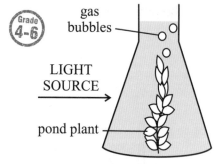

Figure 1

(a) Suggest how the student could measure the rate of photosynthesis.

[1 mark]

(b) State the dependent variable and the independent variable in this experiment.

[2 marks]

2 The graph in **Figure 2** shows how changing the light intensity affected the rate of photosynthesis of a plant.

During the experiment, the plant was kept at a constant temperature and a constant concentration of carbon dioxide.

(Grade 6-7)

Figure 2

(a) State what factor was limiting the rate of photosynthesis of the plant between points **A** and **B** on the graph. Explain your answer.

[2 marks]

(b) Explain why the graph flattens off after point **B**.

[2 marks]

3 A student is investigating the effect of light intensity on the rate of photosynthesis by placing a lamp at various distances from a plant and measuring the rate of photosynthesis.

(Grade 7-9)

Use the inverse square law to calculate the light intensity when the lamp is 7.5 cm from the plant. Give your answer in arbitrary units (a.u.) to 2 significant figures.

[2 marks]

Transport in Plants

Plants need to get stuff from <u>A to B</u>. Flowering plants have <u>two types</u> of <u>transport vessel</u> — xylem and <u>phloem</u>. Both types of vessel go to <u>every part</u> of the plant, but they are totally <u>separate</u>.

Root Hairs Take In Minerals and Water

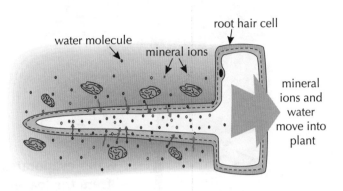

1) The cells on the surface of plant roots grow into "<u>hairs</u>", which stick out into the soil.
2) Each branch of a root will be covered in <u>millions</u> of these microscopic hairs.
3) This gives the plant a <u>large surface area</u> for absorbing <u>water</u> and <u>mineral ions</u> from the soil.
4) The concentration of mineral ions is usually <u>higher</u> in the <u>root hair cells</u> than in the <u>soil</u> around them, so mineral ions are absorbed by <u>active transport</u> (see page 35).
5) Water is absorbed by <u>osmosis</u>.

Phloem Tubes Transport Food

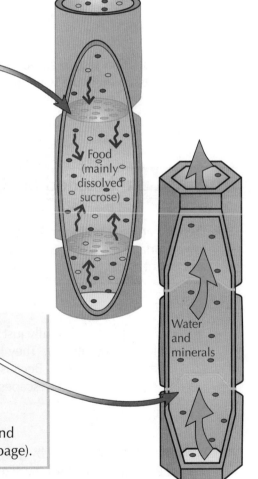

1) Phloem tubes are made of columns of <u>elongated</u> living cells with small <u>pores</u> in the <u>end walls</u> to allow stuff to flow through.
2) They transport <u>food substances</u> (mainly <u>sucrose</u>) made in the leaves to the rest of the plant for <u>immediate use</u> (e.g. in growing regions) or for <u>storage</u>.
3) This process is called <u>translocation</u> and it requires <u>energy</u> from respiration (see page 159). The transport goes in <u>both directions</u>.

Xylem Tubes Take Water UP

1) Xylem tubes are made of <u>dead cells</u> joined end to end with <u>no</u> end walls between them and a hole down the middle. They're strengthened with a material called <u>lignin</u>.
2) They carry <u>water</u> and <u>mineral ions</u> from the <u>roots</u> to the <u>stem</u> and <u>leaves</u>.
3) The movement of water <u>from</u> the <u>roots</u>, <u>through</u> the <u>xylem</u> and <u>out</u> of the <u>leaves</u> is called the <u>transpiration stream</u> (see next page).

Xylem vessels carry water, phloem vessels carry sucrose

Make sure you don't get your phloem <u>mixed up</u> with your xylem. To help you to learn which is which, you could remember that ph<u>lo</u>em transports substances in b<u>o</u>th directions, but xylem only transports things upwards — x<u>y</u> to the sky. It might just bag you a mark or two on exam day...

Transpiration and Stomata

Plants need <u>water</u> and <u>gases</u> such as carbon dioxide and oxygen.

Transpiration is the Loss of Water from the Plant

1) Transpiration is caused by the <u>evaporation</u> and <u>diffusion</u> (see p.35) of water from a plant's surface. Most transpiration happens at the <u>leaves</u>.

2) The loss of water creates a slight <u>shortage</u> of water in the leaf, and so more water is drawn up from the rest of the plant through the <u>xylem vessels</u> to replace it.

3) This in turn means more water is drawn up from the <u>roots</u>, and so there's a constant <u>transpiration stream</u> of water through the plant.

4) The transpiration stream carries <u>mineral ions</u> that are dissolved in the water along with it.

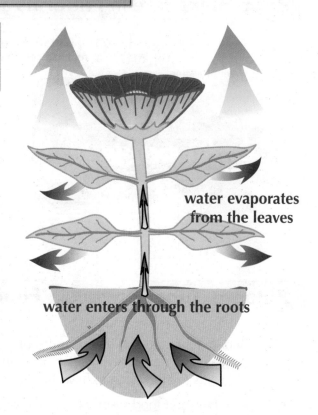

water evaporates from the leaves

water enters through the roots

Stomata are Needed for Gas Exchange

1) Stomata are <u>tiny pores</u> on the surface of a plant. They're mostly found on the lower surface of <u>leaves</u>. Stomata allow CO_2 and <u>oxygen</u> to <u>diffuse</u> directly in and out of a leaf. They also allow <u>water vapour</u> to escape during <u>transpiration</u>.

It's one stoma, but two or more stomata.

2) Transpiration is really just a <u>side-effect</u> of the way leaves are adapted for <u>photosynthesis</u>. They have to have <u>stomata</u> so that gases can be exchanged easily. Because there's more water <u>inside</u> the plant than in the <u>air outside</u>, the water escapes from the leaves through the stomata by diffusion.

3) Stomata are surrounded by <u>guard cells</u>, which <u>change shape</u> to control the size of the pore — when the guard cells are <u>turgid</u> (swollen with water) the stomata are <u>open</u> and when the guard cells are <u>flaccid</u> (low on water and limp) the stomata are <u>closed</u>.

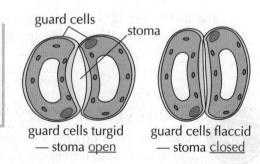

guard cells

stoma

guard cells turgid — stoma <u>open</u>

guard cells flaccid — stoma <u>closed</u>

Transpiration Rate

The rate of transpiration varies according to the environmental conditions.

Transpiration Rate is Affected by Environmental Factors

Light Intensity

1) The brighter the light, the greater the transpiration rate.

2) Stomata begin to close as it gets darker. Photosynthesis can't happen in the dark, so they don't need to be open to let CO_2 in. When the stomata are closed, very little water can escape.

Temperature

1) The warmer it is, the faster transpiration happens.

2) When it's warm the water particles have more energy to evaporate and diffuse out of the stomata.

The faster the transpiration rate, the faster the water uptake by the plant.

Air Flow

1) The better the air flow around a leaf (e.g. stronger wind), the greater the transpiration rate.

2) If air flow around a leaf is poor, the water vapour just surrounds the leaf and doesn't move away. This means there's a high concentration of water particles outside the leaf as well as inside it, so diffusion doesn't happen as quickly.

3) If there's good air flow, the water vapour is swept away, maintaining a low concentration of water in the air outside the leaf. Diffusion then happens quickly, from an area of higher concentration to an area of lower concentration.

The opening and closing of stomata is important for plants to survive

Plants need stomata for gas exchange but they let out a lot of water too. A big tree can lose about a thousand litres of water from its leaves every single day. That's a lot of water, which is why closing the stomata in certain conditions (e.g at night) is really important to stop too much water being lost.

Transpiration Rate

Sorry, more on <u>transpiration</u>, but at least this page is about a <u>practical</u>.

You Can **Estimate Transpiration Rate**

You can use a special piece of apparatus called a <u>potometer</u> to <u>estimate transpiration rate</u>. It actually <u>measures water uptake</u> by a plant, but it's <u>assumed</u> that water uptake by the plant is <u>directly related</u> to water loss from the leaves (transpiration). Here's what you do:

1) Set up the apparatus as in the diagram, and then record the <u>starting position</u> of the air bubble.

2) Start a stopwatch and record the <u>distance moved</u> by the bubble per unit time, e.g. per hour. Calculating the <u>speed</u> of <u>air bubble movement</u> gives an <u>estimate</u> of the <u>transpiration rate</u>.

reservoir of water

As the plant takes up water, the air bubble moves along the scale.

Tap is shut off during experiment.

Water moves this way.

Bubble moves this way.

capillary tube with a scale

Beaker of water.

 EXAMPLE:

A potometer was used to estimate the transpiration rate of a plant cutting. The bubble moved 25 mm in 10 minutes. Estimate the transpiration rate.

To estimate the <u>rate of transpiration</u>, divide the <u>distance</u> the bubble moved by the <u>time taken</u>.

$$\frac{distance\ moved}{time\ taken} = \frac{25\ mm}{10\ min} = 2.5\ mm\ min^{-1}$$

mm min⁻¹ is the same as mm/min.

You can use a potometer to estimate how <u>light intensity</u>, <u>temperature</u> or <u>air flow</u> around the plant affect the transpiration rate. Just remember to <u>only change one variable at a time</u> and control the rest.

 EXAM TIP

Make sure you know how to work out transpiration rate

You need to know how to <u>calculate</u> the rate of transpiration using measurements taken in a practical like the one above. Watch out for the <u>units</u> — you might be asked to use different ones in the exam. Don't panic though, just make sure your units match all the way through the calculation.

Warm-Up & Exam Questions

There's a fair few diagrams on the previous pages. Make sure you familiarise yourself with the labels and content of each one, don't just look at the pretty colours... Anyway you know what's next by now...

Warm-Up Questions

1) Where are most of a plant's stomata located?
2) True or false? Substances pass in both directions through xylem vessels.
3) State the three main factors that affect the rate of transpiration in plants.

Exam Questions

1 Plants absorb water and mineral ions through their root hair cells.

   (a) Name the vessels that transport water and mineral ions from the roots of a plant to the leaves.

[1 mark]

   (b) Describe the structure of the vessels you named in **1(a)**.

[3 marks]

   (c) Name the process by which water is transported through and lost from a plant.

[1 mark]

2 Aphids are insects. They feed on liquid which they extract from a plant's transport vessels, using their sharp mouthparts to pierce the stem. This liquid contains dissolved sucrose.

   (a) Name the type of transport vessel that the aphids extract their liquid food from.

[1 mark]

   (b) Describe and explain how the structure of this type of transport vessel is adapted to its function.

[4 marks]

3 A student investigated the effect of temperature and air flow on transpiration in basil plants. She put groups of three plants in four different conditions. She weighed the plants before and after the experiment and calculated the % loss in mass for each plant. Her results are shown in **Figure 1**.

plant	% loss in mass			
	Group A: 20 °C Still Room	Group B: 20 °C Next to a Fan	Group C: 25 °C Still Room	Group D: 25 °C Next to a Fan
1	5	8	10	13
2	5	9	11	15
3	4	11	9	13
mean	4.7	9.3		13.6

Figure 1

   (a) Calculate the mean % loss in mass for the three plants in Group **C**.

[2 marks]

   (b)* Explain why keeping the plants in Group **D** at 25 °C and placing them next to a fan meant that they lost more mass than the plants in Group **A**.

[6 marks]

Adaptations of Leaves and Plants

The <u>leaves</u> of plants are <u>adapted</u> so that efficient <u>photosynthesis</u> and <u>gas exchange</u> can take place.

Leaves are Adapted for Photosynthesis and Gas Exchange

The diagram below shows the structure of a <u>typical leaf</u>. You need to know how it's adapted for efficient photosynthesis and gas exchange.

Mesophyll just means 'middle of a leaf'.

Labels: waxy cuticle; upper epidermis; palisade mesophyll tissue; spongy mesophyll tissue; lower epidermis; xylem; phloem; air space; stomata; guard cell

1) Leaves are <u>broad</u>, so there's a large surface area exposed to <u>light</u>, which is needed for <u>photosynthesis</u>.

2) The <u>palisade layer</u> has lots of <u>chloroplasts</u>. This means that they're near the top of the leaf where they can get the most <u>light</u>.

3) The <u>upper epidermis</u> is <u>transparent</u> so that light can pass through it to the <u>palisade layer</u>.

4) The <u>xylem</u> and <u>phloem</u> form a network of vascular bundles, which <u>provide</u> the leaf with <u>water</u> for photosynthesis and <u>take away</u> the <u>glucose</u> produced. They also help <u>support</u> the structure.

5) The epidermal tissues are covered with a <u>waxy cuticle</u>, which helps to <u>reduce water loss</u> by evaporation.

6) The <u>tissues</u> of leaves are also adapted for efficient <u>gas exchange</u>. E.g. the <u>lower epidermis</u> has lots of <u>stomata</u>, which let CO_2 diffuse directly into the leaf. Also, the <u>spongy mesophyll</u> tissue contains <u>air spaces</u> which <u>increase</u> the rate of diffusion of gases into and out of the leaf's cells.

Some Plants are Adapted to Live in Extreme Environments

Some plants are adapted to live in extreme environments, e.g. places that are very <u>hot</u> or very <u>dry</u> (like <u>deserts</u>). Adaptations tend to affect the <u>size</u> and <u>shape</u> of the plant's <u>leaves</u>, its <u>cuticle</u>, and the <u>number</u> and <u>position</u> of its <u>stomata</u>. For example, plants living in deserts (like <u>cacti</u>) tend to have the following <u>adaptations</u>, which help them to <u>conserve water</u>:

Adaptations are features that help an organism to survive in its environment.

1) <u>Small leaves</u>, or <u>spines</u> instead of leaves — this <u>reduces</u> the <u>surface area</u> for water loss by evaporation. Spines also help to <u>stop</u> animals <u>eating</u> the plant to get water.

2) <u>Curled leaves</u>, or <u>hairs</u> on the surface of leaves — this <u>reduces air flow</u> close to the leaf, trapping water vapour near the surface and reducing diffusion from the leaf to the air. (<u>Spines</u> also reduce air flow near the surface of the plant and so do a similar job.)

3) <u>Thick waxy cuticles</u> — again to reduce water loss by evaporation.

4) A <u>thick</u>, <u>fleshy stem</u>, which <u>stores water</u>.

5) <u>Fewer stomata</u> or stomata that <u>only open at night</u> — to reduce water loss by evaporation.

6) Stomata <u>sunken</u> in <u>pits</u> — this makes the stomata lower than the surface of the leaf, which <u>reduces air flow</u> close to the stomata. This reduces water loss in the same way as curled leaves or hairs.

Plant Hormones

Plants produce chemicals called <u>hormones</u>, which regulate the plant's <u>growth</u> and <u>development</u>.

Auxins are Plant **Growth Hormones**

1) <u>Auxins</u> are <u>plant hormones</u> which control <u>growth</u> at the <u>tips</u> of <u>shoots</u> and <u>roots</u>. They move through the plant in <u>solution</u> (dissolved in water).

2) Auxin is produced in the <u>tips</u> and <u>diffuses backwards</u> to stimulate the <u>cell elongation process</u> which occurs in the cells <u>just behind</u> the tips.

3) Auxin <u>promotes</u> growth in the <u>shoot</u>, but actually <u>inhibits</u> growth in the <u>root</u>.

4) Auxins are involved in the <u>growth</u> responses of plants to <u>light</u> (phototropism) and <u>gravity</u> (gravitropism).

Auxins Change the **Direction** of **Shoot Growth**

Shoots are **Positively Phototropic (grow towards light)**

1) When a <u>shoot tip</u> is exposed to <u>light</u>, it accumulates <u>more auxin</u> on the side that's in the <u>shade</u> than the side that's in the light.

2) This makes the cells grow (elongate) <u>faster</u> on the <u>shaded side</u>, so the shoot bends <u>towards</u> the light.

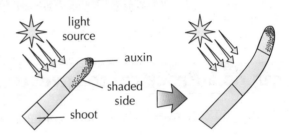

By bending towards the light, the shoot will be able to <u>absorb more light</u> for <u>photosynthesis</u>, which enables the plant to <u>grow</u>. Shoots growing completely in the <u>dark</u> will be <u>tall</u> and <u>spindly</u> — the auxin in the tips makes them <u>elongate quickly</u> on <u>all sides</u>. A <u>taller shoot</u> has a better chance of <u>finding light</u>.

Shoots are **Negatively Gravitropic (grow away from gravity)**

1) When a <u>shoot</u> is growing sideways, <u>gravity</u> produces an unequal distribution of auxin in the tip, with <u>more auxin</u> on the <u>lower side</u>.

2) This causes the lower side to grow <u>faster</u>, bending the shoot <u>upwards</u>.

Auxins coordinate growth in plants

By responding to <u>stimuli</u> in their environment, plants increase their chances of <u>survival</u>. For example, by growing towards the light, plants increase the amount of light they receive for photosynthesis.

Plant Hormones

Auxins Change the Direction of Root Growth

Roots are Positively Gravitropic (grow towards gravity)

1) A root growing sideways will have more auxin on its lower side.

2) But in a root the extra auxin inhibits growth. This means the cells on top elongate faster, and the root bends downwards.

Roots are Negatively Phototropic (grow away from light)

1) If a root starts being exposed to some light, more auxin accumulates on the more shaded side.

2) The auxin inhibits cell elongation on the shaded side, so the root bends downwards, back into the ground.

Roots that are completely underground aren't exposed to light — they grow downwards due to positive gravitropism.

You can do a Practical to Investigate Plant Growth Responses

For example, you can investigate the effect of light on the growth of cress seeds like this...

1) Put some cress seeds in a Petri dish lined with moist filter paper.

2) Surround the Petri dish with black card. (You might want to make a box out of black card and put the dish in that.)

3) Cut a hole in one side of the card only.

4) Shine a light into the box through the hole.

5) Leave your cress seeds alone for one week until you can observe their response — you should find the seedlings grow towards the light. You can even measure the angle they're growing at.

Light should only be able to reach the dish through the hole because the card will stop light entering from other directions.

Auxins work differently in different parts of the plant

Remember: if part of a plant grows towards a stimulus, it is growing positively with respect to that stimulus, and if a plant grows away from a stimulus, it is growing negatively with respect to that stimulus.

Commercial Use of Plant Hormones

Plant hormones can be <u>extracted</u>, or <u>artificial copies</u> can be made. This comes in pretty handy...

Plant Hormones Have Many Commercial Uses

As Selective Weedkillers

1) Most <u>weeds</u> growing in fields of crops or in a lawn are <u>broad-leaved</u>, in contrast to <u>grasses</u> and <u>cereals</u> which have very <u>narrow leaves</u>.

2) <u>Selective weedkillers</u> have been developed from <u>auxins</u>, which only affect the <u>broad-leaved plants</u>.

3) The weedkillers totally <u>disrupt</u> their normal growth patterns, which soon <u>kills</u> them, while leaving the grass and crops <u>untouched</u>.

Growing from Cuttings with Rooting Powder

1) A <u>cutting</u> is part of a plant that has been <u>cut off it</u>, like the end of a branch with a few leaves on it.

2) Normally, if you stick cuttings in the soil they <u>won't grow</u>, but if you add <u>rooting powder</u>, which contains <u>auxins</u>, they will <u>produce roots</u> rapidly and start growing as <u>new plants</u>.

3) This enables growers to produce lots of <u>clones</u> (exact copies) of a really good plant <u>very quickly</u>.

Controlling Flower and Fruit Formation

1) <u>Gibberellins</u> are plant hormones that stimulate <u>seed germination</u> (growth of a seed into a plant), <u>stem growth</u> and <u>flowering</u>. They can be used to make plants flower <u>earlier</u> than they would usually do so, or under <u>conditions</u> in which they wouldn't usually flower (e.g. when it's <u>warmer</u> than usual).

2) They can also be used to <u>reduce flower formation</u>, which can <u>improve fruit quality</u>. (Fruit grows from pollinated flowers, see below.) E.g. <u>apricot trees</u> often produce too many flowers. This causes too many fruits to form — the tree can't support them all and they grow quite small. Fewer flowers means fewer fruits, which are able to grow nice and big.

Producing Seedless Fruit

1) Fruit (with seeds in the middle) normally only grows on flowering plants which have been <u>pollinated by insects</u>. If the flower <u>doesn't</u> get pollinated, the fruit and seeds <u>don't grow</u>.

2) If <u>plant hormones</u> such as <u>gibberellins</u> are applied to the <u>unpollinated flowers</u> of some types of plant, the <u>fruit will grow</u> but the <u>seeds won't</u>. Some <u>seedless citrus fruits</u> can be grown this way.

Controlling the Ripening of Fruits

1) The <u>ripening</u> of fruits can be controlled either while they are still on the plant, or during <u>transport</u> to the shops. This allows the fruit to be picked while it's still <u>unripe</u> (and therefore firmer and <u>less easily damaged</u>).

2) A <u>ripening hormone</u> called <u>ethene</u> is then added and the fruit will ripen on the way to the supermarket and be <u>perfect</u> just as it reaches the shelves.

Controlling Seed Germination

1) Lots of seeds won't <u>germinate</u> until they've been through <u>certain conditions</u> (e.g. a period of <u>cold</u> or of <u>dryness</u>).

2) <u>Seeds</u> can be treated with <u>gibberellins</u> to make them germinate at <u>times of year</u> that they <u>wouldn't</u> normally. It also helps to make sure <u>all</u> the seeds in a batch germinate at the <u>same time</u>.

Warm-Up & Exam Questions

You could skim through this page in a few minutes, but there's no point unless you check over any bits you don't know and make sure you understand everything. It's not quick but it's the only way.

Warm-Up Questions

1) Which layer of plant tissue contains lots of chloroplasts?
2) Why is having fewer stomata helpful to a plant living in dry conditions?
3) Name the plant hormone responsible for both phototropism and gravitropism.
4) Explain what causes plant shoots to grow towards the light.
5) Give one way that gibberellin is used commercially.

Exam Questions

1 Leaves contain many types of tissue.

Which type of plant tissue contains air spaces for the diffusion of gases?

☐ **A** epidermal tissue   ☐ **C** spongy mesophyll tissue

☐ **B** palisade mesophyll tissue   ☐ **D** meristem tissue

[1 mark]

2 A gardener frequently uses products containing plant hormones in her garden.

(a) The gardener has a problem with weeds in her lawn.
She uses a weedkiller that targets the weeds without affecting the growth of the lawn.
Name the hormone likely to be present in the weedkiller.

[1 mark]

(b) The gardener has a cutting of a plant she would like to grow more of.
Explain how a plant hormone could help the gardener to grow a new plant from the cutting.

[2 marks]

3 A student placed some germinating beans on the surface of some damp soil and left them in the dark for five days. The appearance of the beans before and after the five day period is shown in **Figure 1**.

Start   After 5 days

Figure 1

Both the shoot and the root have undergone a gravitropic response after 5 days.

(a) Describe the gravitropic response of the shoot.

[1 mark]

(b) Explain the mechanism behind this response.

[2 marks]

Revision Summary for Topic 6

<u>Plants</u>, <u>plants</u> and more <u>plants</u> — that pretty much sums up <u>Topic 6</u> for you.

- Try these questions and <u>tick off each one</u> when you <u>get it right</u>.
- When you've done <u>all the questions</u> under a heading and are <u>completely happy</u>, tick it off.

Photosynthesis and Limiting Factors (p.121-123) ☑

1) In what part of a cell does photosynthesis take place?
2) Apart from water vapour, what gas is needed for photosynthesis?
3) Name the two products of photosynthesis.
4) Why is photosynthesis described as an endothermic reaction?
5) Describe the relationship between light intensity and distance from a light source.
6) What effect would a low carbon dioxide concentration have on the rate of photosynthesis?
7) Describe how you could investigate the effect of light intensity on the rate of photosynthesis.

Transport in Plants and Transpiration (p.125-128) ☑

8) How are root hair cells adapted to their function?
9) By what process do phloem tubes transport sucrose around a plant?
10) What effect does a faster transpiration rate have on water uptake by the plant?
11) a) What are stomata?
    b) What is the role of stomata in transpiration?
12) How does light intensity affect the rate of transpiration?
13) Describe how you'd use a potometer to estimate the rate of transpiration.

Adaptations of Leaves and Plants (p.130) ☑

14) Give three ways in which a typical leaf is adapted to absorb the maximum amount of light for photosynthesis.
15) Give two ways in which a leaf is adapted for efficient gas exchange.
16) How do curled leaves help a plant living in dry conditions?

Plant Hormones (p.131-133) ☑

17) What are auxins?
18) Shoots are positively phototropic. What does this mean?
19) Roots are positively gravitropic. Explain the role of auxin in this response.
20) Explain how selective weedkillers work.
21) List three things that gibberellins stimulate in plants.
22) Describe a commercial use of the plant hormone ethene.

Hormones

Way back in Topic 2 you learnt how information is passed around the body via neurones.
Well the body also uses hormones as a way to communicate, which is what this page is all about.

Hormones Are **Chemical Messengers** Sent in the **Blood**

1) Hormones are chemical molecules released directly into the blood.

2) They are carried in the blood to other parts of the body, but only affect particular cells in particular organs (called target organs).

3) Hormones control things in organs and cells that need constant adjustment.

4) Hormones are produced in (and secreted by) various glands, called endocrine glands. These glands make up your endocrine system.

Endocrine Glands Are Found in **Different Places** in the Body

PITUITARY GLAND

1) The pituitary gland produces many hormones that regulate body conditions.

2) It is sometimes called the 'master gland' because these hormones act on other glands, directing them to release hormones that bring about change.

THYROID

This produces thyroxine, which is involved in regulating things like the rate of metabolism, heart rate and temperature (see page 138) .

ADRENAL GLAND

This produces adrenaline, which is used to prepare the body for a 'fight or flight' response (see page 138).

OVARIES (females only)

Produce oestrogen, which is involved in the menstrual cycle (see pages 140-141).

PANCREAS

This produces insulin, which is used to regulate the blood glucose level (see page 146).

TESTES (males only)

Produce testosterone, which controls puberty and sperm production in males.

Comparing Neurones and Hormones

Now you know that there are two ways information can be sent round the body — via the nervous or hormonal systems — here's a page comparing the differences between them...

Hormones and Nerves Carry Messages in Different Ways

Hormones and nerves do similar jobs — they both carry information and instructions around the body. But there are some important differences between them:

Nerves

Very FAST action.

Act for a very SHORT TIME.

Act on a very PRECISE AREA.

Hormones

SLOWER action.

Act for a LONG TIME.

Act in a more GENERAL way.

If you're not sure whether a response is nervous or hormonal, have a think about the speed of the reaction and how long it lasts.

If the Response is Really Quick, It's Probably Nervous

1) Some information needs to be passed to effectors really quickly. For example:

   - Signals telling you that a part of your body is feeling pain (so you can take action quickly to avoid your body being damaged).
   - Information from your eyes telling you there's something dangerous heading your way.

2) It's no good using hormones to carry messages like these — they would be too slow.

If a Response Lasts For a Long Time, It's Probably Hormonal

Hormonal responses tend to carry on having an effect for a longer time than nervous responses.

For example, when you get a shock, a hormone called adrenaline is released into the body (causing the fight or flight response, where your body is hyped up ready for action). You can tell it's a hormonal response (even though it kicks in pretty quickly) because you feel a bit wobbly for a while afterwards.

There's more about adrenaline on the next page.

Nerves, hormones — no wonder revision makes me tense...

Hormones control various organs and cells in the body, though they tend to control things that aren't immediately life-threatening (so things like sexual development, blood sugar level, water content, etc.).

Adrenaline and Thyroxine

On the previous two pages you learnt what hormones are. Now it's time to look at a couple of examples...

Adrenaline Prepares You for 'Fight or Flight'

1) Adrenaline is a hormone released by the adrenal glands (which are located just above the kidneys — see page 136).

2) Adrenaline prepares the body for 'fight or flight' — in other words, standing your ground in the face of a threat (e.g. a predator) or bravely running away. It does this by activating processes that increase the supply of oxygen and glucose to cells. For example:

> - Adrenaline binds to specific receptors in the heart. This causes the heart muscle to contract more frequently and with more force, so heart rate and blood pressure increase.
> - This increases blood flow to the muscles, so the cells receive more oxygen and glucose for increased respiration.
> - Adrenaline also binds to receptors in the liver. This causes the liver to break down its glycogen stores (see. p.146) to release glucose.
> - This increases the blood glucose level, so there's more glucose in the blood to be transported to the cells.

3) When your brain detects a stressful situation, it sends nervous impulses to the adrenal glands, which respond by secreting adrenaline. This gets the body ready for action.

Hormone Release can be Affected by Negative Feedback

Your body can control the levels of hormones (and other substances) in the blood using negative feedback systems. When the body detects that the level of a substance has gone above or below the normal level, it triggers a response to bring the level back to normal again. Here's an example of just that:

Thyroxine Regulates Metabolism

An underactive thyroid gland can cause weight gain. Less thyroxine is produced, so your metabolic rate drops. This means that less of the glucose you take in gets broken down in respiration, so more is stored as fat.

1) Thyroxine is a hormone released by the thyroid gland.

2) It plays an important role in regulating metabolic rate — the speed at which chemical reactions in the body occur.

3) A negative feedback system keeps the amount of thyroxine in the blood at the right level:

- When the blood thyroxine level is lower than normal, the hypothalamus (a structure in the brain) is stimulated to release thyrotropin releasing hormone (TRH).
- TRH stimulates the pituitary gland to release thyroid stimulating hormone (TSH).
- TSH stimulates the thyroid gland to release thyroxine, so the blood thyroxine level rises back towards normal.
- When the blood thyroxine level becomes higher than normal, the release of TRH from the hypothalamus is inhibited, which reduces the production of TSH, so the blood thyroxine level falls.

A higher than normal thyroxine level also directly inhibits the secretion of TSH from the pituitary gland.

Warm-Up and Exam Questions

Yep, that's right this topic is no different from the last — there are still plenty of questions for you to get practising what you've learnt. Don't worry, the warm-up questions will ease you in gently.

Warm-Up Questions

1) What term is used to describe an organ whose cells are affected by a particular hormone?
2) a) Name five endocrine glands found in the male human body.
   b) Name one type of endocrine gland found in the female human body that is not found in the male human body.
3) Name the glands that produce adrenaline.
4) Name the gland that produces thyroxine.

Exam Questions

1   **Figure 1** shows thyroxine undergoing regulation in the human body.
    Changes from the normal thyroxine level trigger a response that returns the level to normal.

    (a) Name the type of system that regulates the level
         of a hormone, such as thyroxine, in the blood.
         [1 mark]

    (b) Which of these things is happening at
         point **X** in **Figure 1**?

         ☐ **A** TRH release is stimulated.

         ☐ **B** TSH production is increased.

         ☐ **C** TSH release is inhibited.

         ☐ **D** Thyroxine release is stimulated.

         [1 mark]

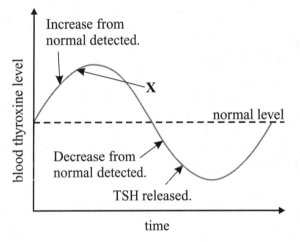

Figure 1

2   Hypopituitarism is a condition in which the pituitary gland
    doesn't secrete enough of one or more of the pituitary hormones.

    People with hypopituitarism may experience tiredness and weight gain.
    These symptoms are linked to low thyroid hormone levels.

    Suggest why someone with hypopituitarism may experience these symptoms.

    [3 marks]

3* A dog suddenly runs towards a cat across the street, which frightens the cat.

    Describe how a hormonal response would affect the cat's heart rate and
    blood glucose level when it sees the dog. Explain why these effects are beneficial.

    [6 marks]

Topic 7 — Animal Coordination, Control and Homeostasis

The Menstrual Cycle

The monthly release of an egg from a woman's ovaries is part of the menstrual cycle.

The Menstrual Cycle Has Four Stages

The menstrual cycle is the monthly sequence of events in which the female body releases an egg and prepares the uterus (womb) in case the egg is fertilised. This is what happens at each stage:

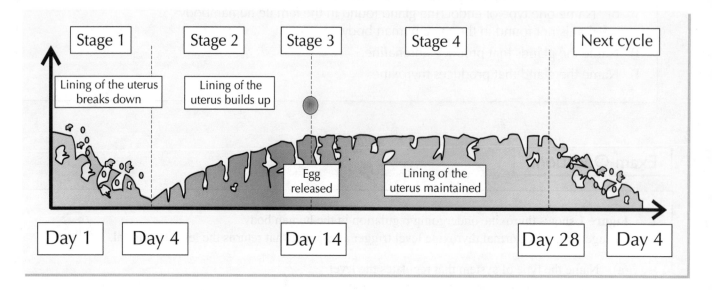

Stage 1

Day 1 is when menstruation starts. The lining of the uterus breaks down and is released.

The lining of the uterus is also called the 'endometrium'.

Stage 2

The uterus lining is repaired. From day 4 to day 14, the uterus lining builds up again until it becomes a thick spongy layer full of blood vessels, ready for a fertilised egg to implant there.

Stage 3

An egg develops and is released from the ovary (ovulation) at about day 14.

Stage 4

The lining is then maintained for about 14 days, until day 28. If no fertilised egg has landed on the uterus wall by day 28, the spongy lining starts to break down again, and the whole cycle starts over.

Examiners love a good menstrual cycle graph...

Make sure you have a good handle on the different stages of the menstrual cycle before moving on to the next page to learn about the hormones that control those stages — examiners like asking about it.

The Menstrual Cycle

The **Menstrual Cycle** is **Controlled** by **Four Hormones**

1. **FSH** (Follicle-Stimulating Hormone)

1) Released by the pituitary gland.
2) Causes a follicle (an egg and its surrounding cells) to mature in one of the ovaries.
3) Stimulates oestrogen production.

2. **Oestrogen**

1) Released by the ovaries.
2) Causes the lining of the uterus to thicken and grow.
3) A high level stimulates an LH surge (a rapid increase).

3. **LH** (Luteinising Hormone)

1) Released by the pituitary gland.
2) The LH surge stimulates ovulation at day 14 — the follicle ruptures and the egg is released.
3) Stimulates the remains of the follicle to develop into a structure called a corpus luteum — which secretes progesterone.

4. **Progesterone**

1) Released by the corpus luteum after ovulation.
2) Maintains the lining of the uterus.
3) Inhibits the release of FSH and LH.
4) When the progesterone level falls, and there's a low oestrogen level, the uterus lining breaks down.
5) A low progesterone level allows FSH to increase and then the whole cycle starts again.

If a fertilised egg implants in the uterus (i.e. the woman becomes pregnant) then the level of progesterone will stay high to maintain the lining of the uterus during pregnancy.

Controlling Fertility

Hormones can be used <u>artificially</u> to help <u>infertile</u> women have babies

Hormones can be Used to Treat Infertility

If a person is <u>infertile</u>, it means they <u>can't reproduce naturally</u>. There are methods an infertile couple can use to become pregnant, many of which involve <u>hormones</u>. You need to learn these <u>two examples</u>:

Clomifene Therapy

1) Some women are infertile because they <u>don't ovulate</u> or they <u>don't ovulate regularly</u>.

2) These women can take a drug called <u>clomifene</u>. This works by causing more <u>FSH</u> and <u>LH</u> to be released by the body, which <u>stimulates egg maturation and ovulation</u> — see previous page.

3) By knowing when the woman will be ovulating, the couple can have intercourse <u>during this time period</u> to improve the chance of becoming pregnant.

IVF ("*in vitro* fertilisation")

1) IVF involves collecting <u>eggs</u> from the woman's ovaries and fertilising them in a <u>lab</u> using the man's <u>sperm</u>. These are then grown into <u>embryos</u>.

2) Once the embryos are <u>tiny balls of cells</u>, one or two of them are <u>transferred</u> to the woman's uterus to improve the chance of <u>pregnancy</u>.

3) <u>FSH</u> and <u>LH</u> are given before egg collection to <u>stimulate egg production</u> (so more than one egg can be collected).

4) IVF is an example of <u>Assisted Reproductive Technology</u> (<u>ART</u>) — a fertility treatment that involves eggs being handled (and usually fertilised) <u>outside of the body</u>.

Understanding how hormones work helps put them to use artificially

Knowing the effects that <u>LH</u> and <u>FSH</u> have on the <u>menstrual cycle</u> allows us the use the hormones to manipulate the menstrual cycle when <u>treating infertility</u>. In <u>clomifene therapy</u> and <u>IVF</u>, FSH and LH are really important because they both <u>stimulate egg production</u>, <u>maturation</u> and <u>ovulation</u>.

Controlling Fertility

<u>Pregnancy</u> can happen if sperm reaches the ovulated egg. <u>Contraception</u> tries to <u>stop</u> this happening.

Contraceptives are Used to Prevent Pregnancy

1) <u>Hormones</u> can also be used as <u>contraceptives</u>. For example, <u>oestrogen</u> can be used to <u>prevent</u> the <u>release</u> of an <u>egg</u>. This may seem kind of strange (since naturally oestrogen helps stimulate the <u>release</u> of eggs). But if oestrogen is taken <u>every day</u> to keep the level of it <u>permanently high</u>, it <u>inhibits</u> the production of <u>FSH</u>, and after a while <u>egg development</u> and <u>production stop</u> and stay stopped.

2) <u>Progesterone</u> can also be used to <u>reduce fertility</u>. It works in several different ways — one of which is by stimulating the production of <u>thick cervical mucus</u>, which <u>prevents</u> any <u>sperm</u> getting through the entrance to the uterus (the <u>cervix</u>) and reaching an egg.

3) Some hormonal contraceptives contain <u>both oestrogen and progesterone</u> — for example, the <u>combined pill</u> (which is an oral contraceptive) and the <u>contraceptive patch</u> (which is worn on the skin).

4) The <u>mini-pill</u> (another oral contraceptive) and the <u>contraceptive injection</u> both contain <u>progesterone only</u>.

5) Pregnancy can also be prevented by <u>barrier methods</u> of contraception — these put a barrier between the <u>sperm</u> and <u>egg</u> so they <u>don't meet</u>. Examples include <u>condoms</u> (both male and female) and <u>diaphragms</u> (flexible, dome-shaped devices that fit over the opening of the uterus and are inserted before sex).

Diaphragms must be used with a spermicide — a chemical that kills sperm.

Hormonal and Barrier Contraceptive Methods Have Pros and Cons

1) Generally, when <u>used correctly</u>, hormonal methods are <u>more effective</u> at <u>preventing pregnancy</u> than barrier methods. Also, hormonal methods mean the couple don't have to stop and think about contraception <u>each time</u> they have intercourse (as they would if they relied on barrier methods).

2) However, hormonal methods can have <u>unpleasant side-effects</u>, such as headaches, acne and mood changes. Also, hormonal methods <u>don't protect</u> against <u>sexually transmitted infections</u> — <u>condoms</u> are the only form of contraception that do this.

People have a choice to make when picking a contraceptive

You might be asked to <u>evaluate</u> different <u>methods of contraception</u> in your exam. If you are, remember: you need to weigh up and write about both the <u>pros</u> and the <u>cons</u> of each method and write a sensible <u>conclusion</u> too. That's how you get your hands on those top marks.

Warm-Up and Exam Questions

Right then, another lot of pages down. Now there's just the small matter of answering some questions...

Warm-Up Questions

1) Name the hormone that stimulates an egg to mature in the ovary.
2) Name the only form of contraception that protects against sexually transmitted infections.
3) What is Assisted Reproductive Technology (ART)?
4) What effect does the drug clomifene have on the release of FSH and LH?

Exam Questions

1   The menstrual cycle is controlled by several different hormones.

   (a)   Describe the effect of progesterone on the release of FSH.

[1 mark]

   (b)   Name the hormone responsible for stimulating the formation of the corpus luteum.

[1 mark]

   (c)   State the day of the menstrual cycle on which the egg released.

[1 mark]

Towards the end of the menstrual cycle oestrogen, levels are low and progesterone levels begin to fall.

   (d)   Describe the effect that this will have on the uterus lining.

[1 mark]

   (e)   When a fertilised egg implants in the uterus, the level of progesterone remains high.
       Suggest why this happens.

[1 mark]

2   A couple are researching which form of contraceptive to use. One option is the combined oral contraceptive pill. The pill contains both oestrogen and progesterone and is taken everyday.

   (a)   Explain how taking oestrogen every day will stop the woman getting pregnant.

[2 marks]

   (b)   State and explain **one** way in which taking a contraceptive pill
       containing progesterone could stop a woman getting pregnant.

[2 marks]

   (c)   The couple are also considering using barrier contraceptives to prevent pregnancy.
       Describe how barrier contraceptives prevent pregnancies.

[1 mark]

   (d)   State **one** advantage and **one** disadvantage for the couple if they choose to use
       a barrier contraceptive instead of a hormonal contraceptive.

[2 marks]

Homeostasis

Homeostasis means maintaining the right conditions inside your body, so that everything works properly. Luckily there are some clever systems in place to keep things plodding along steadily.

Homeostasis is Maintaining a Constant Internal Environment

1) Conditions in your body need to be kept steady — this is really important because your cells need the right conditions in order to function properly, including the right conditions for enzyme action (see p.27). It can be dangerous for your health if conditions vary too much from normal levels.

2) To maintain a constant internal environment, your body needs to respond to both internal and external changes, whilst balancing inputs (stuff going into your body) with outputs (stuff leaving).

3) Examples of homeostasis in action include:

Blood glucose regulation — you need to make sure the amount of glucose in your blood doesn't get too high or too low (see next page).

Thermoregulation (regulating body temperature) — you need to reduce your body temperature when you're hot, but increase it when the environment is cold. See p.148.

Osmoregulation (regulating water content) — you need to keep a balance between the water you gain (in drink, food, and from respiration) and the water you pee, sweat and breathe out. See pages 149-151.

4) Negative feedback systems (see p.138) help to keep conditions in your body steady. This means that if a condition changes away from the normal level, a response is triggered that counteracts the change. E.g. a rise in blood glucose level causes a response that lowers blood glucose level (and vice versa).

Homeostasis is really important to keep your body "normal"

Without negative feedback systems, changes in your body conditions would go unregulated. This would be really bad because your body wouldn't function properly. So we need homeostasis to keep things in check.

Blood Glucose Regulation

Insulin and glucagon are hormones that control how much glucose there is in your blood.

Insulin and Glucagon Control Blood Glucose Concentration

1) Eating foods containing carbohydrate puts glucose into the blood from the small intestine.
2) The normal metabolism of cells removes glucose from the blood.
3) Vigorous exercise removes much more glucose from the blood.
4) Excess glucose can be stored as glycogen in the liver and in the muscles.
5) When these stores are full then the excess glucose is stored as lipid (fat) in the tissues.
6) Changes in blood glucose are monitored and controlled by the pancreas, using the hormones insulin and glucagon, as shown:

Blood glucose concentration
too HIGH — INSULIN is added.

So insulin removes
glucose from the blood.

Blood glucose concentration
too LOW — GLUCAGON is added.

And people used to think the pancreas was just a cushion...

This stuff can seem a bit confusing at first, but you could have a go at remembering it like this:
If blood glucose is increasing, insulin's added. If blood glucose is almost gone, glucagon's added.

Diabetes

Diabetes is an example of when homeostasis <u>doesn't work</u>. Make sure you fully understand how <u>insulin</u> affects <u>blood glucose concentration</u> (on the previous page) before you try getting your head around diabetes.

Type 1 Diabetes — Caused by a **Lack of Insulin**

1) <u>Type 1 diabetes</u> is a condition where the <u>pancreas produces little or no insulin</u>. The result is that a person's blood glucose can <u>rise</u> to a level that can <u>kill them</u>.

Remember, insulin reduces blood glucose level.

2) A person with type 1 diabetes will need to be <u>treated</u> with <u>insulin therapy</u> — this usually involves <u>injecting insulin</u> into the <u>subcutaneous tissue</u> (fatty tissue under the skin), from where it will enter the bloodstream. This is often done at mealtimes to make sure that the <u>glucose</u> is removed from the blood <u>quickly</u> once the food has been <u>digested</u>. This stops the level of glucose in the blood from getting too high and is a <u>very effective treatment</u>. The <u>amount of insulin</u> that needs to be injected depends on the person's <u>diet</u> and how <u>active</u> they are.

3) As well as insulin therapy, people with type 1 diabetes also need to think about:

Injecting too much insulin could result in a dangerously low blood glucose level.

   - <u>Limiting their intake</u> of foods rich in simple carbohydrates, i.e. sugars (which cause the blood glucose level to rise rapidly).
   - Taking <u>regular exercise</u> — this helps to <u>remove excess glucose</u> from the blood.

Type 2 Diabetes — a Person is **Resistant to Insulin**

1) <u>Type 2 diabetes</u> is a condition where the <u>pancreas doesn't produce enough insulin</u> or when a person becomes <u>resistant to insulin</u> (their body's cells <u>don't respond</u> properly to the hormone). In both of these cases, blood glucose level <u>rises</u>.

2) There is a <u>correlation</u> (see p.14) between <u>obesity</u> and <u>type 2 diabetes</u> — this means that obese people have an <u>increased risk</u> of developing type 2 diabetes. People are classified as <u>obese</u> if they have a <u>body mass index</u> (<u>BMI</u>) of <u>over 30</u>. BMI is worked out using this formula:

$$BMI = \frac{mass\ (kg)}{(height\ (m))^2}$$

See page 116 for more on calculating BMI and waist-to-hip ratios.

3) Where the body <u>stores excess fat</u> is also important — storing a lot of fat around the <u>abdomen</u> (tummy area) is associated with an <u>increased risk</u> of developing type 2 diabetes. Calculating a person's <u>waist-to-hip ratio</u> gives an indication of how fat is stored. This is the formula you need:

$$Waist\text{-}to\text{-}hip\ ratio = \frac{waist\ circumference\ (cm)}{hip\ circumference\ (cm)}$$

4) A ratio above <u>1.0 for men</u> and above <u>0.85 for women</u> is associated with an increased risk of type 2 diabetes because it indicates that a lot of fat is being stored around the abdomen.

5) Type 2 diabetes can be <u>controlled</u> by eating a <u>healthy diet</u>, getting regular <u>exercise</u> and <u>losing weight</u> if needed. Some people with type 2 diabetes also have <u>medication</u> or <u>insulin injections</u>.

Thermoregulation

Thermoregulation is the process your body uses to keep its internal temperature steady.

Body Temperature is Controlled by the Hypothalamus

1) All enzymes have an optimum temperature — this is the temperature at which they work best.

2) The enzymes in the human body work best at about 37 °C. Below this temperature enzyme activity slows down and above this temperature enzymes may start to denature so they can't work at all.

3) Homeostasis maintains our core body temperature at a steady 37 °C. Any change in body temperature triggers a response that counteracts it, e.g. a rise in body temperature triggers a response to bring it back down again.

> See page 27 for more on how temperature affects enzyme activity.

4) The thermoregulatory centre in the hypothalamus (a structure in the brain) acts as your own personal thermostat.

5) It contains receptors that are sensitive to the blood temperature in the brain. It also receives impulses from receptors in the skin (nerve endings) that provide information about the external temperature. These receptors are located in the epidermis (the outer layer of the skin) and in the dermis (a deeper layer of skin just below the epidermis).

6) When the hypothalamus detects a change, it causes a response in the skin:

When You're Too Hot...

1) Erector muscles relax, so hairs lie flat.

2) Lots of sweat (containing water and salts) is produced in sweat glands in the dermis. The sweat is released onto the surface of the skin through pores in the epidermis. When the sweat evaporates it transfers energy from your skin to the environment, cooling you down.

temperature receptors (nerve endings) — epidermis — dermis — sweat gland — hair erector muscle — blood vessels widen

3) Blood vessels close to the surface of the skin dilate (widen). This is called vasodilation. It allows more blood to flow near the surface, so it can transfer more energy into the surroundings, which cools you down.

When You're Too Cold...

no sweat — hairs erect — blood supply reduced

1) Erector muscles contract. Hairs stand on end to trap an insulating layer of air near the surface of the skin, which helps keep you warm.

2) Very little sweat is produced.

3) Blood vessels near the surface of the skin constrict (vasoconstriction). This means less blood flows near the surface, so less energy is transferred to the surroundings.

4) When you're cold you also shiver (your muscles contract automatically). This increases your rate of respiration, which transfers more energy to warm the body.

Osmoregulation and the Kidneys

The <u>kidneys</u> play a big part in this whole homeostasis thing too. They're important for regulating <u>water content</u> in the blood — this is <u>osmoregulation.</u>

Regulating Water Content is Really Important

1) It's really important that the <u>water content</u> of the <u>blood</u> is <u>controlled</u> to keep <u>cells functioning normally</u>.

2) If the concentration of water in the blood is <u>too high</u> then water will move <u>into</u> the body cells by <u>osmosis</u> (see p.36). If too much water moves into the cells then the cells may <u>burst</u>.

Animal cells burst when they contain too much water because they don't have a rigid cell wall (unlike plant cells).

3) If the concentration of water in the blood is <u>too low</u> then water will move <u>out of</u> the cells into the blood by osmosis. This causes the cells to <u>shrink</u>.

4) The <u>kidneys</u> help to regulate water content by controlling how much water is <u>reabsorbed</u> and how much is <u>lost in urine</u>.

The Kidneys are Part of the Urinary System

Kidneys have <u>three main roles</u>:

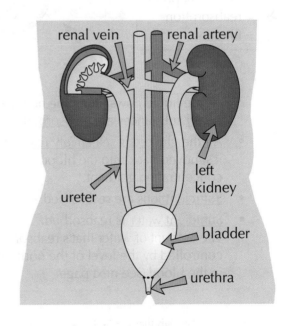

1) <u>Removal of urea</u> from the blood. Urea is produced in the <u>liver</u> from the breakdown of <u>excess amino acids</u>.

2) <u>Adjustment of ion levels</u> in the blood.

3) <u>Adjustment of water content</u> of the blood.

They do this by <u>filtering</u> stuff out of the blood under <u>high pressure</u>, and then <u>reabsorbing</u> the useful things. The end product is <u>urine</u>.

You need to be able to describe the structure of the urinary system.

Topic 7 — Animal Coordination, Control and Homeostasis

Osmoregulation and the Kidneys

Your kidneys are full of lots and lots of <u>nephrons</u> (about 1 million of them in each kidney).
They have the job of <u>filtering the blood</u> to get rid of <u>waste substances</u>, as well as <u>excess water and ions</u>.

Nephrons are the Filtration Units in the Kidneys

This is what happens in each <u>nephron</u>:

1) The <u>liquid</u> part of the blood (containing water, urea, ions and glucose) is <u>forced out</u> of the <u>glomerulus</u> and into the <u>Bowman's capsule</u> at <u>high pressure</u> (<u>ultrafiltration</u>). <u>Bigger</u> molecules (e.g. proteins) and <u>blood cells</u> can't pass through the membranes and are <u>not forced out</u>.

a kidney
urine
a single nephron
urine

Filtration happens here.

<u>Enlarged view of a single nephron</u>

capillary network

glomerulus

Reabsorption happens here, as does water regulation.

blood to renal vein

blood from renal artery

Bowman's capsule

proximal convoluted tubule

distal convoluted tubule

from another nephron

collecting duct

loop of Henle

Key:
= blood
= fluid in nephron
= reabsorption
= filtration

Release of wastes.

urine

2) As the liquid flows along the nephron, <u>useful</u> substances are <u>reabsorbed</u>:

• <u>All</u> the <u>glucose</u> is <u>selectively reabsorbed</u> — it's moved back into the blood <u>against</u> the concentration gradient.
• <u>Sufficient ions</u> are reabsorbed.
• <u>Sufficient water</u> is reabsorbed. The amount of water that's reabsorbed is controlled by the level of the hormone <u>ADH</u> in the blood (see next page).

3) Whatever isn't reabsorbed (e.g. urea, excess water, excess ions) continues <u>out</u> of the <u>nephron</u> via the <u>collecting duct</u>. It then passes into the <u>ureter</u> and down to the <u>bladder</u> as <u>urine</u>. Urine is released through the <u>urethra</u>.

Animals that live in drought conditions have longer loops of Henle to allow them to reabsorb more water.

Osmoregulation and the Kidneys

As you might have been expecting, the kidneys' work is controlled by a <u>hormone</u>.

Water Content is Controlled by a Negative Feedback System

1) The amount of water reabsorbed in the kidney nephrons is <u>controlled</u> by <u>anti-diuretic hormone</u> (ADH).

2) The brain <u>monitors the water content of the blood</u> and instructs the <u>pituitary gland</u> to release <u>ADH</u> into the bloodstream according to how much is needed.

3) ADH makes the <u>collecting ducts</u> of the <u>nephrons more permeable</u> so that <u>more water</u> is <u>reabsorbed</u> back into the blood. This stops the body from becoming <u>dehydrated</u>.

4) The whole process of water content regulation is controlled by a <u>negative feedback system</u>:

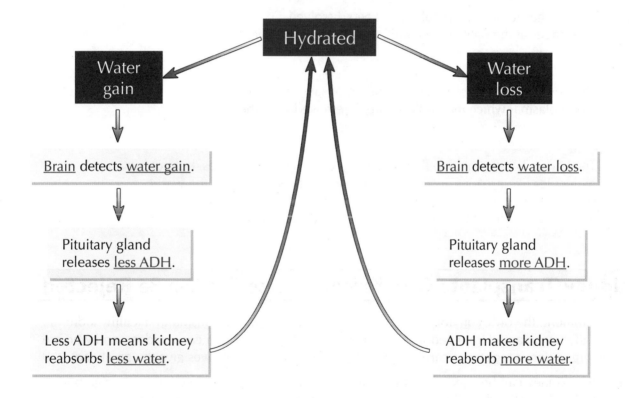

E.g. if the amount of <u>sodium ions</u> in the blood <u>increases</u>, the <u>concentration of water</u> in the blood will <u>fall</u>. The brain will detect that the blood needs <u>more water</u>, so it will release <u>more ADH</u>. <u>More water</u> will be <u>reabsorbed</u> from the collecting ducts so the water content of the blood will <u>rise</u>.

More ADH = less urine produced...

If you <u>lose water</u> (e.g. you <u>sweat</u> during exercise and <u>don't drink enough</u> to replace it), your blood water content will drop and your pituitary gland will release more ADH. <u>More water</u> will be <u>reabsorbed</u> from the collecting ducts and you'll end up producing a <u>smaller volume</u> of <u>more concentrated</u> (darker) <u>urine</u>.

More on the Kidneys

If someone's kidneys stop working, there are basically two treatments — regular dialysis or a transplant.

Dialysis Filters the Blood Mechanically

1) Patients who have kidney failure can't filter their blood properly — but a dialysis machine can be used to filter their blood for them:

2) Dialysis has to be done regularly to keep dissolved substances at the right concentrations, and to remove waste.

3) Dialysis fluid has the same concentration of salts and glucose as blood plasma (which means those aren't removed from the blood).

4) The barrier is permeable to things like ions and waste substances, but not big molecules like proteins (just like membranes in the kidney). So the waste substances (e.g. urea), plus excess ions and water from the blood, move across the membrane into the dialysis fluid. Cells and proteins stay in the blood.

Kidney Transplants Cure Kidney Disease But Can Be Rejected

At the moment, the only cure for kidney disease is to have a kidney transplant. Healthy kidneys are usually transplanted from people who have died suddenly, say in a car accident, and who are on the organ donor register or carry a donor card (provided their relatives give the go-ahead).

The donor kidney can be rejected by the patient's immune system — treated like a foreign body and attacked by antibodies. To help prevent this happening, precautions are taken:

1) A donor with a tissue type that closely matches the patient is chosen.
2) The patient is treated with drugs that suppress the immune system, so that their immune system won't attack the transplanted kidney.

Dialysis or transplant? Both have their downsides...

Donor kidneys are matched by blood type (and a few other things) to the recipient, which makes them less likely to be rejected. However, it means a potentially long waiting time for a suitable kidney.

Warm-Up and Exam Questions

Would you look at that — more questions. There are quite a few, but that just makes for great practice.

Warm-Up Questions

1) What is homeostasis?
2) What does insulin do?
3) What is Type 2 diabetes?
4) Name one factor that increases your risk of developing Type 2 diabetes.
5) Name the area of the brain that controls body temperature.
6) Aside from urea, give two substances that are removed from the body in the urine.
7) Which hormone controls the reabsorption of water in the kidneys?

Exam Questions

1   The substances that are filtered out of the blood in the kidneys form a fluid called a filtrate inside the nephron.

(a)   **Figure 1** shows some substances that are present either in the blood or in the filtrate just after filtration has taken place.

Complete **Figure 1** by filling in the blanks in each column.

[2 marks]

Substances	Blood	Filtrate
glucose	✗	✓
urea		
	✗	✓

Figure 1

(b)   Glucose is present in the blood that leaves the kidneys.
By which of the following processes does glucose move from the filtrate into the blood?

☐   **A**   ultrafiltration   ☐   **C**   osmosis

☐   **B**   selective reabsorption   ☐   **D**   diffusion

[1 mark]

2   A hospital patient is suffering from kidney failure. She has dialysis three times a week.

(a)   Explain why the patient does not lose glucose from her blood during dialysis.

[2 marks]

(b)   Explain why proteins are not removed from the patient's blood during dialysis.

[1 mark]

The patient is on the waiting list to receive a kidney transplant.

(c)   Give **one** disadvantage of kidney transplants.

[1 mark]

Exam Questions

3   **Figure 2** shows how the blood glucose level is regulated in humans.

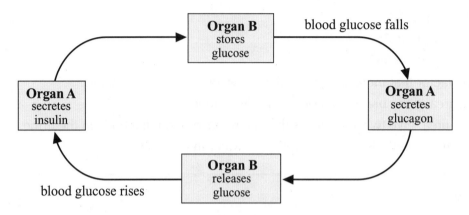

Figure 2

(a)   Identify organs **A** and **B** in **Figure 2**.

[2 marks]

(b)   Apart from organ **B** releasing glucose, suggest **one** reason
why a person's blood glucose level might rise.

[1 mark]

(c)   With reference to **Figure 2**, explain what goes wrong with
the regulation of blood glucose level in people with Type 1 diabetes.

[3 marks]

(d)   Describe what the hormone glucagon does.

[1 mark]

4   Changes in the skin are an important part of temperature regulation.
Figure 3 shows a cross section through the skin of a person who is cold.

(a)   In **Figure 3** the blood vessels close to
the surface of the skin have narrowed.

Give the scientific name for this
process and explain why it happens.

[3 marks]

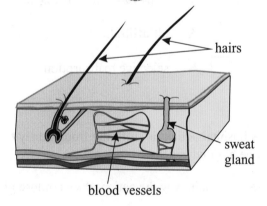

(b)   Describe and explain the response of a
sweat gland when a person is cold.

[2 marks]

Figure 3

5*   A runner went for a 10 mile run on a warm day. When she got home,
the runner noticed that her urine was darker in colour than normal.

Explain why she produced darker coloured urine.

[6 marks]

Revision Summary for Topic 7

Yay, you've made it to the end of Topic 7 — now for some questions to make sure you've been paying attention...

Try these questions and tick off each one when you get it right.

When you've done all the questions under a heading and are completely happy, tick it off.

Hormones (p.136-138) ☑

1) What is a hormone?

2) How do hormones travel to target organs?

3) What is an endocrine gland?

4) Name the gland where each of the following hormones is produced:
   a) oestrogen,   b) testosterone,   c) insulin.

5) Which hormone prepares the body for the 'fight or flight' response?

6) Describe how a negative feedback system works in the body.

7) Which hormone, released by the thyroid gland, controls metabolic rate?

The Menstrual Cycle and Fertility (p.140-143) ☐

8) Draw and label a timeline of the 28 day menstrual cycle.

9) Describe two effects of FSH on the body.

10) Describe two effects of oestrogen on the body.

11) Which hormone is secreted by a corpus luteum?

12) What is clomifene therapy? Who might use it?

13) Briefly describe how IVF is carried out.

14) Write down two pros and two cons of hormonal contraceptives.

Homeostasis (p.145-152) ☐

15) Name the two hormones that are involved in controlling blood glucose concentration in the human body.

16) Explain how type 1 and type 2 diabetes can be treated.

17) What is thermoregulation? Why is it important for enzymes in the body?

18) Explain how changes in the skin help to control body temperature when you're too hot.

19) What is osmoregulation?

20) Describe what might happen to body cells if the concentration of water in the blood is too low.

21) Excess amino acids are broken down in the liver. Name the waste product of this process, which must be removed in urine.

22) List the main structures in the urinary system.

23) Sketch a nephron and label all the parts.

24) Describe how urine is formed.

25) Describe how the brain responds when it detects a fall in the water content of the blood.

26) Give two treatments for kidney failure and briefly describe each one.

Exchange of Materials

Like all organisms, animals need to <u>exchange</u> things with their environment — but being <u>multicellular</u> makes things a little bit complicated...

Organisms **Exchange Substances** with their Environment

1) All organisms must <u>take in</u> substances that they <u>need</u> from the environment and <u>get rid</u> of any <u>waste products</u>. For example:

> Cells need <u>oxygen</u> for <u>aerobic respiration</u> (see page 159), which produces <u>carbon dioxide</u> as a waste product. These two <u>gases</u> move between <u>cells</u> and the <u>environment</u> by <u>diffusion</u> (see next page).

> <u>Water</u> is taken up by cells by <u>osmosis</u>. In animals, dissolved <u>food molecules</u> (the products of digestion, e.g. glucose, amino acids) and <u>mineral ions</u> diffuse along with it.

> <u>Urea</u> (a waste product produced by animals from proteins, see p.150) diffuses from <u>cells</u> to the <u>blood plasma</u> for removal from the body by the kidneys.

There's more on diffusion and osmosis on pages 35-36.

2) How <u>easy</u> it is for an organism to exchange substances with its environment depends on the organism's <u>surface area to volume ratio</u> (<u>SA : V</u>).

You Can Compare **Surface Area to Volume Ratios**

A ratio shows <u>how big</u> one value is <u>compared</u> to another. The <u>larger</u> an organism is, the <u>smaller</u> its surface area is compared to its volume. You can show this by calculating <u>surface area to volume ratios</u>:

A hippo can be represented by a 2 cm × 4 cm × 4 cm block.

The area of a surface is found by the equation: LENGTH × WIDTH

So the hippo's total <u>surface area</u> is:

$\qquad$ (4 × 4) × 2 (top and bottom surfaces of block)
$\qquad$ + (4 × 2) × 4 (four sides of the block)
$\qquad$ = 64 cm².

The volume of a block is found by the equation: LENGTH × WIDTH × HEIGHT
So the hippo's <u>volume</u> is 4 × 4 × 2 = 32 cm³.

The surface area to volume ratio of the hippo can be written as <u>64 : 32</u>.
To <u>simplify</u> the ratio, <u>divide both sides</u> of the ratio by the <u>volume</u>.

So the surface area to volume ratio of the hippo is <u>2 : 1</u>.

A mouse can be represented by a 1 cm × 1 cm × 1 cm block.
Its <u>surface area</u> is (1 × 1) × 6 = 6 cm².
Its <u>volume</u> is 1 × 1 × 1 = 1 cm³.
So the surface area to volume ratio of the mouse is <u>6 : 1</u>.

> The block mouse's surface area is <u>six</u> times its volume, but the block hippo's surface area is only <u>twice</u> its volume. So the <u>mouse</u> has a <u>larger</u> surface area compared to its volume.

Exchange Surfaces and the Alveoli

The alveoli are an <u>exchange surface</u> found in the lungs of mammals. They're <u>well-adapted</u> for the <u>efficient exchange</u> of two important <u>gases</u> — oxygen and carbon dioxide.

Multicellular Organisms Need Exchange Surfaces

1) In <u>single-celled organisms</u>, gases and dissolved substances can diffuse <u>directly into</u> (or out of) the cell across the cell membrane — it's because they have a <u>large surface area</u> compared to their <u>volume</u>, so <u>enough substances</u> can be exchanged across the membrane to supply the volume of the cell.

2) <u>Multicellular organisms</u> (such as <u>animals</u>) have a <u>smaller surface area</u> compared to their <u>volume</u>. This makes it difficult to exchange <u>enough substances</u> to supply their <u>entire volume</u> across their <u>outside surface</u> alone. So they need some sort of <u>exchange surface</u> for efficient diffusion and a <u>mass transport system</u> to move substances between the exchange surface and the rest of the body.

3) The exchange surfaces have to allow <u>enough</u> of the necessary substances to pass through, so they are <u>adapted</u> to maximise effectiveness (see next page).

Gas Exchange in Mammals Happens in the Alveoli

1) The job of the lungs is to transfer <u>oxygen</u> (O_2) to the <u>blood</u> and to <u>remove</u> waste <u>carbon dioxide</u> (CO_2) from it.

2) To do this, the lungs contain millions of little air sacs called <u>alveoli</u> where <u>gas exchange</u> takes place.

3) Blood <u>arriving</u> at the alveoli has just returned to the lungs from the <u>rest of the body</u>, so it contains <u>lots of CO_2</u> and <u>not much O_2</u>. This maximises the <u>concentration gradient</u> for the diffusion of both gases.

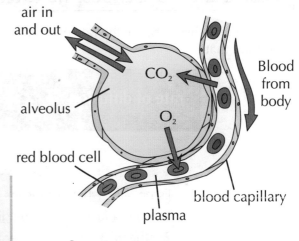

Remember — one alveolus, many alveoli.

4) O_2 <u>diffuses out</u> of the <u>air</u> in the <u>alveoli</u> (where the concentration of O_2 is <u>high</u>) and into the <u>blood</u> (where the concentration of O_2 is <u>low</u>). CO_2 diffuses in the <u>opposite direction</u> to be breathed out.

5) The alveoli are specialised to maximise the <u>diffusion</u> of O_2 and CO_2. They have:
   - A moist lining for <u>dissolving</u> gases.
   - A good <u>blood supply</u> to maintain the concentration gradients of O_2 and CO_2.
   - <u>Very thin</u> walls — minimising the <u>distance</u> that gases have to move.
   - An enormous <u>surface area</u> (about 75 m² in humans).

O_2 and CO_2 diffuse across the membranes of the cells that make up the walls of the capillary and alveolus. These membranes are partially permeable — see page 36.

Humans need alveoli for gas exchange...

You might well get asked to explain how the <u>adaptations</u> of the alveoli help gas exchange, so make sure you know what those adaptations are and why they affect the <u>rate of diffusion</u>.

Rate of Diffusion

So diffusion is pretty important in the transport of substances into and out of organisms.
On this page you'll see how the rate of diffusion is affected by different factors.

The Rate of Diffusion Depends on Three Main Things

Gases are exchanged in the lungs by diffusion. (There's more on diffusion on page 35.)
The rate of diffusion of any substance is affected by these three factors:

Distance — substances diffuse more quickly when they haven't as far to move.

Concentration difference (gradient) — substances diffuse faster if there's a big difference in concentration between the area they are diffusing from and the area they are diffusing to. If there are lots more particles on one side, there are more there to move across.

Surface area — the more surface there is available for molecules to move across, the faster they can get from one side to the other.

Fick's Law Describes the Rate of Diffusion

The relationship between the rate of diffusion and the factors that affect it is described by Fick's Law. It states that:

$$\text{rate of diffusion} \propto \frac{\text{surface area} \times \text{concentration difference}}{\text{thickness of membrane}}$$

'$\propto$' means 'is proportional to'.

Essentially, what this means is that the rate of diffusion will DOUBLE if:
1) the surface area or the difference in concentration DOUBLES, OR
2) the thickness of the membrane HALVES.

You can use the expression $\dfrac{\text{surface area} \times \text{concentration difference}}{\text{thickness of membrane}}$ as a measure of the rate of diffusion.

EXAMPLE:

An exchange surface has a surface area of 11 µm². It is 0.01 µm thick.
The concentration of oxygen on one side of the exchange surface is 0.4 M.
The concentration on the other side is 0.2 M. Calculate the rate of diffusion.

1) Write out the formula that you need:

$$\text{rate of diffusion} = \frac{\text{surface area} \times \text{concentration difference}}{\text{thickness of membrane}}$$

2) Fill in the values you know. You can work out the concentration difference by taking the smaller concentration away from the larger concentration.

$$\text{rate of diffusion} = \frac{11 \times (0.4 - 0.2)}{0.01}$$

$$= \frac{11 \times 0.2}{0.01} = \frac{2.2}{0.01}$$

3) Calculate the answer:

$$= 220 \text{ a.u}$$ a.u. stands for 'arbitrary units'.

Respiration

You need energy to keep your body going. Energy comes from food, and it's released by respiration.

Cellular Respiration Releases Energy

1) Respiration is NOT breathing in and breathing out.

2) Respiration actually goes on in every cell of all living organisms — and it happens continuously.

3) It's the process of transferring (releasing) energy from the breakdown of organic compounds (usually glucose). The energy is then used for things like:

Organic compounds are compounds containing carbon. They include carbohydrates, lipids and proteins.

- metabolic processes — such as making larger molecules from smaller ones (e.g. proteins from amino acids),
- contracting muscles (in animals),
- maintaining a steady body temperature (in mammals and birds).

4) Because energy is transferred to the environment, respiration is an exothermic reaction. Some of this energy is transferred by heating.

5) There are two types of respiration, aerobic and anaerobic.

Aerobic Respiration Needs Plenty of Oxygen

1) Aerobic respiration is what happens when there's plenty of oxygen available.
2) Aerobic just means "with oxygen" and it's the most efficient way to transfer energy from glucose.
3) This type of respiration goes on all the time in plants and animals. Here's the equation:

glucose + oxygen $\longrightarrow$ carbon dioxide + water

$$C_6H_{12}O_6 + 6O_2 \longrightarrow 6CO_2 + 6H_2O$$

This is the reverse of the photosynthesis equation (see page 121).

Respiration

Anaerobic Respiration Doesn't Use Oxygen At All

1) When you do really <u>vigorous exercise</u> your body can't supply enough <u>oxygen</u> to your muscles for aerobic respiration — even though your <u>heart rate</u> and <u>breathing rate</u> increase as much as they can. Your muscles have to start <u>respiring anaerobically</u> as well.

2) Anaerobic just means "<u>without</u> oxygen". It transfers much <u>less energy</u> than aerobic respiration so it's much less <u>efficient</u>. In anaerobic respiration, the glucose is only <u>partially</u> broken down, and <u>lactic acid</u> is also produced.

3) The <u>lactic acid</u> builds up in the muscles — it gets <u>painful</u> and leads to <u>cramp</u>.

4) This is the <u>word equation</u> for anaerobic respiration in <u>animals</u>:

$$\text{glucose} \longrightarrow \text{lactic acid}$$

Anaerobic Respiration in **Plants** is Slightly **Different**

1) <u>Plants</u> can respire <u>without oxygen</u> too, but they produce <u>ethanol</u> (alcohol) and CO_2 <u>instead</u> of lactic acid.

2) This is the <u>word equation</u> for anaerobic respiration in <u>plants</u>:

Fungi such as yeast also do anaerobic respiration like this.

$$\text{glucose} \longrightarrow \text{ethanol} + \text{carbon dioxide}$$

Respiration releases energy from glucose

You need to be able to compare <u>anaerobic</u> and <u>aerobic</u> respiration for your exam. Remember, anaerobic respiration has <u>different products</u> to aerobic respiration and transfers much <u>less energy</u>, as well as taking place <u>without oxygen</u>. Both aerobic and anaerobic respiration are <u>exothermic</u> though — don't forget that.

Investigating Respiration PRACTICAL

The rate at which an organism respires will change depending on different factors.
You can do experiments to see how these factors affect the rate of respiration.

You Can Measure the Rate of Respiration Using a Respirometer

In aerobic respiration, organisms use up oxygen from the air. By measuring the amount of
oxygen consumed by organisms in a given time, you can calculate their rate of respiration.

Here's an experiment which uses woodlice, a water bath and a piece of equipment called a respirometer.
It allows you to measure the effect of temperature on the rate of respiration of the woodlice. (You could use
germinating peas or beans instead of woodlice. Germinating seeds respire to provide energy for growth.)

1) Some soda lime granules are added to two test tubes. The soda lime
absorbs the CO_2 produced by the respiring woodlice in the experiment.
(You could use cotton wool soaked in a few drops of potassium
hydroxide solution to absorb the CO_2 produced by the woodlice instead.)

*Soda lime is corrosive.
Safety goggles and gloves
are worn when handling it
to protect the eyes and skin.*

2) A ball of cotton wool is placed above the soda lime in each tube. Woodlice are
placed on top of the cotton wool in one tube. Glass beads with the same mass as
the woodlice are used in the control tube. (There's more on controls on page 6.)

3) The respirometer is then set up as shown in the diagram.

4) The syringe is used to set the fluid
in the manometer to a known level.

5) The apparatus is then left for a set period
of time in a water bath set to 15 °C.

6) During this time, there'll be a decrease in the
volume of the air in the test tube containing
the woodlice. This is because the woodlice
use up oxygen in the tube as they respire.
(The CO_2 they produce is absorbed by the
soda lime so it doesn't affect the experiment.)

7) The decrease in volume reduces the pressure in the tube, causing the coloured
liquid in the manometer to move towards the test tube containing the woodlice.

8) The distance moved by the liquid in a given time is measured. From this you can calculate the volume
of oxygen taken in by the woodlice per minute — this is the rate of respiration in, e.g. cm^3 min^{-1}.

9) Repeat steps 1-8 with the water bath set at different temperatures, e.g. 20 °C and 25 °C.
This will allow you to see how changing the temperature affects the rate of respiration.

Any live animals you use in this experiment should be treated ethically (e.g. it's
important not to leave woodlice in a respirometer for too long, or they may run out
of oxygen and die). There's more about treating organisms ethically on page 194.

*You should make sure that
the woodlice can't come into
contact with the soda lime too.*

Warm-Up and Exam Questions

There's no better way to practice exam questions than doing... err... practice exam questions.
Hang on, what's this I see...

Warm-Up Questions

1) Give two examples of how animals use the energy transferred by respiration.
2) Name two substances that diffuse out from cells into the bloodstream.
3) What are the reactants of aerobic respiration?
4) Name a piece of scientific equipment that can be used to measure the rate of respiration in living organisms.

Exam Questions

1   The lungs contain millions of air sacs, called alveoli, which are adapted for the efficient exchange of oxygen and carbon dioxide in respiration.   *Grade 4-6*

(a)   Which of the following is a correct description of the diffusion of oxygen in gas exchange?

☐   **A**   Oxygen diffuses out of the blood, where the concentration of oxygen is high, into the alveoli, where the concentration of oxygen is low.

☐   **B**   Oxygen diffuses out of the blood, where the concentration of oxygen is low, into the alveoli, where the concentration of oxygen is high

☐   **C**   Oxygen diffuses out of the air in the alveoli, where the concentration of oxygen is high, into the blood, where the concentration of oxygen is low.

☐   **D**   Oxygen diffuses out of the air in the alveoli, where the concentration of oxygen is low, into the blood, where the concentration of oxygen is high.

[1 mark]

(b)   Describe how the thickness of the alveoli walls improves the efficiency of gas exchange in the lungs.

[2 marks]

2   Respiration is a process carried out by all living cells. It can take place aerobically or anaerobically.   *Grade 4-6*

(a)   State the purpose of respiration.

[1 mark]

(b)   Give **two** differences between aerobic and anaerobic respiration.

[2 marks]

(c)   Write the word equation for anaerobic respiration in humans.

[2 marks]

3   A bacterial cell can be represented by a $2\ \mu m \times 2\ \mu m \times 1\ \mu m$ block. Calculate the cell's surface area to volume ratio.   *Grade 7-9*

[3 marks]

Circulatory System — Blood

Blood is a tissue. One of its jobs is to act as a huge transport system. There are four main things in blood...

Red Blood Cells Carry Oxygen

1) The job of red blood cells (also called erythrocytes) is to carry oxygen from the lungs to all the cells in the body.
2) They have a biconcave disc shape (in other words, they look a bit like a jam doughnut that's being pressed in at the top and bottom) to give a large surface area for absorbing oxygen.
3) They don't have a nucleus — this allows more room to carry oxygen.
4) They contain a red pigment called haemoglobin, which contains iron.
5) In the lungs, haemoglobin binds to oxygen to become oxyhaemoglobin. In body tissues, the reverse happens — oxyhaemoglobin splits up into haemoglobin and oxygen, to release oxygen to the cells.

The more red blood cells you've got, the more oxygen can get to your cells. At high altitudes there's less oxygen in the air — so people who live there produce more red blood cells to compensate.

White Blood Cells Defend Against Infection

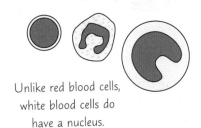

Unlike red blood cells, white blood cells do have a nucleus.

1) Phagocytes are white blood cells that can change shape to engulf (gobble up) unwelcome microorganisms — this is called phagocytosis.
2) Lymphocytes are white blood cells that produce antibodies against microorganisms (see p.102). Some also produce antitoxins to neutralise any toxins produced by the microorganisms.
3) When you have an infection, your white blood cells multiply to fight it off — so a blood test will show a high white blood cell count.

Platelets Help Blood Clot

1) These are small fragments of cells. They have no nucleus.
2) They help the blood to clot at a wound — to stop all your blood pouring out and to stop microorganisms getting in. (So platelets basically float about waiting for accidents to happen.)
3) Lack of platelets can cause excessive bleeding and bruising.

Plasma is the Liquid That Carries Everything in Blood

This is a pale, straw-coloured liquid which carries just about everything:
1) Red and white blood cells and platelets.
2) Nutrients like glucose and amino acids. These are the soluble products of digestion which are absorbed from the gut and taken to the cells of the body.
3) Carbon dioxide from the organs to the lungs.
4) Urea, from the liver to the kidneys.
5) Hormones.
6) Proteins.
7) Antibodies and antitoxins produced by the white blood cells.

Circulatory System — Blood Vessels

<u>Blood</u> needs a good set of 'tubes' to carry it round the body. Here's a page on the different types:

Blood Vessels are **Designed** for Their **Function**

There are <u>three</u> different types of <u>blood vessel</u>:
1) <u>ARTERIES</u> — these carry the blood <u>away</u> from the heart.
2) <u>CAPILLARIES</u> — these are involved in the <u>exchange of materials</u> at the tissues.
3) <u>VEINS</u> — these carry the blood <u>to</u> the heart.

Arteries Carry Blood Under **Pressure**

1) The heart pumps the blood out at <u>high pressure</u> so the artery walls are <u>strong</u> and <u>elastic</u>.
2) The walls are <u>thick</u> compared to the size of the hole down the middle (the "<u>lumen</u>").
3) They contain thick layers of <u>muscle</u> to make them <u>strong</u>, and <u>elastic fibres</u> to allow them to stretch and <u>spring back</u>.

elastic fibres and smooth muscle
lumen

Capillaries are Really **Small**

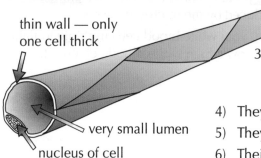
thin wall — only one cell thick
very small lumen
nucleus of cell

1) Arteries branch into <u>capillaries</u>.
2) Capillaries are really <u>tiny</u> — too small to see.
3) They are very <u>narrow,</u> so they can squeeze into the gaps between cells. This means they can carry the blood <u>really close</u> to <u>every cell</u> in the body to <u>exchange substances</u> with them.
4) They have <u>permeable</u> walls, so substances can <u>diffuse</u> in and out.
5) They supply <u>food</u> and <u>oxygen</u>, and take away <u>waste</u> like CO_2.
6) Their walls are usually <u>only one cell thick</u>. This <u>increases</u> the rate of diffusion by <u>decreasing</u> the <u>distance</u> over which it occurs.

Veins Take Blood **Back** to the Heart

1) Capillaries eventually <u>join up</u> to form <u>veins</u>.
2) The blood is at <u>lower pressure</u> in the veins so the walls don't need to be as <u>thick</u> as artery walls.
3) They have a <u>bigger lumen</u> than arteries to help the blood <u>flow</u> despite the lower pressure.
4) They also have <u>valves</u> to help keep the blood flowing in the <u>right direction</u>.

elastic fibres and smooth muscle
large lumen

valve

Blood vessels carry blood around the body...

It's easy to forget which vessels carry blood where. Remember, <u>a</u>rteries carry the blood <u>a</u>way from the heart, <u>ve</u>ins carry the blood back <u>in</u>to the heart and <u>c</u>apillaries carry blood <u>c</u>lose to <u>c</u>ells.

Circulatory System — The Heart

The heart plays a major role in the circulatory system. It is needed to pump the blood through the blood vessels so that material can be transported to and from the cells.

Mammals Have a Double Circulatory System

1) This means that the heart pumps blood around the body in two circuits.

   In the first circuit, the heart pumps deoxygenated blood to the lungs to take in oxygen. Oxygenated blood then returns to the heart.

   In the second circuit, the heart pumps oxygenated blood around all the other organs of the body to deliver oxygen to the body cells. Deoxygenated blood then returns to the heart.

2) Fish have a single circulatory system — deoxygenated blood from the fish's body travels to the heart, which then pumps it right round the body again in a single circuit (via the gills where it picks up oxygen).

Lungs

Heart

Rest of Body

The Heart Pumps Blood Through the Blood Vessels

The mammalian heart has four chambers and four major blood vessels. *A fish's heart only has two chambers.*

1) The right atrium of the heart receives deoxygenated blood from the body (through the vena cava).

2) The deoxygenated blood moves through to the right ventricle, which pumps it to the lungs (via the pulmonary artery).

3) The left atrium receives oxygenated blood from the lungs (through the pulmonary vein).

4) The oxygenated blood then moves through to the left ventricle, which pumps it out round the whole body (via the aorta).

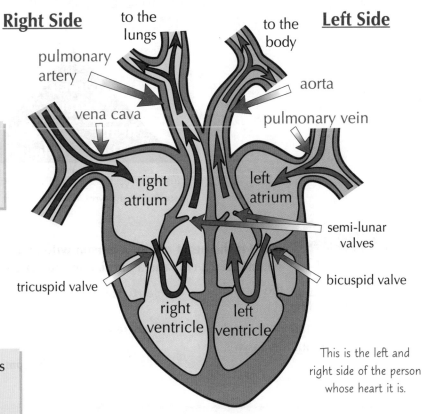

Right Side to the lungs

pulmonary artery

vena cava

right atrium

tricuspid valve

right ventricle

to the body **Left Side**

aorta

pulmonary vein

left atrium

semi-lunar valves

bicuspid valve

left ventricle

This is the left and right side of the person whose heart it is.

Blue = deoxygenated blood. Red = oxygenated blood.

The left ventricle has a much thicker wall than the right ventricle. It needs more muscle because it has to pump blood around the whole body at high pressure, whereas the right ventricle only has to pump it to the lungs. Valves prevent the backflow of blood in the heart.

Circulatory System — The Heart

You Can Calculate How Much Blood is Pumped Every Minute

1) Cardiac output is the total volume of blood pumped by a ventricle every minute.

2) You can calculate it using this equation:

$$\text{cardiac output} = \text{heart rate} \times \text{stroke volume}$$

in cm³ min⁻¹   in beats per minute (bpm)   in cm³

3) The heart rate is the number of beats per minute (bpm).

4) The stroke volume is the volume of blood pumped by one ventricle each time it contracts.

5) You might be asked to find the stroke volume or the heart rate in the exam instead of the cardiac output — if so, you can just rearrange the equation above. You can use this formula triangle to help you:

$$\frac{\text{cardiac output}}{\text{heart rate} \quad \times \quad \text{stroke volume}}$$

Just cover up the thing you want to find with your finger and write down what's left showing.

EXAMPLE:

What is the heart rate of a person with an average stroke volume of 72 cm³ and a cardiac output of 5420 cm³ min⁻¹?

1) Rearrange the formula to find heart rate.

Heart rate (bpm) = cardiac output (cm³ min⁻¹) ÷ stroke volume (cm³)

2) Fill in the values and work out the answer.

Heart rate (bpm) = 5420 ÷ 72
= 75.27...
= 75 bpm (2 s.f.)

For more on rounding to significant figures, see page 9.

Make sure you learn the equation...

MATHS TIP

If you're struggling to remember the equation, think it through logically — if you know the volume of blood pumped during each ventricle contraction (stroke volume), and how many contractions there are a minute (heart rate), you can multiply them to find the total volume of blood pumped each minute (cardiac output).

Topic 8 — Exchange and Transport in Animals

Warm-Up and Exam Questions

Who knew the circulatory system had so many different parts, with so many different functions?
Time to check you remember them all...

Warm-Up Questions

1) What do veins do?
2) Describe the purpose of platelets in blood.
3) Give three things that are carried in blood plasma.
4) Give the equation for calculating cardiac output.

Exam Questions

1   Blood is a tissue which transports important components, such as red blood cells, around the body.

   (a)   Name the other main type of blood cell, and state its function.

   [2 marks]

   (b)   Blood cells are carried in the bloodstream inside blood vessels.
         Capillaries are one type of blood vessel.
         State and explain **two** ways that the structure of a capillary enables it to carry out its function.

   [4 marks]

2   **Figure 1** shows the human heart and four blood vessels, as seen from the front.
    The left ventricle has been labelled.

Figure 1

   (a)   Name the parts labelled A, B and C.

   [1 mark]

   (b)   Describe the function of the left ventricle.

   [1 mark]

   (c)   Give the function of the valves in the heart.

   [1 mark]

   (d)   Describe the passage of deoxygenated blood from the body through the heart to reach the lungs.

   [4 marks]

Revision Summary for Topic 8

So that's Topic 8 — lots of information about exchange and transport in animals. Time to test yourself...
- Try these questions and tick off each one when you get it right.
- When you've done all the questions under a heading and are completely happy, tick it off.

Exchange of Materials, the Alveoli and Diffusion (p.156-158) ☑

1) Name three substances that animals have to exchange with their environment.
2) Why do multicellular organisms need specialised exchange surfaces?
3) Why do multicellular organisms need mass transport systems?
4) Where does gas exchange take place within the lungs?
5) Explain the movement of oxygen between the alveoli and the blood.
6) What three factors affect the rate of diffusion across a membrane?
7) State Fick's Law.

Respiration (p.159-161) ☑

8) Is respiration exothermic or endothermic? Explain your answer.
9) What are the products of aerobic respiration?
10) Under what circumstances do muscles perform anaerobic respiration?
11) When using a respirometer to measure the oxygen consumption of respiring organisms, what is the purpose of the soda lime in the respirometer?

The Circulatory System (p.163-166) ☑

12) Describe the shape of an erythrocyte.
13) What is the name of the pigment contained within red blood cells and what does it do?
14) What is the function of lymphocytes?
15) Name the component of blood that helps blood to clot at a wound.
16) What is the function of blood plasma?
17) Do arteries carry blood away from or towards the heart?
18) How are arteries adapted for carrying blood at high pressure?
19) Why are the walls of capillaries so thin?
20) What is the function of the valves found within veins?
21) Write the name of the blood vessel that:
    a) carries blood into the right atrium.
    b) carries blood towards the lungs.
    c) carries blood into the left atrium.
22) What is the equation for cardiac output?
23) How would you calculate the heart rate of an individual if you were given values for their cardiac output and stroke volume?

Topic 8 — Exchange and Transport in Animals

Ecosystems and Interactions Between Organisms

Organisms live together in ecosystems. They depend on other organisms in their ecosystem for survival.

Ecosystems are Organised into Different Levels

Ecosystems have different levels of organisation:

Level	Definition
Individual	A single organism.
Population	All the organisms of one species in a habitat.
Community	All the organisms of different species living in a habitat.
Ecosystem	A community of organisms along with all the non-living (abiotic) conditions (see next page).

A habitat is the place where an organism lives, e.g. a rocky shore or a field.

A species is a group of similar organisms that can reproduce to give fertile offspring.

Organisms in a Community Are Interdependent

1) Organisms depend on each other for things like food and shelter in order to survive and reproduce. This is known as interdependence. It means that a change in the population of one species can have huge knock on effects for other species in the same community.

2) Mutualism is a relationship between two organisms, from which both organisms benefit. E.g. bees and flowering plants have a mutualistic relationship. When bees visit flowers to get nectar, pollen is transferred to their bodies. The bees then spread the pollen to other plants when they land on their flowers. The bees get food and the plants get help reproducing. Everyone's a winner.

3) Parasites live very closely with a host species (e.g. in or on them). The parasite takes what it needs to survive, but the host doesn't benefit. E.g. fleas are parasites of mammals such as dogs. Fleas feed on their host's blood, but don't offer anything in return.

Interdependence is the key to communities

Because all organisms in a community share the same habitat, different species are often dependent on each other. Some species rely on each other so much that one couldn't survive without the other.

Ecosystems and Interactions Between Organisms

The environment in which organisms live <u>changes</u> all the time. The things that change are either <u>abiotic</u> (non-living) or <u>biotic</u> (living) factors. These can have a big <u>effect</u> on a community...

Environmental Changes **Affect Communities** in **Different Ways**

The <u>environment</u> in which plants and animals live <u>changes all the time</u>. These changes are caused by <u>abiotic</u> (non-living) and <u>biotic</u> (living) factors. They will affect communities in different ways — for some species <u>population size</u> may <u>increase</u>, for others it may <u>decrease</u>, or the <u>distribution</u> of populations (where they live) may change. Here are some <u>examples</u> of the effects of changes in <u>abiotic</u> and <u>biotic</u> factors:

Abiotic Factors Affect Communities...

Temperature

E.g. the distribution of <u>bird species</u> in Germany is probably changing because of a rise in average temperature. For instance, the <u>European Bee-Eater bird</u> is a <u>Mediterranean</u> species but it's now present in parts of <u>Germany</u>.

Amount of Water

E.g. <u>daisies</u> grow best in soils that are <u>slightly damp</u>. If the soil becomes <u>waterlogged</u> or <u>too dry</u>, the population of daisies will <u>decrease</u>.

Light Intensity

E.g. as trees grow and provide more <u>shade</u>, <u>grasses</u> may be replaced by <u>fungi</u> (or <u>mosses</u>, etc.) which are better able to <u>cope</u> with the <u>lower light intensity</u>.

Levels of pollutants

E.g. <u>lichen</u> are unable to survive if the concentration of <u>sulfur dioxide</u> (an <u>air pollutant</u>) is too <u>high</u> (see page 189).

...and so do **Biotic** Factors

Competition

Organisms <u>compete with other species</u> (and members of their own species) for the <u>same resources</u>. E.g. red and grey <u>squirrels</u> live in the same habitat and eat the same food. Competition with the grey squirrels for these resources in some areas means there's not enough food for the reds — the <u>population</u> of red squirrels is <u>decreasing</u>, partly as a result of this.

Predation

E.g. if the <u>number of lions</u> (predators) <u>decreases</u> then the number of <u>gazelles</u> (their prey) might <u>increase</u> because <u>fewer</u> of them will be <u>eaten</u> by the lions.

Investigating Ecosystems

This is where the <u>fun</u> starts. Studying <u>ecosystems</u> gives you the chance to <u>rummage around</u> in bushes, get your hands <u>dirty</u> and look at some <u>real organisms</u>, living in the <u>wild</u>.

Use Quadrats to Study the Distribution of Small Organisms

A <u>quadrat</u> is a <u>square</u> frame enclosing a <u>known area</u>, e.g. 1 m².
To compare <u>how common</u> an organism is in <u>two sample areas</u> just follow these simple steps:

1) Place a <u>1 m² quadrat</u> on the ground at a <u>random point</u> within the <u>first</u> sample area. You could do this by dividing the sample area into a grid and using a random number generator to pick coordinates to place your quadrats at. This will help to make sure the results you get are representative of the whole sample area.

2) <u>Count</u> all the organisms you're interested in <u>within</u> the quadrat.

3) <u>Repeat</u> steps 1 and 2 lots of times.

4) <u>Work out</u> the <u>mean</u> number of organisms per quadrat within the first sample area — this is the <u>total number of organisms</u> you counted <u>divided by</u> the <u>number of quadrats</u> you placed.

A quadrat

1m

1m

Anna counted the number of daisies in 7 quadrats that she placed at random in her first sample area. She recorded the following results: 18, 20, 22, 23, 23, 23, 25.

Here the MEAN is: $\dfrac{\text{TOTAL number of organisms}}{\text{NUMBER of quadrats}} = \dfrac{154}{7}$ = 22 daisies per quadrat

5) <u>Repeat</u> steps 1 to 4 in the <u>second</u> sample area.

6) Finally, <u>compare</u> the two means. E.g. you might find a mean of 2 daisies per m² in one area, and 22 daisies per m² (lots more) in another area.

You Can Also Estimate the Population Size of an Organism in an Area

1) To work out the <u>population size</u> of an organism in a sample area, first you need to use a quadrat to find the <u>mean number of organisms per m²</u>. (If you use a quadrat with an area of 1 m², this is the same as the mean number of organisms per quadrat, as shown above.)

2) Then just <u>multiply the mean</u> by the <u>total area</u> of your sample area:

Students used quadrats, each with an area of 0.5 m², to randomly sample daisies in a field. They found a mean of 10 daisies per quadrat. The area of the field was 800 m². Estimate the population of daisies in the field.

1) Work out the <u>mean number of organisms per m²</u>.

1 ÷ 0.5 = 2
2 × 10 = 20 daisies per m²

Because the quadrat is only 0.5 m², first you need to work out how many quadrats make up 1 m².

2) Then multiply the <u>mean</u> by the <u>total area</u> (in m²) of the habitat.

20 × 800
= 16 000 daisies on the field

Investigating Ecosystems

So, now you think you've learnt all about quadrats. Well hold on — there's more fun to be had.

Use **Belt Transects** to Study **Distribution Along** a **Gradient**

Sometimes abiotic factors will change across a habitat. The change is known as a gradient. You can use quadrats to help find out how organisms (like plants) are distributed along a gradient. For example, how a species becomes more or less common as you move from an area of shade (near a hedge at the edge of a field) to an area of full sun (the middle of the field). The quadrats are laid out along a line, forming a belt transect. Here's what you do:

1) Mark out a line in the area you want to study, e.g. from the hedge to the middle of the field.

2) Then collect data along the line using quadrats placed next to each other. If your transect is long, you could place the quadrats at regular intervals (e.g. every 2 metres) instead. Collect data by counting all the organisms of the species you're interested in, or by estimating percentage cover. This means estimating the percentage area of a quadrat covered by a particular type of organism.

Make sure you can correctly identify the organisms you're investigating. If necessary, use books or information from the internet to help you.

tape measure

quadrat 1

3) You could also record other data, such as the mean height of the plants you're counting or the abiotic factors in each quadrat (e.g. you could use a light meter to measure the light intensity).

4) Repeat steps 1 and 2 several times, then find the mean number of organisms or mean percentage cover for each quadrat.

5) Plot graphs to see if the changing abiotic factor is correlated with a change in the distribution of the species you're studying.

Organisms have a relationship with their environment

You could be asked to interpret some data showing the relationship between the distribution of a species and an abiotic factor. But remember, just because two things are correlated, it doesn't always mean a change in one is causing the change in the other. There might be other factors involved.

Ecosystems and Energy Transfers

There's a lot of <u>energy</u> moving around in ecosystems. Energy gets transferred through <u>food chains</u>.

Some **Energy** Passes **Along The Food Chain** — But Most **Doesn't**

<u>Food chains</u> show what's eaten by what within an ecosystem. Here is an example of a simple <u>food chain</u>.

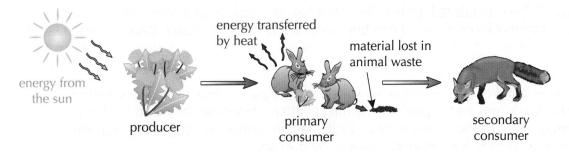

Producers make their own food using energy from the Sun, and are eaten by primary consumers. Primary consumers are then eaten by secondary consumers. (If the food chain is longer, secondary consumers are eaten by tertiary consumers.)

1) The <u>Sun</u> is the <u>source of energy</u> for nearly <u>all life on Earth</u>.

2) <u>Plants</u> use <u>a small percentage</u> of the light energy that falls on them to convert carbon dioxide and water <u>into glucose</u>, via photosynthesis. They use some of the glucose <u>immediately</u> in <u>respiration</u> and <u>store</u> some of the rest as <u>biomass</u> (the mass of living material that makes up an organism).

3) A <u>primary consumer</u>, like the <u>rabbit</u>, then <u>eats</u> the <u>plant</u>. It <u>uses</u> some of the energy it gets from the plant, and some of the rest is <u>stored</u> in its body as <u>biomass</u>.

4) Then a <u>secondary consumer</u>, like the <u>fox</u>, <u>eats</u> the primary consumer and gets some of the energy stored in its biomass. This is a simple <u>food chain</u>.

Each stage of a food chain is called a trophic level.

5) Energy is used by organisms at each stage to <u>stay alive</u>, i.e. in <u>respiration</u>, which transfers energy for <u>all life processes</u>, including <u>movement</u>. A lot of energy is <u>transferred to the surroundings</u> by <u>heat</u>.

6) This energy <u>isn't stored</u> as biomass, so it <u>isn't transferred</u> to the organisms in the next <u>trophic level</u>. (It's 'lost' to the food chain.)

7) Energy that does get stored as biomass <u>doesn't all get transferred</u> to the next trophic level either. That's because <u>not all</u> of an organism <u>gets eaten</u> (e.g. bones) and because not all of the bits that do get eaten can be digested — <u>undigested material</u> is <u>lost</u> from the food chain in <u>faeces</u>.

8) This explains why you hardly ever get <u>food chains</u> with more than about <u>five trophic levels</u>. So much energy is lost at each stage that there's not enough left to support more organisms after four or five stages. You also tend to get <u>fewer organisms</u> at each trophic level (although this <u>isn't always</u> the case).

Ecosystems and Energy Transfers

Pyramids of biomass are a handy way of illustrating the amount of biomass at each level in a food chain.

Pyramids of Biomass Show Weight

1) A pyramid of biomass shows how much the creatures at each level of a food chain would weigh if you put them together. Since biomass is a store of energy (see previous page), a pyramid of biomass also shows how much energy there is at each stage in the food chain.

2) The pyramid of biomass below shows the food chain of a mini meadow ecosystem. The dandelions are the producer (starting point) — they make their own food using energy from the Sun. They're eaten by the rabbits (primary consumers), which are eaten by the fox (secondary consumer)... and so on.

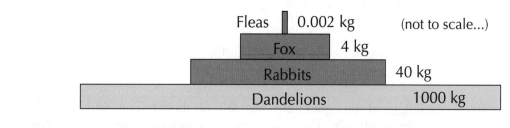

Fleas   0.002 kg   (not to scale...)
Fox   4 kg
Rabbits   40 kg
Dandelions   1000 kg

3) If you weighed them, all the dandelions would have a big biomass and the hundreds of fleas would have a very small biomass.

4) Each time you go up one trophic level, the mass of organisms goes down. This is because most of the biomass (or energy) is lost and so does not become biomass in the next level up. This gives rise to the pyramid shape that almost every pyramid of biomass has.

You could be asked to construct a pyramid of biomass in your exam.
Luckily it's pretty simple — they'll give you all the information that you need to do it.
If you do get asked to draw a pyramid of biomass, just remember:

- The first level is always the producer, the second level is the primary consumer, the third level is the secondary consumer, and so on.

- Make sure you draw each bar to a sensible scale — e.g. 5 small squares on a grid = 1 kg.

Pyramids of biomass are nearly always pyramid shaped

There are actually a couple of exceptions where pyramids of biomass aren't quite pyramid-shaped. It happens when the producer has a very short life but reproduces loads, like with plankton at certain times of year. But it's very rare, so you don't need to worry about it.

More on Ecosystems and Energy Transfers

If you like <u>food chains</u>, <u>numbers</u> and <u>formulas</u>, then this page might just be the most <u>exciting</u> thing you've ever seen. If not, just power through and make sure you've got it all in your head.

You Need to be Able to **Interpret Data** on **Energy Transfers**

The diagram below shows an example of a <u>food chain</u>.

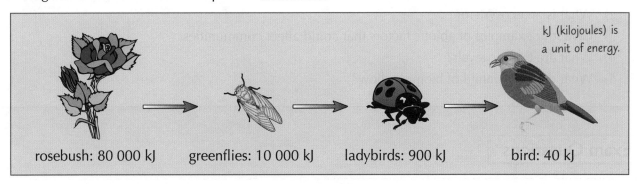

rosebush: 80 000 kJ   greenflies: 10 000 kJ   ladybirds: 900 kJ   bird: 40 kJ

kJ (kilojoules) is a unit of energy.

The arrows in a food chain show you the direction of energy transfer, e.g. energy is transferred from the rosebush to the greenflies, when the greenflies eat the rosebush.

1) The numbers show the <u>amount of energy</u> transferred to the <u>next level</u>. So <u>80 000 kJ</u> is the amount of energy transferred to the <u>greenflies</u>, and <u>10 000 kJ</u> is the amount transferred to the <u>ladybirds</u>.

2) You can work out how much energy has been <u>lost</u> at each level by <u>taking away</u> the energy that is transferred to the <u>next</u> level from the energy that was available at the <u>previous</u> level.

> **EXAMPLE:** **Calculate the energy lost between the first and second trophic levels.**
>
> energy lost = energy available at previous level − energy transferred to next level
> = 80 000 kJ − 10 000 kJ
> = 70 000 kJ lost

3) You can also calculate the <u>efficiency of energy transfer</u> between levels using this handy formula:

$$\text{efficiency} = \frac{\text{energy transferred to next level}}{\text{energy available at previous level}} \times 100$$

Here's an example:

> **EXAMPLE:** **Calculate the efficiency of energy transfer between the first and second trophic levels.**
>
> efficiency = $\dfrac{\text{energy transferred to next level}}{\text{energy available at previous level}} \times 100 = \dfrac{10\ 000}{80\ 000} \times 100$
>
> = **12.5% efficient** —— Efficiency is usually pretty low (around 10%).

4) You can also calculate the <u>biomass</u> lost between trophic levels or the efficiency of biomass transfer using the formulas above — just substitute the word 'energy' for 'biomass'.

Warm-Up and Exam Questions

This Ecosystems and Material Cycles topic's a long one — so make sure you've got these first few pages stuck in your head before moving on and learning the rest. These questions should help you.

Warm-Up Questions

1) What is the correct scientific term for all the organisms of different species living in a habitat?
2) What is an ecosystem?
3) Give four examples of abiotic factors that could affect communities.
4) What are trophic levels?
5) What does a pyramid of biomass show?

Exam Questions

PRACTICAL

1   Some students investigated the distribution of poppies across a field next to a wood. A sketch of the area is shown in **Figure 1**.

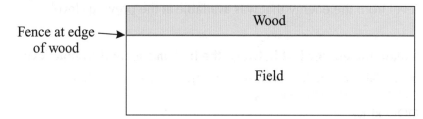

Figure 1

The students' results are shown in **Figure 2**.

| Number of poppies per m² | 5 | 9 | 14 | 19 | 26 |
| Distance from wood (m) | 2 | 4 | 6 | 8 | 10 |

Figure 2

(a) Describe how the students could have used quadrats to obtain the results in **Figure 2**.

[3 marks]

(b) Describe the trend in the results in **Figure 2**.

[1 mark]

2   Cutthroat trout are present in lakes in Yellowstone National Park. In the last few decades, lake trout have been introduced to the lakes. However, lake trout have emerged as predators and have been eating the cutthroat trout.

(a) Suggest and explain how the introduction of the lake trout might cause the population sizes of both species of fish to fluctuate over time.

[4 marks]

(b) Give **one** other biotic factor that could affect the size of the cutthroat trout population.

[1 mark]

Human Impacts on Biodiversity

However you look at it, <u>humans</u> have a <u>big impact</u> on the environment, including on <u>biodiversity</u>.

Human Activities Affect Biodiversity

1) <u>Biodiversity</u> is the <u>variety of living organisms</u> in an <u>ecosystem</u>.
2) Human <u>interactions</u> within ecosystems often affect biodiversity.
3) Sometimes we have a <u>positive</u> impact on biodiversity (e.g. by carrying out <u>conservation schemes</u> or <u>reforestation</u>, see page 179), but we often have a <u>negative</u> effect. Here are some examples:

Fertilisers can Leach into Water and Cause Eutrophication

<u>Nitrates</u> are put onto fields as <u>fertilisers</u> (see p.187). If <u>too much fertiliser</u> is applied and it <u>rains</u> afterwards, nitrates easily find their way into rivers and lakes. The result is <u>eutrophication</u> — an <u>excess of nutrients</u> in water — which can lead to the <u>death</u> of many of the species present in the water, <u>reducing</u> the <u>biodiversity</u> of the habitat. Here's how it happens:

Pollution by sewage can cause eutrophication in the same way that fertilisers do.

1) <u>Fertilisers</u> enter the water, adding <u>excess nitrates</u> (more than plants in the water can take in).

2) The excess nitrates cause <u>algae</u> to <u>grow fast</u> and <u>block out the light</u>.

3) <u>Plants can't photosynthesise</u> due to lack of light and <u>start to die</u> and <u>decompose</u>.

4) With more food available, microorganisms that feed on decomposing plants <u>increase</u> in <u>number</u> and <u>use up oxygen</u> in the water.

5) Organisms that need oxygen for aerobic respiration (e.g. <u>fish</u>) <u>die</u>.

Fertilisers need to be used responsibly

Unfortunately, it's difficult to <u>stop using fertilisers</u> altogether because farmers worldwide are under pressure to <u>produce enough food</u> — and using fertilisers helps them <u>improve</u> their <u>crop yields</u>.
As you'll see on the next page our <u>demand</u> for <u>fish</u> is also <u>affecting</u> the <u>biodiversity</u> of our lakes and seas.

Human Impacts on Biodiversity

Fish can be Farmed in Holding Nets in Open Water

Fish farms in areas of open water (e.g. lakes or the sea) can reduce biodiversity in the surrounding area. It can happen like this:

1) Food is added to the nets to feed the fish, which produce huge amounts of waste. Both the food and the waste can leak into the open water, causing eutrophication and the death of wild species.

2) Fish farms in open water often act as a breeding ground for large numbers of parasites. These parasites can get out of the farm and infect wild animals, sometimes killing them.

3) Predators (e.g. sea lions) are attracted to the nets and can become trapped in them and die.

4) Sometimes farmed fish can escape into the wild, which can cause problems for wild populations of indigenous species (see below).

Sometimes fish are farmed in large tanks rather than in open water nets. These farms are low in biodiversity because often only one species is farmed, the tanks are often kept free of plants and predators, and any parasites and microorganisms are usually killed.

The Introduction of Non-Indigenous Species Can Reduce Biodiversity

1) A non-indigenous species is one that doesn't naturally occur in an area. They can be introduced intentionally (e.g. for food or hunting) or unintentionally (e.g. as a stowaway in international cargo). The introduction of a non-indigenous species may cause problems for indigenous (native) species.

2) Non-indigenous species compete with indigenous species for resources like food and shelter. Sometimes, they are better at getting these resources and out-compete the indigenous species, which decrease in number and eventually die out. For example, signal crayfish were introduced to the UK for food, but they prey on and out-compete many indigenous river species, reducing biodiversity.

3) Non-indigenous species sometimes also bring new diseases to a habitat. These often infect and kill lots of indigenous species, reducing the habitat's biodiversity.

Adding a new species to a habitat can reduce biodiversity

You'd think that introducing a new species into an ecosystem would increase biodiversity. But when they out-compete the indigenous species, the numbers of their competitors decline. And since many organisms in an ecosystem are interdependent (see p.169), this can have big knock-on effects in the community.

Conservation and Biodiversity

Trying to conserve biodiversity can be tricky, given all the challenges that face different ecosystems (many of which are a result of human activities). There are benefits of doing this though, so it's pretty worthwhile...

There Are **Lots** of Ways to **Conserve** and **Maintain** Biodiversity

Lots of human activities can reduce biodiversity (see the previous two pages). However, there are plenty of things that we can do to increase biodiversity. Here are a couple of examples...

Reforestation Can Increase Biodiversity in **Deforested Areas**

1) Reforestation is when land where a forest previously stood is replanted to form a new forest.

2) Forests generally have a high biodiversity because they contain a wide variety of trees and other plants, and these provide food and shelter for lots of different animal species.

3) Deforestation reduces this biodiversity by removing the trees (either by chopping them down or burning them). Reforestation helps to restore it.

4) Reforestation programmes need to be carefully planned to maximise positive effects and minimise negative ones. For example, replanting a forest with a variety of tree species will result in a higher biodiversity than replanting using only a single type of tree.

Conservation Schemes Protect At-Risk Species

1) Conservation schemes can help to protect biodiversity by preventing species from dying out.
2) Conservation methods include:

1) Protecting a species' natural habitat (so that individuals have a place to live).
2) Protecting species in safe areas outside of their natural habitat (e.g. animals can be protected in zoos) and introducing captive breeding programmes to increase numbers.
3) The use of seed banks to store and distribute the seeds of rare and endangered plants.

It's not all lost — biodiversity can be increased

There are ways in which we can improve the biodiversity of an area — but the scale of efforts to maintain or increase biodiversity often isn't large enough to combat the huge negative impact of other human activities.

Conservation and Biodiversity

The last few pages have been all about what biodiversity is, how humans affect biodiversity and how we might go about maintaining it. But why is it important for us to maintain biodiversity? Read on...

Maintaining Biodiversity Has Many Benefits

There are lots of benefits to both wildlife and humans of maintaining biodiversity on a local and global scale.

1) Protecting the human food supply — over-fishing has greatly reduced fish stocks in the world's oceans. Conservation programmes can ensure that future generations will have fish to eat.

2) Ensuring minimal damage to food chains — if one species becomes extinct it will affect all the organisms that feed on and are eaten by that species, so the whole food chain is affected. This means conserving one species may help others to survive.

3) Providing future medicines — many of the medicines we use today come from plants. Undiscovered plant species may contain new medicinal chemicals. If these plants are allowed to become extinct, e.g. through rainforest destruction, we could miss out on valuable medicines.

4) Cultural aspects — individual species may be important in a nation's or an area's cultural heritage, e.g. the bald eagle is being conserved in the USA as it is regarded as a national symbol.

5) Ecotourism — people are drawn to visit beautiful, unspoilt landscapes with a variety of animal and plant species. Ecotourism (environmentally-friendly tourism) helps bring money into biodiverse areas where conservation work is taking place.

6) Providing new jobs — things such as ecotourism, conservation schemes and reforestation schemes provide employment opportunities for local people.

Biodiversity is important for us all

In some way or another the loss of biodiversity affects everyone — after all we are part of the biodiversity on earth. Make sure you know and can explain the benefits of maintaining biodiversity.

Food Security

As the population of planet Earth increases, growing enough food for everyone isn't going to get any easier...

Not Everyone Has 'Food Security'

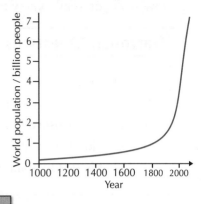

1) The world's population is rising very quickly and it's not slowing down.

2) This means that global food production must increase too, so that we all have access to enough food that is safe for us to eat and has the right balance of nutrition — this is known as 'food security'.

3) As the world's population continues to grow we need to produce more food, so that each person still has the same amount of food to eat.

Biological Factors Affect the Level of Food Security

The increasing human population is a biological factor affecting food security. So are:

Increasing consumption of meat and fish, and increasing animal farming

1) As people become wealthier, their diets are likely to change to include a wider variety of foods, including more meat and fish (which are expensive to buy). This can be bad news for food security.

2) There's less energy and less biomass every time you move up a stage in a food chain, so for a given area of land, you can produce a lot more food for humans by growing crops rather than by having grazing animals. Plus, animals and fish being reared to be eaten are often fed crops that would otherwise be eaten by humans (e.g. corn).

3) There's also a risk of over-fishing wild fish, so there won't be enough for us to catch in the future.

Environmental changes caused by human activity

1) Burning fossil fuels (coal, oil and natural gas) releases lots of carbon dioxide, a greenhouse gas. Greenhouse gases trap energy in the atmosphere, helping to keep the Earth warm. But increasing levels of greenhouse gases are causing the global temperature to rise. This is global warming.

2) Global warming is a type of climate change. It causes other forms of climate change, e.g. changing rainfall patterns. Climate change may affect the growth of crops, which could reduce yields.

3) Other changes caused by humans, such as soil pollution, could also reduce our ability to grow crops.

Yield means 'the amount of useful product made'.

Sustainability

1) Sustainability means meeting the needs of today's population without affecting the ability of future generations to meet their needs. We must think about sustainability when addressing food security.

2) For example, diesel and petrol are made from crude oil, a non-renewable fossil fuel that will run out eventually. There's currently an increase in the growth of crops to make biofuels, e.g. bioethanol, which is made by fermenting the sugar in corn and sugar cane. Biofuels are renewable alternatives to fossil fuels — but the crops take up land that could be used for food crops. We need to balance our need for this land to make biofuels with the need to grow more food, now and in the future.

3) Also, the high input costs of farming (e.g. the price of fertilisers, fuel and machinery) may make it too expensive for farmers in some areas to continue farming and maintain food production in the future.

New pests and pathogens

1) Pests (e.g. some insects) and pathogens (e.g. bacteria, fungi) can damage crops and livestock.

2) When new pests and pathogens emerge, they can have a negative impact on yields. E.g. if a new disease spreads to a crop, lots of the plants may not be resistant to the disease. This means a large number of crop plants will be damaged, reducing the yield and the amount that can be sold as food.

Warm-Up and Exam Questions

You can't just stare at these pages and expect all of the information to go in. Do these questions to see how well you really know the stuff. If you get stuck you can always go back to the page for a quick recap.

Warm-Up Questions

1) What is biodiversity?
2) Explain how excess nitrates in water systems can lead to the death of fish living in the water.
3) How do conservation schemes affect biodiversity? Explain your answer.
4) Describe two ways that an open water fish farm can reduce the biodiversity of an area.
5) What is sustainability?

Exam Questions

1 Black rats were accidentally introduced into an island habitat by a tourist boat which visited the island. Local biologists are worried that the introduction of the non-indigenous rat species will have a negative impact on biodiversity.

Suggest and explain **two** ways that the introduction of black rats to the island could reduce biodiversity.

[4 marks]

2 A group of conservationists are working to replant the trees in an area of forest which has been badly damaged by a forest fire.

(a) There is a suggestion that the whole area should be replanted with white spruce, a tree species which will be cheap to plant.
Explain why only planting white spruce will result in low biodiversity.

[2 marks]

(b) Several years after the area was successfully reforested, the conservationists found a few individuals of an endangered small mammal species living in the forest. The conservationists want to protect the species. Suggest **one** way they could do this.

[1 mark]

3 Current methods of fishing and farming may have to be changed in order to be more sustainable, so that there is greater human food security in the future.

(a) Explain what is meant by the term 'food security'.

[1 mark]

Over the past 50 years, the amount of animal farming happening globally has increased. This is largely due to an increased demand for meat.

(b) Explain why an increase in animal farming is a threat to global food security.

[3 marks]

(c) State **two** other threats to global food security and explain why each one is a threat.

[4 marks]

The Carbon Cycle

<u>Recycling</u> may be a buzz word for us but it's old school for nature. All the <u>nutrients</u> in our environment are constantly being <u>recycled</u> — there's a nice balance between what <u>goes in</u> and what <u>goes out</u> again.

Materials are Constantly Recycled in an Ecosystem

1) An <u>ecosystem</u> is all the <u>organisms</u> living in an area, as well as all the <u>non-living</u> conditions, e.g. soil quality, availability of water, temperature.

There's more on ecosystems on page 169.

2) Materials are <u>recycled</u> through <u>both</u> the <u>living</u> (<u>biotic</u>) and <u>non-living</u> (<u>abiotic</u>) components of ecosystems:

1) <u>Living things</u> are made of <u>elements</u> they take from the <u>environment</u>, e.g. plants take in <u>carbon</u> and <u>oxygen</u> from the air and <u>nitrogen</u> from the soil.
2) They turn these elements into the <u>complex compounds</u> (carbohydrates, proteins and fats) that make up living organisms. Elements are <u>passed along</u> food chains when <u>animals eat the plants</u> and each other.
3) The <u>elements</u> are <u>recycled</u> — <u>waste products</u> and <u>dead organisms</u> are broken down by <u>decomposers</u> (usually microorganisms) and the elements in them are <u>returned</u> to the <u>soil</u> or <u>air</u>, ready to be taken in by new plants and put back into the food chain.

The Carbon Cycle Shows How Carbon is Recycled

<u>Carbon</u> is an important element in the materials that living things are made from. But there's only a <u>fixed amount</u> of carbon in the world. This means it's constantly <u>recycled</u>:

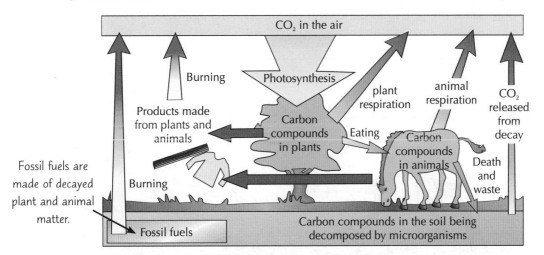

This diagram isn't half as bad as it looks. <u>Learn</u> these important points:

1) There's only <u>one arrow</u> going <u>down</u> from CO_2 in the <u>air</u>. The whole thing is 'powered' by <u>photosynthesis</u>. Green <u>plants</u> use the carbon from CO_2 to make <u>carbohydrates</u>, <u>fats</u> and <u>proteins</u>.
2) <u>Eating</u> passes the carbon compounds in the plants along to <u>animals</u> in a food chain (see p.173).
3) Both plant and animal <u>respiration</u> while the organisms are alive <u>releases CO_2</u> back into the <u>air</u>.
4) Plants and animals eventually <u>die</u> and <u>decompose</u>, or are killed and turned into <u>useful products</u>.
5) When plants and animals <u>decompose</u> they're broken down by <u>microorganisms</u>, like bacteria and fungi. These <u>decomposers release CO_2</u> into the air by <u>respiration</u>, as they break down the material.
6) Some useful plant and animal <u>products</u>, e.g. wood and fossil fuels, are <u>burned</u> (<u>combustion</u>). This process also <u>releases CO_2</u> back into the air.
7) <u>Decomposition</u> of materials means that <u>habitats</u> can be <u>maintained</u> for the organisms that live there, e.g. <u>nutrients</u> are <u>returned</u> to the soil, and <u>waste material</u>, such as dead leaves, doesn't just <u>pile up</u>.

The Water Cycle

The <u>amount</u> of water on Earth is pretty much <u>constant</u> — but <u>where</u> it is changes.
Water moves between <u>rivers</u>, <u>lakes</u>, <u>oceans</u> and the <u>atmosphere</u> in what's known as the <u>water cycle</u>.

The **Water Cycle** Means Water is **Endlessly Recycled**

The water here on planet Earth is constantly <u>recycled</u>.
There are four key steps you should understand:

As warm water vapour rises it
cools down and forms clouds.

1) <u>Energy</u> from the <u>Sun</u> makes water <u>evaporate</u> from the land
and sea, turning it into <u>water vapour</u>. Water also evaporates
from plants — this is known as <u>transpiration</u> (see p.126).

2) The warm water vapour is <u>carried upwards</u>
(as warm air rises). When it gets higher up
it <u>cools</u> and <u>condenses</u> to form <u>clouds</u>.

3) Water falls from the clouds as <u>precipitation</u> (usually
rain, but sometimes snow or hail) onto <u>land</u>,
where it provides <u>fresh water</u> for <u>plants</u> and <u>animals</u>.

4) It then <u>drains</u> into the <u>sea</u>, before the whole process starts again.

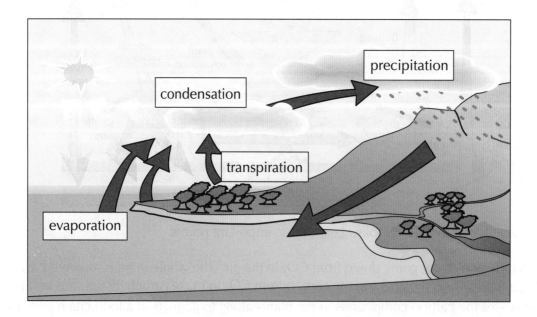

If it wasn't for the water cycle constantly recycling water, we'd quickly <u>run out</u> of the stuff.
That would be <u>really bad</u> news because all living things on our planet <u>need</u> water to <u>survive</u>.

Evaporation, transpiration, condensation, precipitation

The water cycle is pretty straightforward, so there's absolutely no excuse not to learn it inside out.
The most important thing to remember is that it's a <u>cycle</u> — a <u>continuous</u> process with no beginning or end.
Water that falls to the ground as rain (or snow, hail etc.) will eventually end up back in the clouds again.

The Water Cycle

A **Drought** Occurs When There **Isn't Enough Precipitation**

Droughts can cause big problems, partly because we rely on precipitation to get fresh water for drinking (sea water is too salty). Luckily, in times of drought, there are methods we can use to produce potable water (water that's suitable for drinking). One of these methods is called desalination.

Desalination Can Be Used to Produce **Potable Water** From **Salt Water**

Desalination removes salts (mineral ions) from salt water (e.g. sea water). There are a few different methods of desalination. One really simple method is thermal desalination:

1) Salt water is boiled in a large enclosed vessel, so that the water evaporates.
2) The steam rises to the top of the vessel, but the salts stay at the bottom.
3) The steam then travels down a pipe from the top of the vessel and cools and condenses back into pure water.

Reverse Osmosis is a Widely Used Modern Method of **Desalination**

1) Osmosis is the net movement of water across a partially permeable membrane, from an area of HIGHER water concentration to an area of LOWER water concentration (see page 36).

2) The higher the salt concentration in a solution, the lower the water concentration, so you could also say that osmosis is the net movement of water from an area of LOWER salt concentration to an area of HIGHER salt concentration.

3) Reverse osmosis reverses this process to get rid of impurities in water. Here's how:

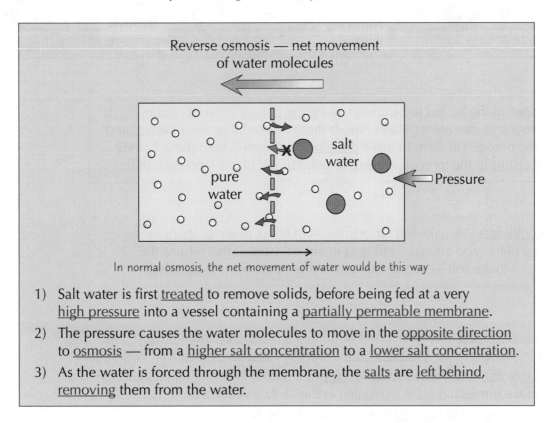

Reverse osmosis — net movement of water molecules

pure water

salt water

Pressure

In normal osmosis, the net movement of water would be this way

1) Salt water is first treated to remove solids, before being fed at a very high pressure into a vessel containing a partially permeable membrane.

2) The pressure causes the water molecules to move in the opposite direction to osmosis — from a higher salt concentration to a lower salt concentration.

3) As the water is forced through the membrane, the salts are left behind, removing them from the water.

The Nitrogen Cycle

Just like carbon and water, nitrogen is constantly being recycled.

Nitrogen is Recycled in the Nitrogen Cycle

1) The atmosphere contains 78% nitrogen gas, N_2. This is very unreactive and so it can't be used directly by plants or animals. Nitrogen is needed for making proteins for growth, so living organisms have to get it somehow.

2) Nitrogen is passed back and forth between the air, living organisms and the soil in the nitrogen cycle. Here's a diagram showing how it works. (Don't worry, it's all explained in more detail below.)

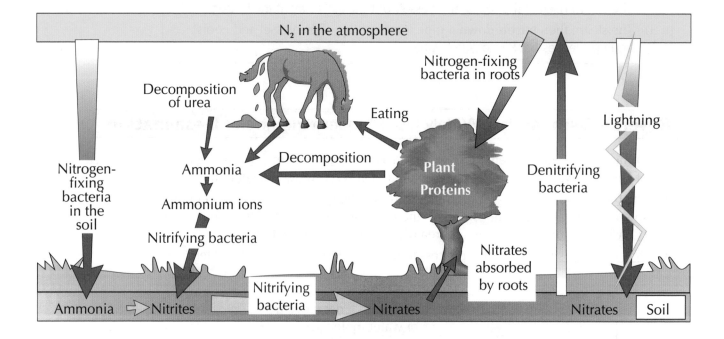

3) Nitrogen in the air has to be turned into mineral ions, such as nitrates, before plants can use it. Plants absorb these mineral ions from the soil and use the nitrogen in them to make proteins. Nitrogen is then passed along food chains in the form of proteins, as animals eat plants (and each other).

4) Decomposers (bacteria and fungi in the soil) break down proteins in rotting plants and animals, and urea in animal waste. This returns the nitrogen to the soil — so the nitrogen in these organisms is recycled.

5) Nitrogen fixation is the process of turning N_2 from the air into nitrogen-containing ions in the soil which plants can use. There are two main ways that this happens:

   a) Lightning — there's so much energy in a bolt of lightning that it's enough to make nitrogen react with oxygen in the air to give nitrates.

   b) Nitrogen-fixing bacteria in roots and soil (see next page).

The Nitrogen Cycle

6) There are four different types of bacteria involved in the nitrogen cycle:

1) DECOMPOSERS — decompose proteins and urea and turn them into ammonia. Ammonia forms ammonium ions in solution that plants can use.

2) NITRIFYING BACTERIA — turn ammonia in decaying matter into nitrites and then into nitrates. Different species of nitrifying bacteria are responsible for producing nitrites and nitrates.

3) NITROGEN-FIXING BACTERIA — turn atmospheric N_2 into ammonia, which forms ammonium ions.

4) DENITRIFYING BACTERIA — turn nitrates back into N_2 gas. This is of no benefit to living organisms. Denitrifying bacteria are often found in waterlogged soils.

7) Some nitrogen-fixing bacteria live in the soil. Others live in nodules on the roots of legume plants (e.g. peas and beans). When these plants decompose, the nitrogen stored in them and in their nodules is returned to the soil. Nitrogen-containing ions can also leak out of the nodules during plant growth. The plants have a mutualistic relationship (see page 169) with the bacteria — the bacteria get food (sugars) from the plant, and the plant gets nitrogen-containing ions from the bacteria to make into proteins.

Farmers Can Increase the Amount of Nitrates in the Soil

1) Like all plants, crops take up nitrates from the soil as they grow.

2) But crops are harvested, rather than being left to die and decompose, so the nitrogen they contain isn't returned to the soil.

3) Over time, the nitrogen content of the soil decreases, leading to poor crop growth and deficiency diseases.

4) So farmers have ways of increasing the amount of nitrates in the soil to help their crops grow better:

Crop Rotation

This is where, instead of growing the same crop in a field year after year, different crops are grown each year in a cycle. The cycle usually includes a nitrogen-fixing crop (e.g. peas or beans), which helps to put nitrates back into the soil for another crop to use the following year.

Fertilisers

Spreading animal manure or compost on fields recycles the nutrients left in plant and animal waste and returns them to the soil through decomposition. Artificial fertilisers containing nitrates (and other mineral ions needed by plants) can also be used, but these can be expensive and can cause environmental problems (see page 177).

Bacteria do a lot of the hard work in the nitrogen cycle

Different types of bacteria play different roles at different points in the nitrogen cycle. You definitely need to get your head around which type of bacteria does what. Make sure that you know before moving on.

Warm-Up and Exam Questions

You know the drill, first some warm-up questions to ease you in, then the slightly trickier exam questions.

Warm-Up Questions

1) How is the carbon that is stored in fossil fuels returned to the atmosphere?
2) Describe how thermal desalination can be used to produce potable water.
3) Describe the role of nitrifying bacteria in the nitrogen cycle.
4) Explain why using nitrogen-containing fertilisers can be beneficial to farmers.

Exam Questions

1   **Figure 1** shows a simplified version of part of the nitrogen cycle.

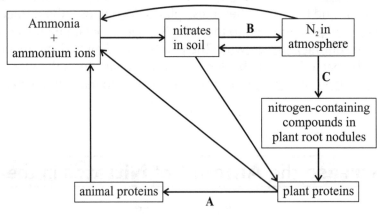

Figure 1

(a) Describe what is happening at stage **A**.

[1 mark]

(b) Name the type of bacteria responsible for stage **B**.

[1 mark]

(c) Name the type of bacteria responsible for stage **C**.

[1 mark]

2   The water cycle describes the constant movement of water molecules on the Earth.

(a) In the water cycle, name the process by which water moves from plants into the air.

[1 mark]

(b) Describe the shortest route a water molecule could take
through the water cycle to get from an ocean to a garden pond.

[4 marks]

3*   An area of woodland is cleared to build a house. The tree trunks are taken away to be
dried and used in furniture making. The smaller tree branches are used for firewood.
The green plants are piled up at the edge of the building site and left there.

Describe how carbon stored in the vegetation that has been cleared could be returned to the atmosphere.

[6 marks]

Indicator Species

The presence or absence of certain organisms in an area can be monitored as an indicator of pollution.

Indicator Species Can Give You Information About Pollution Levels

Some organisms are very sensitive to changes in their environment and so can be studied to see the effect of human activities — these organisms are known as indicator species.

Water Pollution

1) If raw sewage or fertilisers containing nitrates are released into a river, the microorganisms in the water increase in number and use up the oxygen (this is eutrophication — see page 177).

2) Some invertebrate animals, like stonefly larvae and freshwater shrimps are good indicators for water pollution levels because they're very sensitive to the concentration of dissolved oxygen in the water. If you find stonefly larvae in a river, it indicates that the water is clean.

3) Other invertebrates have adapted to live in polluted conditions, so if you see lots of them you know there's a problem. E.g. bloodworms and sludgeworms indicate a very high level of water pollution.

The absence of an indicator species could tell you the opposite too, e.g. the absence of stonefly larvae could indicate polluted water.

Air Pollution

1) Air pollution can be monitored by looking at particular types of lichen that are very sensitive to the concentration of sulfur dioxide in the atmosphere. (Sulfur dioxide is a pollutant released from car exhausts and power stations.) The number and type of lichen at a particular location will indicate how clean the air is. E.g. the air is clean if there are lots of lichen — especially bushy lichen, which need cleaner air than crusty lichen.

2) Blackspot fungus is found on rose leaves. It is also sensitive to the level of sulfur dioxide in the air, so its presence will indicate clean air.

3) You might get some data on indicator species in the exam, e.g. data showing there are more lichen species further away from a city centre. This is probably because outside the city centre, there is less pollution and the air contains less sulfur dioxide and other pollutants.

Bushy lichen

Crusty lichen

The Use of Indicator Species Isn't Without Flaws

There are a couple of ways of using indicator species to measure pollution:

1) You could do a simple survey to see if a species is present or absent from an area. This is a quick way of telling whether an area is polluted or not. But it's no good for telling how polluted an area is.

2) Counting the number of times an indicator species occurs in an area will give you a numerical value, allowing you to see roughly how polluted one area is in comparison with another.

Using indicator species is a simple and cost-effective way of saying whether or not an area is polluted. But indicator species can't give accurate figures for exactly how much pollution is present. There may also be factors other than pollution playing a role in the presence or absence of a species in an environment. Sometimes, it's better to use non-living indicators. For example:

1) Dissolved oxygen meters and chemical tests are used to accurately measure the concentration of dissolved oxygen in water, to show how the level of water pollution is changing.

2) Electronic meters and various laboratory tests are also used to accurately measure the concentration of sulfur dioxide in air, to show how air pollution is changing.

Decomposition

Decomposition is really important. Without it there'd be dead stuff everywhere. Let's break it down...

Things Decompose Because of Microorganisms

1) Living things (and the waste they produce) are made of elements taken from the world around them. When living things die or release waste, decomposition returns these elements to the soil or air.

2) Nearly all decomposition is done by microorganisms like soil bacteria and fungi. They are known as decomposers.

3) The rate of decay of a material depends on three main things:

Temperature
A warm temperature speeds up the rate of enzyme-controlled reactions in microbes, so decay happens faster. Enzymes denature if the temperature gets too high (see p.27).

Water Content
Decay takes place faster in moist environments because the organisms involved in decay need water to survive and carry out biological processes.

Oxygen Availability
The rate of decomposition is faster where there is plenty of oxygen available. Many microorganisms need oxygen for aerobic respiration (see page 159). Some decomposers don't need oxygen to respire, but these decomposers work slower anyway.

Food Preservation Methods Reduce the Rate of Decay

To preserve food, we use methods that slow decomposition by making the oxygen availability, water content and temperature less suitable for microorganisms' survival and reproduction. For example:

Storing foods in a fridge or freezer lowers the temperature of the food. This slows down the decomposers' rate of reproduction (or stops it altogether in the case of freezing).

Storing food in airtight containers stops microorganisms and oxygen from getting in. Tin cans are a good example of this — once the food is in, the can is sealed and sterilised (by exposing it to a high pressure and temperature) to kill any microorganisms present.

Drying food removes the water that microorganisms need to survive and reproduce, as does adding salt or sugar (which causes the microorganisms to lose water by osmosis — see p.36).

Keep food cold, dry and in airtight containers
The basic principles about how to store food safely come from knowing about the rate of food decay.

Decomposition

Compost is really useful stuff — so let's take a look at how to make it in as fast a time as possible.

Ideal Conditions Are Maintained to Make Compost

1) Compost is decomposed organic matter (e.g. food waste and garden waste) that is used as a fertiliser for crops and garden plants.

2) It's produced fastest in warm, moist conditions when there's plenty of oxygen available.

3) Compost bins create the ideal conditions for decomposers. For example,

   - Some have mesh sides to increase the oxygen availability.
   - The decomposing material is kept moist and heat is generated by the decomposers themselves.
   - Some compost bins are insulated to increase the temperature further.

You can Calculate the Rate of Decomposition

You could be asked to calculate how fast some lovely organic matter is decomposing. Here's an example:

EXAMPLE:

A block of cheese was left out of the fridge. The graph below shows the amount of mould that formed on the cheese. Moulds are fungi that decompose the cheese. Calculate the average rate at which the cheese decomposed during the first week, giving your answer as units of mould day^{-1}.

1) 1 week is 7 days, so first find 7 days on the x-axis of the graph.

2) From that point, draw a line straight up to the point that it meets the line of the graph.

3) Now draw a line straight across from there to the y-axis. Read off the amount of mould that had formed in 7 days.

4) Divide the amount of mould by the number of days.

5) Finally, calculate the answer (and don't forget to give the units).

Rate of decomposition = 25 units of mould ÷ 7 days

= 3.571...

= 3.6 units of mould day^{-1} (to 2 s.f.)

You might even get asked to calculate the change in the rate of decomposition during two different time periods. To do this, just find both rates and then subtract the lower rate from the higher rate.

Don't get tripped up by rate of decay

In the exam, the amount of decay could be shown in a number of ways, e.g. the amount of mould formed, the change in mass of the material or the percentage loss in mass of the material. But don't panic — calculating the rate of decay will always use the same principle. Rate is a measure of how much something changes over time, so to find the rate of decay, you just need to divide the quantity that changes (e.g amount of mould or mass) by the time it takes to change.

Warm-Up and Exam Questions

Don't assume that you've remembered everything you just read. Give these questions a go to find out.

Exam Questions

1 A group of students are investigating how the sulfur dioxide released by a local power station has affected the distribution of lichen in two woodland areas, woodland **A** and woodland **B**. **Figure 1** shows the mean percentage cover of lichen on a sample of tree trunks in each area.

Species	Mean percentage cover on tree trunks (%)	
	Woodland **A**	Woodland **B**
Bushy Lichen	11	34
Crusty Lichen	19	25

Figure 1

(a) Suggest and explain **one** conclusion that you could draw from the data in **Figure 1** about the levels of sulfur dioxide in the two woodlands.

[3 marks]

(b) Suggest **one** disadvantage of using indicator species to collect data on air pollution.

[1 mark]

2 A gardener recycles her garden waste in a compost bin.

Grade 7-9

Figure 2 shows the change in mass of the waste over 8 weeks as a percentage of its original mass, as it decomposes.

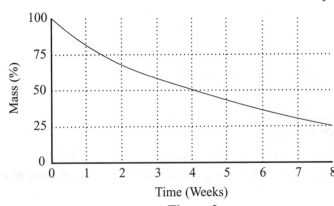

Figure 2

(a) The mean rate of decomposition during the first four weeks was 12.5 % of mass per week. Use **Figure 2** to calculate the change in the mean rate of decomposition between the first four weeks and the last four weeks.

[3 marks]

(b)* Suggest how the gardener could maximise the rate of decomposition in the compost bin. In your answer you should explain the conditions needed for fast decay and suggest how the gardener could create these conditions in her compost bin.

[6 marks]

Revision Summary for Topic 9

Congratulations, you've made it to the end of <u>Topic 9</u> — now it's time to test how much you've taken in...
- Try these questions and <u>tick off each one</u> when you <u>get it right</u>.
- When you've done <u>all the questions</u> under a heading and are <u>completely happy</u> with it, tick it off.

Ecosystems (p.169-175) ☑

1) Define the following terms: a) population, b) community.
2) What does it mean if two species are interdependent?
3) Give an example of a mutualistic relationship.
4) Give two biotic factors and explain how each one could affect a community.
5) Briefly describe how you could use quadrats to investigate the population size of a species.
6) What is a belt transect?
7) Explain why food chains rarely have more than five trophic levels.
8) What is biomass?
9) True or false? Producers always go at the top of a pyramid of biomass.
10) What is the formula for calculating the efficiency of energy transfer between levels of a food chain?

Biodiversity and Food Security (p.177-181) ☑

11) a) What is meant by the term 'eutrophication'?
    b) Explain how having an open water fish farm in a water system can cause eutrophication.
12) What is a non-indigenous species?
13) Give three examples of types of conservation schemes.
14) Give three benefits of maintaining biodiversity.
15) Give five biological factors that affect food security.

The Carbon, Water and Nitrogen Cycles (p.183-187) ☑

16) Name the only process that removes carbon dioxide from the air in the carbon cycle.
17) Name two processes that put carbon dioxide back into the air in the carbon cycle.
18) Produce a labelled diagram of the water cycle.
19) Why is the ability to produce potable water important in times of drought?
20) What does desalination mean?
21) Name a common method of desalination.
22) Describe the role of nitrogen-fixing bacteria in the nitrogen cycle.
23) What is crop rotation? Why is it beneficial to farmers?

Indicator Species and Decomposition (p.189-191) ☑

24) Name two indicator species found in clean water.
25) An area contains lots of rose plants. The plants all have blackspot fungus on their leaves. What does this tell you about the level of air pollution in the area?
26) Explain why cold conditions can help to preserve food.
27) Explain why compost is usually kept moist.

Safety and Ethics

Science can be quite dangerous at times, so it's important that you keep yourself (and others) safe in the lab. Some experiments can also involve ethical issues that you must deal with respectfully and responsibly.

Make Sure You're **Working Safely** in the **Lab**

1) Before you start any experiment, make sure you know about any safety precautions to do with your method or the chemicals you're using. You need to follow any instructions that your teacher gives you carefully. The chemicals you're using may be hazardous — for example, they might be flammable (catch fire easily), or they might irritate or burn your skin if it comes into contact with them.

2) Make sure that you're wearing sensible clothing when you're in the lab (e.g. open shoes won't protect your feet from spillages). When you're doing an experiment, you should wear a lab coat to protect your skin and clothing. Depending on the experiment, you may need to also wear safety goggles and gloves.

3) You also need to be aware of general safety in the lab, e.g. keep anything flammable away from lit Bunsen burners, don't directly touch any hot equipment, handle glassware (including microscope slides) carefully to avoid breakages, etc.

You Need to Think About **Ethical Issues** In Your Experiments

1) Any organisms involved in your investigations need to be treated safely and ethically.

2) Animals need to be treated humanely — they should be handled carefully and any wild animals captured for studying should be returned to their original habitat. Any animals kept in the lab should also be cared for in a humane way, e.g. they should not be kept in conditions that are too hot.

3) If you are carrying out an experiment involving other students, they should not be forced to participate against their will or feel pressured to take part.

BEWARE — hazardous biology experiments about...

Before you carry out an experiment, you must consider all of the hazards. They can be anything from chemicals to sharp objects, pathogens to heating equipment. Whatever the hazard, make sure you know all the safety precautions you should follow to keep yourself, and others, safe.

Heating Substances

Some more useful lab stuff for you now — a bit about <u>heating things up</u>.

Bunsen Burners Have a **Naked Flame**

Bunsen burners are good for <u>heating things quickly</u>. But you need to make sure you're using them <u>safely</u>:

- You should always use a Bunsen burner on a <u>heat-proof mat</u>.
- If your Bunsen burner is alight but not heating anything, make sure you <u>close</u> the hole so that the flame becomes <u>yellow</u> and <u>clearly visible</u>.
- Use the <u>blue</u> flame to heat things. If you're heating a vessel <u>in</u> the flame, hold it at the <u>top</u> (e.g. with <u>tongs</u>) and point the opening <u>away from</u> yourself (and others).
- If you're heating something <u>over</u> the flame (e.g. a beaker of water), you should put a <u>tripod and gauze</u> over the Bunsen burner before you light it, and place the vessel on this.
- Whenever you use a Bunsen burner, you should wear <u>safety goggles</u> to protect your eyes.

Hole is closed

Heat-proof mat

to gas

The Temperature of **Electric Water Baths** Can Be **Set**

1) A <u>water bath</u> is a container filled with water that can be heated to a <u>specific temperature</u>. A <u>simple</u> water bath can be made by heating a <u>beaker of water</u> over a <u>Bunsen burner</u> and monitoring the temperature with a <u>thermometer</u> (see p.28). However, it is difficult to keep the temperature of the water <u>constant</u>.

2) An <u>electric water bath</u> will monitor and adjust the temperature for you. It's a much easier way of keeping the temperature of a reaction mixture constant. Here's how you use one:

- <u>Set</u> the temperature on the water bath, and allow the water to <u>heat up</u>.
- To make sure it's reached the right temperature, use a <u>thermometer</u>.
- Place the vessel containing your substance in the water bath using <u>test tube holders</u> or <u>tongs</u>. The level of water outside the vessel should be <u>just above</u> the level of the substance in the vessel.
- The substance will then be warmed to the <u>same temperature</u> as the water. As the substance in the vessel is surrounded by water, the heating is very <u>even</u>.

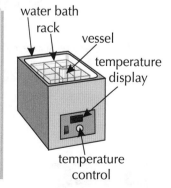

water bath rack

vessel

temperature display

temperature control

Electric water baths are great for keeping the temperature constant

Make sure you're clear on how to use <u>Bunsen burners</u> and <u>electric water baths</u>, and more importantly, on how to use them <u>safely</u>. Obviously flames and hot things are <u>very dangerous</u>, so <u>take care</u>.

Measuring Substances

Get your lab coats on, it's time to find out about some of the skills you'll need in experiments...

Use the **Right Apparatus** to Take **Accurate Readings**

1. Length

1) <u>Length</u> can be <u>measured</u> in different <u>units</u> (e.g. mm, cm, m). Smaller units have a higher degree of <u>accuracy</u>. For example, it's more <u>accurate</u> to measure the length of a potato cylinder to the nearest <u>mm</u> than the nearest <u>cm</u>.

2) You'll need to decide on the <u>appropriate level of accuracy</u> for your experiment. For example, the length of a <u>leaf</u> would be better measured in <u>millimetres</u>, but the length of a <u>transect line</u> would be better measured in <u>metres</u>.

3) It is also important to <u>choose</u> the <u>right equipment</u> when measuring length — a <u>ruler</u> would probably be best for small things, but a <u>metre rule</u> or <u>tape measure</u> would be better for larger distances.

2. Area

In biology, you might need to measure the <u>area</u> of something (e.g. part of a habitat, a living thing). Living things are usually quite <u>complex shapes</u>, but you can make their area easier to work out by comparing them to a <u>simpler shape</u> and working out the area of that (e.g. <u>inhibition zones</u> on agar plates spread with bacteria are roughly <u>circular</u> — see p.112). To find the area of something:

1) First, you'll need to take <u>accurate measurements</u> of its dimensions.

> If you want to <u>measure</u> the area of a <u>field</u> (see page 171) that is <u>rectangular</u>, you'll need to use a <u>tape measure</u> or a <u>trundle wheel</u> to measure the <u>length</u> and <u>width</u> of the field. Record your readings in metres.

2) Then you can <u>calculate</u> its <u>area</u>.

> Area of a <u>rectangle</u> = <u>length</u> × <u>width</u>.
> So, if your field is 30 m by 55 m, the <u>area</u> would be 30 × 55 = <u>1650 m^2</u>.

Don't forget the units of area are always something squared, e.g. mm^2.

3) Here are some examples of other <u>area formulas</u> that may come in useful:

> **Area of a triangle = ½ × base × height**
> **Area of a circle = πr^2**

3. Mass

To weigh a substance, start by putting the <u>container</u> you are weighing your substance into on a <u>balance</u>. Set the balance to exactly <u>zero</u> and then weigh out the correct amount of your substance.

Measuring Substances

4. Time

1) If your experiment involves <u>timing</u> something (e.g. how long a reaction takes to happen) or taking measurements at <u>regular intervals</u>, it's probably best to use a <u>stopwatch</u>.

2) Using a <u>stopwatch</u> that measures to the nearest <u>0.1 s</u> will make your results more <u>accurate</u>.

3) Always make sure you <u>start</u> and <u>stop</u> the stopwatch at exactly the right time. For example, if you're investigating the rate of a reaction, you should start timing at the <u>exact moment</u> you mix the reagents and start the reaction.

4) It's a good idea to get the <u>same person</u> to do the timing so the results are as <u>precise</u> as possible.

5. Temperature

1) You can use a <u>thermometer</u> to measure temperature.

2) Make sure that the <u>bulb</u> of the thermometer is <u>completely submerged</u> in the substance you're measuring and that you wait for the temperature to <u>stabilise</u> before you take your initial reading.

3) Read off the <u>scale</u> on the thermometer at <u>eye level</u> to make sure your reading is correct.

When you're reading off a scale, write down the value of the graduation that the amount is closest to. If it's exactly halfway between two values, round up.

6. Volume of a Liquid

There's more than one way to measure the volume of a <u>liquid</u>. Whichever method you use, always read the volume from the <u>bottom of the meniscus</u> (the curved upper surface of the liquid) when it's at <u>eye level</u>.

Read volume from here — the bottom of the meniscus.

Using a pipette

1) <u>Pipettes</u> are used to suck up and <u>transfer</u> volumes of liquid between containers.

2) <u>Dropping pipettes</u> are used to transfer <u>drops</u> of liquid.

3) <u>Graduated pipettes</u> are used to transfer <u>accurate</u> volumes.

4) A <u>pipette filler</u> is attached to the end of a graduated pipette, to <u>control</u> the amount of liquid being drawn up.

Using a measuring cylinder

1) <u>Measuring cylinders</u> come in all different <u>sizes</u>.

2) Make sure you choose one that's the right size for the measurement you want to make. It's no good using a huge 1 dm³ cylinder to measure out 2 cm³ of a liquid — the graduations will be too big, and you'll end up with <u>massive errors</u>. It'd be much better to use one that measures up to 10 cm³.

Measuring Substances

7. Volume of a Gas

1) To accurately measure the <u>volume</u> of gas, you should use a <u>gas syringe</u>.
2) Alternatively, you can use an <u>upturned measuring cylinder</u> filled with <u>water</u>. The gas will <u>displace</u> the water so you can <u>read the volume</u> off the <u>scale</u>.
3) You could also <u>count the bubbles</u> of gas released. But the bubbles could be <u>different sizes</u> and if they're produced quickly you might <u>miss some</u> — so this method is <u>less accurate</u>.
4) When you're measuring a gas, you need to make sure that the equipment is set up so that none of the gas can <u>escape</u>, otherwise your results won't be <u>accurate</u>.

8. pH

The method you should use to measure pH depends on what your experiment is.

1) <u>Indicators</u> are dyes that <u>change colour</u> depending on whether they're in an <u>acid</u> or an <u>alkali</u>. You use them by adding a couple of drops of the indicator to the solution you're interested in. <u>Universal indicator</u> is a <u>mixture</u> of indicators that changes colour <u>gradually</u> as pH changes. It's useful for <u>estimating</u> the pH of a solution based on its colour.
2) <u>Indicator paper</u> is useful if you don't want to colour the entire solution that you're testing. It <u>changes colour</u> depending on the pH of the solution it touches. You can also hold a piece of <u>damp indicator paper</u> in a <u>gas sample</u> to test its pH.
3) <u>pH meters</u> have a <u>digital display</u> that gives an <u>accurate value</u> for the pH of a solution.

Blue litmus paper turns <u>red</u> in acidic conditions and
red litmus paper turns <u>blue</u> in alkaline conditions.

9. Continuous Sampling

1) <u>Continuous sampling</u> is when <u>lots of samples</u> are taken at <u>regular intervals</u> over a particular time period. This means you can see what is happening <u>during the experiment</u>, not just its outcome.
2) Using a <u>data logger</u> connected to a computer is an <u>example</u> of continuous sampling. Data loggers can be used to measure a range of variables, including <u>temperature</u>, <u>pH</u> and <u>O_2 concentration</u>.

Make Sure You Can Draw Diagrams of Your Equipment

When you're writing out a <u>method</u> for your experiment, it's always a good idea to draw a <u>labelled diagram</u> showing how your apparatus will be <u>set up</u>. The easiest way to do this is to use a scientific drawing, where each piece of apparatus is drawn as if you're looking at its <u>cross-section</u> (with no shading or colouring).

For example:

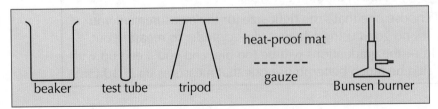

beaker   test tube   tripod   heat-proof mat   gauze   Bunsen burner

The pieces of glassware are drawn without tops so they aren't sealed. If you want to draw a closed system, remember to draw a bung in the top.

Practice Exams

Once you've been through all the questions in this book, you should feel pretty confident about the exams.
As final preparation, here is a set of **practice exams** to really get you set for the real thing. The time allowed for
each paper is 1 hour 45 minutes. These papers are designed to give you the best possible preparation for your exams.

CGP Practice Exam Paper
GCSE Biology

GCSE Biology

Paper 1

Higher Tier

In addition to this paper you should have:
• A ruler.
• A calculator.

Centre name			
Centre number			
Candidate number			

Time allowed:
• 1 hour 45 minutes

Surname	
Other names	
Candidate signature	

Instructions to candidates
• Write your name and other details in the spaces provided above.
• Answer **all** questions in the spaces provided.
• Do all rough work on the paper.
• Cross out any work you do not want to be marked.
• You are allowed to use a calculator.

Information for candidates
• The marks available are given in brackets at the end of each question.
• There are 100 marks available for this paper.
• You should use good English and present your answers in a
clear and organised way.
• For questions marked with an asterisk (*) ensure that your answers
have a logical structure, with points that link together clearly, and
include detailed, relevant information.

Advice to candidates
• In calculations show clearly how you worked out your answers.
• Read each question carefully before answering it.
• Check your answers if you have time.

For examiner's use							
Q	Attempt Nº			Q	Attempt Nº		
	1	2	3		1	2	3
1				6			
2				7			
3				8			
4				9			
5				10			
Total							

1 **Figure 1** shows an animal cell.

Figure 1

(a) Give **two** ways in which the cell in **Figure 1** is different from a bacterial cell.

....

....

....

[2 marks]

(b) Not all animal cells have the same structures as the cell in **Figure 1**.
Explain why.

....

....

[1 mark]

Figure 2 shows a single-celled organism called *Euglena*, found in pond water.

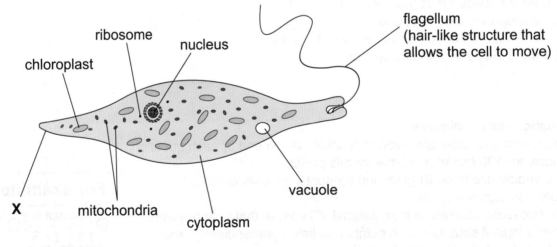

Figure 2

(c) Name part **X**.

....

[1 mark]

(d) A scientist viewed an individual *Euglena* under a microscope with × 150 magnification.
He calculated the real length of the *Euglena* to be 0.054 mm.
Which of the following is the length of the image of the *Euglena*? Use the formula:

$$\text{magnification} = \frac{\text{image size}}{\text{real size}}$$

☐ **A** 27.8 mm

☐ **B** 15 mm

☐ **C** 8.1 mm

☐ **D** 0.00036 mm

[1 mark]

(e) When *Euglena* was first discovered, scientists disagreed over whether it was
a plant or an animal.
Give **two** similarities and **two** differences between plant and animal cells.

....

....

....

....

....

....

....

[4 marks]
[Total 9 marks]

Turn over for the next question

Turn over ▶

2 Antibiotics can be used to kill bacteria and help a patient fight disease.

Scientists developing antibiotics were comparing the effectiveness of two different antibiotics, **X** and **Y**, against a bacterium. They spread the bacteria on agar jelly in 20 Petri dishes — forming an even covering of bacteria on the top of the agar.

They took three identical discs of paper and soaked each of them in one of three different liquids, shown in **Figure 3**.

Disc	Liquid soaked in
1	Antibiotic **X**
2	Antibiotic **Y**
3	Distilled water

Figure 3

The discs were then placed onto the agar in each dish. The dishes were kept in an incubator at 35 °C for two days, and then they were examined.

Figure 4 shows a typical dish.

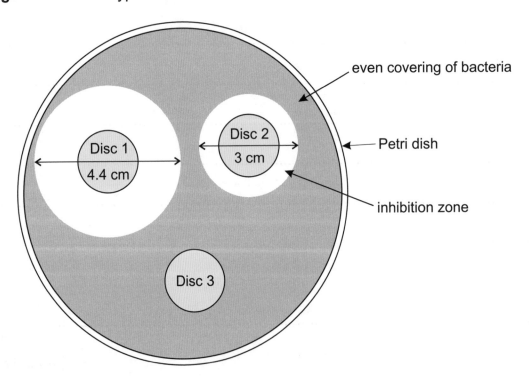

Figure 4

(a) Give **two** things that the scientists should have done to avoid contaminating the bacterial cultures.

....

....

....

....

[2 marks]

(b) The diameter of each inhibition zone is shown on **Figure 4**.
Calculate the areas of the inhibition zones for antibiotics **X** and **Y**.
Use the equation area = πr^2.
Use the areas to compare the effectiveness of the two antibiotics.

....Turn over...

....

....

....

....

....

[3 marks]

(c) Explain why antibiotics are harmful to bacteria but not to humans.

....

....

....

[2 marks]

The most effective antibiotic was manufactured and prescribed to patients.
Two years later, scientists repeated the experiment with a fresh sample of the bacteria and found that no inhibition zone was produced around the disc soaked in this antibiotic.

(d) Suggest an explanation for this observation.

....

....

....

....

[2 marks]
[Total 9 marks]

Turn over for the next question

Turn over ▶

3 **Figure 5** shows the structure of a DNA double-stranded helix.
The two strands are held together by cross-linking between their bases.

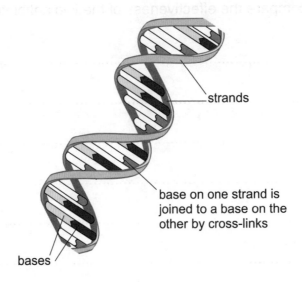

strands

base on one strand is
joined to a base on the
other by cross-links

bases

Figure 5

(a) Explain why there will always be equal amounts of bases A and T in a
molecule of DNA.

....

....
[1 mark]

(b) Name the part of a cell where strands of human DNA are found.

....
[1 mark]

A sequence of bases in a section of DNA is shown in **Figure 6**.

A T C A G G C T A G T T

Figure 6

(c) How many amino acids would be coded for by this base sequence.

☐ **A** 3

☐ **B** 4

☐ **C** 6

☐ **D** 10

[1 mark]

During protein synthesis, the DNA sequence in **Figure 6** is used as a template.
A complementary strand of mRNA is produced from the template through transcription.

(d) Give the sequence of the complementary mRNA strand that is transcribed.

....
[2 marks]

A mutation occurs in another section of DNA. The mutation results in a change
of phenotype, where there is an over production of a protein.

(e) (i) Which of the following describes the term phenotype?

☐ **A** The combination of alleles that an individual has.

☐ **B** Having two alleles that are the same.

☐ **C** The characteristics produced by alleles.

☐ **D** Having two different dominant alleles.

[1 mark]

(ii) Suggest an explanation for how this mutation causes a change in phenotype.

....

....

....

....
[3 marks]
[Total 9 marks]

Turn over for the next question

4 Communicable diseases can be spread between individuals.

(a) Zika virus disease is an example of a communicable disease.
The virus that causes the disease is spread by a mosquito vector.
Suggest **two** ways that the spread of the Zika virus disease could be reduced.

....

....

....
[2 marks]

(b) Which of the following communicable diseases is also spread by a vector?

☐ **A** influenza

☐ **B** malaria

☐ **C** HIV

☐ **D** athlete's foot

[1 mark]

(c) Tuberculosis (TB) is a communicable disease caused by *Mycobacterium tuberculosis* bacteria. A strain of this bacteria was observed to have cells that divided every 18 hours on average.

Give the number of cells that would be produced from one bacterium of this strain in 3 days.

.... cells
[2 marks]

(d) The TB vaccine protects against tuberculosis.
Explain how immunisation helps to protect the body against a disease.

....

....

....

....

....

....

....

....

[4 marks]
[Total 9 marks]

Turn over for the next question

Turn over ▶

208

5   Research from the Human Genome Project can be used to improve human health.

(a) What is meant by the term 'genome'?

☐   **A** A section of DNA that codes for a particular protein.

☐   **B** All of an organism's DNA.

☐   **C** A long coiled up molecule of DNA.

☐   **D** A unit containing a sugar, a phosphate group and a base.

[1 mark]

Cystic fibrosis is an inherited disorder caused by a recessive allele.

(b) Suggest how the Human Genome Project could have the potential to help people with cystic fibrosis.

....

....
[1 mark]

A couple have a baby boy. The doctor tells them that the baby has inherited cystic fibrosis. Neither parent shows signs of the disorder.

(c) In the space below, construct a diagram to show how the baby inherited cystic fibrosis.

Your diagram should show the genotypes of both parents, the genotypes of their gametes, and all the possible genotypes of their offspring.

Use **F** to represent the dominant allele and **f** to represent the recessive allele.

[3 marks]

The family pedigree in **Figure 7** shows a family with a history of cystic fibrosis.

Figure 7

(d) Using the information in **Figure 7**, state what Leina's genotype must be.
Explain your answer.

....

....

....

....

[2 marks]

(e) Carys and Beth are sisters. Carys has a scar on her hand. Beth does not.

Explain whether this is an example of genetic variation, environmental variation, or a combination of both.

....

....

....

[2 marks]
[Total 9 marks]

Turn over for the next question

Turn over ▶

6 The peppered moth is an insect that lives on the trunks of trees in Britain.
The moths are prey for birds such as thrushes.
The peppered moth exists in two varieties, shown in **Figure 8**.

1. A light-coloured variety — they are better camouflaged on tree trunks in unpolluted areas.

2. A dark-coloured variety — they are better camouflaged on sooty tree trunks in badly polluted areas.

Figure 8

The bar charts in **Figure 9** show the percentages of dark- and light-coloured peppered moths in two different towns.

Figure 9

(a) State which town, **A** or **B**, is the most polluted. Give a reason for your answer.

....

....

[1 mark]

(b) Calculate the difference in percentage between the dark-coloured moth population in Town **A** and Town **B**. Show your working.

...............................%
[2 marks]

Collecting the data shown in **Figure 9** involved leaving traps overnight, with lights inside to attract moths. The scientists then counted the moths that had been captured, before releasing them.

(c) Suggest **one** way that the scientists carrying out this investigation could have helped to ensure the humane treatment of the moths.

....

....
[1 mark]

The dark variety of the moth was first recorded in the north of England in 1848.
It became increasingly common in polluted areas until the 1960s, when the
number of soot-covered trees declined because of the introduction of new laws.

(d) Using the idea of natural selection, explain why the dark variety of moth became more common in soot-polluted areas.

....

....

....

....

....

....

....

....
[4 marks]
[Total 8 marks]

Turn over for the next question

7   Statins are a type of drug used to reduce the risk of coronary heart disease, a type of cardiovascular disease.

A new statin has been developed and was initially put through preclinical testing. Following this, the drug was given to thirty healthy volunteers in a clinical trial.

A trial was then carried out on a large sample of patients who had previously had a heart attack. Half were randomly allocated the drug and half were randomly allocated a placebo.

Figure 10 shows the results after five years of treatment.

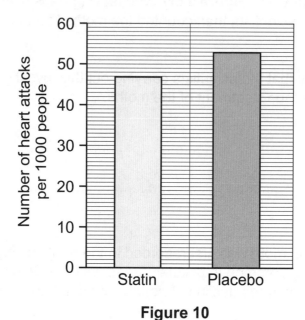

Figure 10

In preclinical testing, new drugs are tested on human cells and tissues and on live animals.

(a) Give **two** reasons why preclinical tests are carried out.

....

....

....

....

[2 marks]

(b) Give **one** reason for giving the drug to healthy human volunteers during the clinical trial.

....

[1 mark]

(c) The scientists carrying out the trial concluded that the statin decreased the risk of having a heart attack for people who had previously had a heart attack.
Evaluate the validity of this conclusion using the information given.

....

....

....

....

....

....

....

....

[4 marks]

Lifestyle changes can also help to reduce the risk of coronary heart disease.

(d) Suggest **one** lifestyle change that could help reduce the risk of a heart attack.

....

....

[1 mark]
[Total 8 marks]

Turn over for the next question

Turn over ▶

8 A student did an experiment to investigate the effect of pH on the action of the enzyme amylase. The method used is shown in **Figure 11**.

> 1. Add a set quantity of starch solution to a test tube and the same quantity of amylase solution to another.
> 2. Add a set quantity of a buffer solution with a pH of 5 to the tube containing starch solution.
> 3. Place all of the test tubes in a water bath at 35 °C.
> 4. Allow the starch and amylase solutions to reach the temperature of the water bath, then mix them together and return the mixture to the water bath.
> 5. Take a small sample of the mixture every minute and test for starch.
> 6. Stop the experiment when starch is no longer present in the sample, or after 30 minutes (whichever is sooner).
> 7. Repeat the experiment using buffer solutions of different pH values.

Figure 11

(a) What happens to the starch during the experiment?

☐ **A** It is converted into amino acids.

☐ **B** It is converted into sugars.

☐ **C** It is converted into glycerol.

☐ **D** It is converted into fatty acids.

[1 mark]

(b) Explain why a set quantity of starch solution was used for each repeat in the experiment.

....

....

[1 mark]

(c) Describe how the student could have tested for the presence of starch in **Step 5**.

....

....

....

....

....

[3 marks]

Figure 12 shows a graph of the student's results.

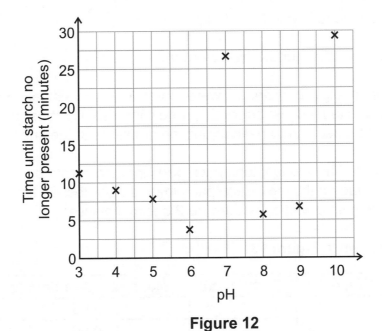

Figure 12

(d) Describe the trend shown in the graph in **Figure 12**, between **pH 3** and **pH 6**.

....

....

[1 mark]

(e) (i) The student thinks that one of the results shown on the graph is likely to be anomalous. Identify the anomalous result and give a reason for your answer.

....

....

....

[2 marks]

(ii) Suggest **two** factors that could have caused this anomalous result.

....

....

....

[2 marks]

[Total 10 marks]

Turn over for the next question

Turn over ▶

9 A scientist was investigating the reflex actions of men and women.

The scientist made the following hypothesis:

'Men have faster reaction times than women.'

The reaction times of eight participants were tested in the investigation.
Each participant was tapped just below the knee with a small rubber hammer.
When the leg was tapped it automatically kicked outwards at the knee.

The scientist recorded how long it took each participant to respond to
the stimulus of the tap on the leg. Each participant did the test 20 times,
and a mean reaction time was calculated (to 2 decimal places).

The results are shown in **Figure 13**.

Sex	Participant	Mean reaction time (s)
Female	1	0.05
	2	0.06
	3	0.06
	4	0.04
Male	5	0.05
	6	0.04
	7	0.04
	8	0.05

Figure 13

(a) Using all the information above, give **two** reasons that support the idea that the
participants' response was a reflex.

....

....

....

[2 marks]

(b) (i) What was the dependent variable in this experiment?

☐ **A** number of participants

☐ **B** stimulus

☐ **C** reaction time

☐ **D** sex

[1 mark]

(ii) What was the independent variable in this experiment?

   ☐ **A** number of participants

   ☐ **B** stimulus

   ☐ **C** reaction time

   ☐ **D** sex

[1 mark]

(c) **Figure 14** shows the mean reaction times for males and females in the investigation.

Figure 14

State whether or not the data shown in **Figure 14** supports the scientist's hypothesis. Explain your answer.

....

....
[2 marks]

(d) Suggest **two** variables that the scientist should have controlled in this experiment.

....

....
[2 marks]

Question 9 continues on the next page

Turn over ▶

Another example of a reflex is the response of moving your hand away from a painful stimulus. **Figure 15** shows the parts of the nervous system involved in this reflex.

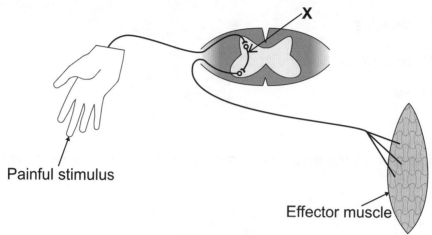

Figure 15

(e) (i) Name part **X** shown in **Figure 15**.

☐ **A** motor neurone

☐ **B** relay neurone

☐ **C** synapse

☐ **D** sensory neurone

[1 mark]

*(ii) The pain stimulus is detected by receptors in the skin and causes a reflex response. Describe the path taken by a nervous impulse in this reflex, beginning at the receptors.

....

....

....

....

....

....

....

....

....

[6 marks]

[Total 15 marks]

10 Some plants can reproduce both sexually and asexually.

(a) Sexual reproduction involves the fusion of gametes.
Gametes are produced by meiosis.

Which of the following is produced when a cell divides by meiosis?

☐ **A** Two genetically different daughter cells.

☐ **B** Four genetically different daughter cells.

☐ **C** Two genetically identical daughter cells.

☐ **D** Four genetically identical daughter cells.

[1 mark]

Strawberry plants reproduce asexually. They produce runners, which are thin stems that grow horizontally along the ground as shown in **Figure 16**. The runners produce shoots and roots which can develop into new plants.

Figure 16

(b) (i) State and explain **one** advantage of asexual reproduction.

....

....

....

[2 marks]

(ii) State and explain **one** disadvantage of asexual reproduction.

....

....

....

[2 marks]

Question 10 continues on the next page

Turn over ▶

DNA can be extracted from strawberries. This involves mixing mashed strawberries with a solution of detergent and salt. The mixture is then filtered and ice-cold ethanol added.

(c) (i) Explain why the detergent and salt are added to the mashed strawberries.

....

....

....

[2 marks]

(ii) State why ice-cold ethanol is added.

....

....

[1 mark]

*(d) Describe the stages of the cell cycle and suggest why disrupting the cell cycle by using herbicides can kill plants.

....

....

....

....

....

....

....

....

....

....

....

....

....

....

[6 marks]

[Total 14 marks]

END OF QUESTIONS

GCSE Biology

Paper 2

Higher Tier

In addition to this paper you should have:
- A ruler.
- A calculator.

Centre name				
Centre number				
Candidate number				

Time allowed:
- 1 hour 45 minutes

Surname
Other names
Candidate signature

Instructions to candidates
- Write your name and other details in the spaces provided above.
- Answer **all** questions in the spaces provided.
- Do all rough work on the paper.
- Cross out any work you do not want to be marked.
- You are allowed to use a calculator.

Information for candidates
- The marks available are given in brackets at the end of each question.
- There are 100 marks available for this paper.
- You should use good English and present your answers in a clear and organised way.
- For questions marked with an asterisk (*) ensure that your answers have a logical structure, with points that link together clearly, and include detailed, relevant information.

Advice to candidates
- In calculations show clearly how you worked out your answers.
- Read each question carefully before answering it.
- Check your answers if you have time.

For examiner's use

Q	Attempt Nº			Q	Attempt Nº		
	1	2	3		1	2	3
1				6			
2				7			
3				8			
4				9			
5				10			
Total							

1 **Figure 1** shows the amount of biomass contained within an area of plants.
It shows how much biomass from the plants is transferred to each trophic level
in a food chain.

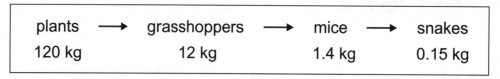

plants   ⟶   grasshoppers   ⟶   mice   ⟶   snakes

120 kg   12 kg   1.4 kg   0.15 kg

Figure 1

(a) What is meant by the term 'producer'?

☐ **A** An organism that eats other organisms.

☐ **B** An organism that eats primary consumers.

☐ **C** An organism that makes its own food.

☐ **D** An organism that releases nutrients into the soil.

[1 mark]

Figure 2 shows four different pyramids of biomass.

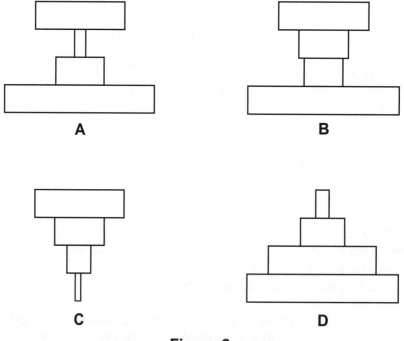

Figure 2

(b) (i) Which pyramid of biomass in **Figure 2** represents the food chain in **Figure 1**?

☐ **A**

☐ **B**

☐ **C**

☐ **D**

[1 mark]

(ii) Give a reason for your answer to **part (i)**.

....

....
[1 mark]

(c) Calculate the efficiency of biomass transfer between the grasshoppers and mice.
Use the equation:

$$\text{efficiency} = \frac{\text{biomass transferred to the next level}}{\text{biomass available at the previous level}} \times 100$$

Efficiency = ... %
[1 mark]

(d) The food chain in **Figure 1** has four trophic levels.
Most food chains have no more than five trophic levels.
Suggest why the length of food chains is limited in this way.

....

....

....
[2 marks]
[Total 6 marks]

Turn over for the next question

Turn over ▶

224

2   A student was investigating the distribution of buttercups in an area around his school.
He counted the number of buttercups in 10 quadrats in five different fields.
His quadrat measured 1 m². His results are shown in **Figure 3**.

Field	Mean number of buttercups per quadrat
A	10
B	35
C	21
D	37
E	21

Figure 3

(a) What is the median of the data in **Figure 3**?

☐ **A** 21

☐ **B** 37

☐ **C** 10

☐ **D** 24.8

[1 mark]

(b) The student used a random number generator to pick the coordinates to place the quadrats.
Suggest why the quadrats were placed randomly.

....

....
[1 mark]

(c) A week later, the student repeated his experiment in a sixth field, Field **F**.
His results for each quadrat are shown below:

6   15   9   14   20   5   3   11   10   7

Using this data, calculate the mean number of buttercups per m² in Field **F**.

Mean = ... buttercups per m²
[1 mark]

(d) (i) Field **F** measures 90 m by 120 m.
Estimate the population of buttercups in Field **F**.

Estimated population = ... buttercups
[2 marks]

(ii) Suggest how the accuracy of the estimate in **part (i)** could be improved.

....

....
[1 mark]

The student observed that the distribution of buttercups changed across Field **A**.
Buttercups grow well in damp soil, so the student thinks that the change in the distribution
of buttercups is due to variability in the moisture level of the soil across the field.
The student wants to investigate this.

(e) (i) Suggest a hypothesis about the distribution of buttercups in Field **A**,
based on the student's observations.

....

....
[1 mark]

(ii) Describe how the student could investigate this hypothesis.

....

....

....

....

....

....

....
[4 marks]
[Total 11 marks]

Turn over for the next question

Turn over ▶

3   A student grew three plants in a windowsill tray.
    She then put the plants in a cardboard box with a cut-out hole.

    Figure 4 shows the same plants before and after three days in the cardboard box.

Start of experiment   After three days

Figure 4

(a) Explain what caused the plants' response.

....

....

....

....

....

....

[3 marks]

(b) Name the response shown by the plants in this experiment.

....

[1 mark]

(c) The student removed one of the plants from the tray.
She observed that the roots of the plant were growing downwards.
What is the name of the stimulus that causes the roots of a plant to grow downwards?

☐ **A** carbon dioxide

☐ **B** gravity

☐ **C** oxygen

☐ **D** temperature

[1 mark]

(d) The hormone which causes the plant growth response shown in **Figure 4**
and described in **part (c)** can be used in a selective weedkiller.
Explain how these weedkillers work.

....

....

....

....

[2 marks]
[Total 7 marks]

Turn over for the next question

Turn over ▶

4 Lactose is a reducing sugar commonly found in dairy products, such as milk and cheese. An enzyme called lactase breaks down lactose during digestion. The resulting products are the sugars glucose and galactose. These are absorbed into the blood from the small intestine.

(a) Suggest an explanation for why the breakdown of sugars like lactose into simpler sugars is necessary for organisms.

....

....

....
[2 marks]

(b) Glucose diffuses from the small intestine into the blood. Describe how the concentration of glucose in the blood compares to that in the small intestine.

....

....
[1 mark]

(c) The optimum pH of lactase is pH 6. State and explain what effect a pH of 12 would have on the break down of lactose by lactase.

....

....
[2 marks]

(d) Lactose intolerance is a digestive problem caused by insufficient production of lactase. To test a person for lactose intolerance, they are given a drink of lactose solution. A blood sample is then taken from them every 30 minutes for two hours. The blood is tested to see how much glucose it contains.

Explain what will happen to the blood glucose level of a person who is lactose intolerant during the test.

....

....

....

....
[2 marks]
[Total 7 marks]

5   The lung is a specialised gas exchange organ.
    It contains millions of air sacs called alveoli.
    Figure 5 shows an alveolus and a blood capillary.

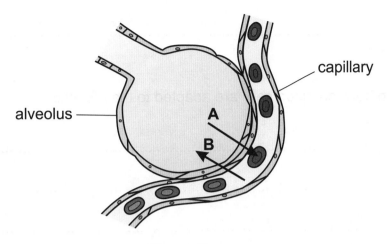

Figure 5

(a) The arrows in **Figure 5** show the net movement of two gases, **A** and **B**.
    What are the names of gases **A** and **B**?

	Gas A	Gas B
A	oxygen	nitrogen
B	carbon dioxide	oxygen
C	oxygen	carbon dioxide
D	carbon dioxide	nitrogen

[1 mark]

(b) Explain why alveoli need a good blood supply.

....

....

....

[2 marks]

Question 5 continues on the next page

Turn over ▶

(c) **Figure 5** shows red blood cells travelling through a capillary.
Red blood cells are flexible, which allows them to fit through capillaries.

(i) State the function of red blood cells.

....

[1 mark]

(ii) Explain how red blood cells are adapted to their function.

....

....

....

....

....

[3 marks]

Sickle cell anaemia is a genetic disorder of the blood where the red blood cells become rigid and sickle-shaped. **Figure 6** shows a sickle-shaped red blood cell and some normal red blood cells.

Figure 6

(d) A person with sickle cell anaemia may experience an increase in breathing rate. Suggest why they may experience this symptom.

....

....

....

....

[2 marks]

[Total 9 marks]

6 **Figure 7** shows the carbon cycle.

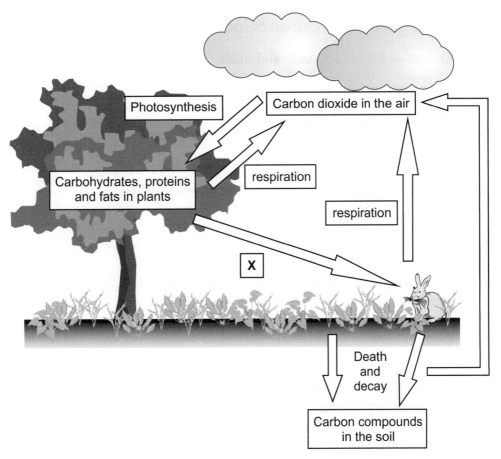

Figure 7

(a) Describe what is occurring at point **X** in the cycle shown in **Figure 7**.

....

....
[1 mark]

(b) Photosynthesis is an important process in the carbon cycle.

   (i) Give **three** factors that limit the rate of photosynthesis.

   1. ....

   2. ....

   3. ....
   [3 marks]

   (ii) Photosynthesis is an endothermic reaction. Explain what this means.

   ....
   [1 mark]

Question 6 continues on the next page

Turn over ▶

(c) What is the word equation for aerobic respiration?

☐ **A** glucose + oxygen → carbon dioxide + water

☐ **B** glucose → ethanol + carbon dioxide

☐ **C** glucose → carbon dioxide + water

☐ **D** glucose + oxygen → carbon dioxide

[1 mark]

(d) Explain how microorganisms are involved in the carbon cycle.

....

....

....

[2 marks]

(e) Microorganisms also play a role in the nitrogen cycle.
Which type of microorganisms turn nitrates in the soil into nitrogen gas?

☐ **A** nitrifying bacteria

☐ **B** denitrifying bacteria

☐ **C** nitrogen fixing bacteria

☐ **D** decomposers

[1 mark]
[Total 9 marks]

7   A scientist measured the rate of transpiration in two plants over 48 hours.
    The results are shown in **Figure 8**.

Figure 8

(a) The rate of transpiration for both plants was slower on **day 2** than on **day 1**.
    Suggest **one** reason for this and explain your suggestion.

    ....

    ....

    ....
    [2 marks]

(b) Explain why the rate of transpiration is lower during the night.

    ....

    ....

    ....

    ....
    [2 marks]

Question 7 continues on the next page

Turn over ▶

234

(c) Describe how a transpiration stream moves water through a plant.

....

....

....

....

....

....

[3 marks]

(d) Plants absorb water from the soil through their roots.
What is the process by which mineral ions are absorbed into the root?

☐ **A** diffusion

☐ **B** active transport

☐ **C** osmosis

☐ **D** transpiration

[1 mark]

(e) Describe how roots are adapted for absorbing water.

....

....

....

[2 marks]
[Total 10 marks]

8   The kidneys play a crucial role in filtering the blood.
    Figure 9 shows a kidney nephron and the blood vessels associated with it.

(a) Label the glomerulus and the loop of Henle on **Figure 9**.

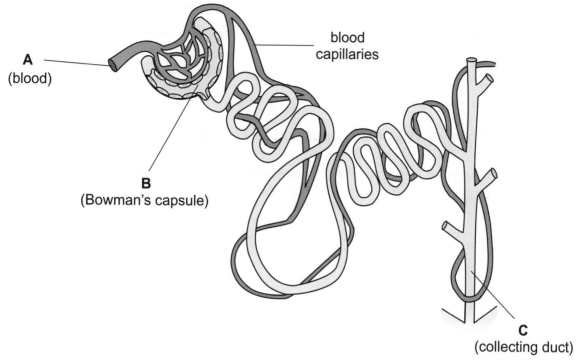

Figure 9

[2 marks]

(b) (i) Many different proteins are found in the blood at point **A**,
        but hardly any are found at point **B**.
        Explain why there is almost no protein at point **B**.

    ....

    ....
                                                                                        [1 mark]

    (ii) Describe an experiment that you could carry out to test whether a sample of liquid
         taken from the nephron tubules contains proteins.

    ....

    ....

    ....

    ....

    ....
                                                                                        [4 marks]

Turn over ▶

(c) Describe how the concentration of glucose at point **C** would compare to the concentration at point **B**. Explain your answer.

....

....

....

[2 marks]

ADH is a hormone involved in the regulation of the water content of the body.

(d) (i) Describe what happens if the brain detects that the water content of the blood is too low.

....

....

....

....

[2 marks]

(ii) The drug ecstasy stimulates the release of ADH. Taking ecstasy can result in too much water entering the body cells, which can cause cell damage. Suggest why taking ecstasy can lead to too much water entering cells from the blood.

....

....

....

....

[2 marks]

People suffering from kidney failure may be treated using a kidney dialysis machine.

Figure 10 shows a type of dialysis machine.

Figure 10

(e) Explain how a dialysis machine works.

....

....

....

....

....

....

[3 marks]

[Total 16 marks]

Turn over for the next question

9 In humans, sexual reproduction involves the reproductive system.

(a) The male reproductive system includes the testes.
What hormone is produced by the testes?

☐ **A** testosterone

☐ **B** adrenaline

☐ **C** oestrogen

☐ **D** insulin

[1 mark]

Figure 11 shows the fluctuations in the levels of four different hormones during one 28 day menstrual cycle.

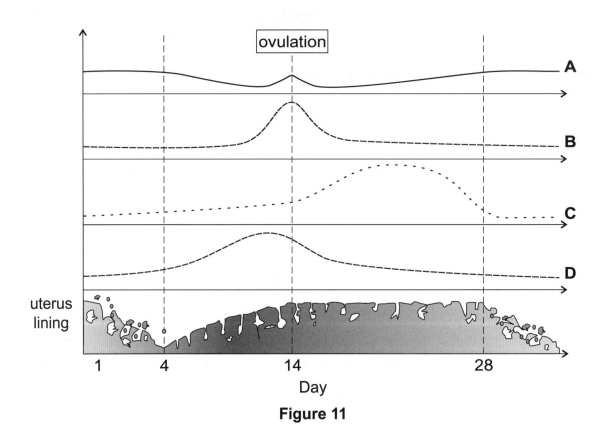

Figure 11

(b) State which line (**A-D**) in **Figure 11** represents progesterone and explain your answer.

....

....

....

[2 marks]

*(c) Describe how progesterone, LH, FSH and oestrogen interact to control the menstrual cycle.

....

....

....

....

....

....

....

....

....

....

....

[6 marks]

Question 9 continues on the next page

Turn over ▶

Some methods of contraception use reproductive hormones to control fertility.
One such method is the contraceptive implant, shown in **Figure 12**.

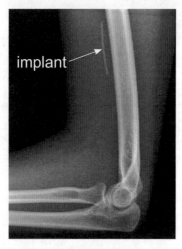

Figure 12

The contraceptive implant:

- is a small, plastic rod that is inserted by a doctor or nurse
- releases progesterone, which reduces fertility
- is effective for three years
- is over 99% effective at preventing pregnancy
- can cause side effects such as headaches and nausea
- can be made less effective by certain medications

Figure 13 shows a condom. The condom is a barrier method of contraception.

Figure 13

The condom:

- is worn over the penis during intercourse
- prevents sperm from entering the vagina
- can only be used once
- is 98% effective at preventing pregnancy when used correctly
- protects against sexually transmitted infections (STIs)

(d) Use the information to evaluate the implant and condom as methods of contraception.
Give a conclusion of which you think is the better method of contraception.
Justify your conclusion.

....

....

....

....

....

....

....

....

[4 marks]

[Total 13 marks]

10 A student is investigating how his heart rate changes during and after exercise.
He measures his heart rate using a portable heart rate monitor.
He takes his resting heart rate before running around the school track
for two minutes. Then he rests again. His results are shown in **Figure 14**.

Time after first heart rate measurement taken (min)	First run — Heart rate (beats/min)
0	72
1	118
2	132
3	129
4	116
5	98
6	84
7	76
8	72
9	72

Figure 14

(a) Complete **Figure 15** using the data from **Figure 14**.

- Complete the *x*-axis. Include a label and use a suitable scale.
- Plot the heart rate.
- Draw a curve of best fit.

Figure 15

[4 marks]

Question 10 continues on the next page

Turn over ▶

(b) Use your graph in **Figure 15** to estimate the student's heart rate after thirty seconds.

heart rate = ... beats/min

[1 mark]

The hormone adrenaline can increase a person's heart rate.

(c) What gland releases adrenaline?

☐ **A** pituitary gland

☐ **B** adrenal gland

☐ **C** thyroid gland

☐ **D** ovaries

[1 mark]

*__(d)__ Explain how adrenaline can prepare a person's body for a 'fight or flight' response.

....

....

....

....

....

....

....

....

....

....

....

....

[6 marks]

[Total 12 marks]

END OF QUESTIONS

Answers

Topic 1 — Key Concepts in Biology

Page 25
Warm-Up Questions
1   mitochondria
2   Any two from: e.g. it has a long tail to help it swim. / It has lots of mitochondria to provide energy for swimming. / It has an acrosome to store the enzymes for digesting the egg cell membrane.
3   electron microscope.
4   4.5×10^{-4} μm

Exam Questions
1   B *[1 mark]*
Remember, DNA in prokaryotic cells floats freely in the cytoplasm — it's not stored in a nucleus.
2 a)   C *[1 mark]*
   b)   It is the site of photosynthesis, which makes food for the plant *[1 mark]*.
   c)   They're involved in translation of genetic material in the synthesis of proteins *[1 mark]*.
3 a)   How to grade your answer:
   Level 0:   There is no relevant information. *[No marks]*
   Level 1:   There is a brief explanation of how to prepare a slide or how to use a light microscope. The points made are basic and not linked together. *[1 to 2 marks]*
   Level 2:   There is some explanation of how to prepare a slide and use a light microscope. Some of the points made are linked together. *[3 to 4 marks]*
   Level 3:   There is a clear and detailed explanation of how to prepare a slide and use a light microscope. The points made are well linked and the answer has a clear and logical structure. *[5 to 6 marks]*
   Here are some points your answer may include:
   To prepare a slide:
   Add a drop of water to the middle of a clean slide.
   Cut up an onion and separate it out into layers.
   Use tweezers to peel off some tissue from the bottom of one of the layers.
   Use tweezers to place the tissue into the water on the slide.
   Add a drop of stain.
   Place a cover slip on top by standing it upright on the slide, next to the water droplet, then carefully tilting and lowering it so it covers the onion tissue without trapping any air bubbles.
   To use a light microscope:
   Clip the slide onto the stage.
   Select the lowest-powered objective lens.
   Use the coarse adjustment knob to move the stage up to just below the objective lens (without looking down the eyepiece).
   Look down the eyepiece and use the coarse adjustment knob to move the stage downwards until the image is roughly in focus.
   Adjust the focus with the fine adjustment knob, until a clear image of the cells is visible.
   To see the cells with greater magnification, swap to a higher-powered objective lens and refocus.
   b)   real size = image size ÷ magnification
        = 7.5 mm ÷ 100
        = 0.075 mm
        $0.075 \times 1000 =$ **75 μm** *[3 marks for correct answer, otherwise 1 mark for correctly rearranging the equation and 1 mark for 0.075 mm.]*

Pages 33-34
Warm-Up Questions
1   The part of an enzyme which joins to a substrate.
2   The pH at which the enzyme works best.
3   temperature and substrate concentration
4 a)   carbohydrase/amylase
   b)   protease
   c)   lipase
Carbohydrases (e.g. amylase) break down carbohydrates, such as starch. Proteases break down proteins, and lipases break down lipids (fats).
5 a)   (simple) sugars
   b)   amino acids
6   amino acids

Exam Questions
1 a)   The active site of the enzyme has a specific shape which will only fit with one type of substrate *[1 mark]*.
   b)   The higher the substrate concentration, the faster the reaction *[1 mark]*, because it is more likely that the enzyme will meet and react with a substrate molecule *[1 mark]*. At a certain point, increasing the substrate concentration stops causing the rate of reaction to increase *[1 mark]*, because all of the active sites are full *[1 mark]*.
2 a)   Temperature change of water = 52.7 − 15.2 = 37.5 °C
        Energy = mass of water × temperature change of water × 4.2
        = 30 × 37.5 × 4.2
        = **4725 J**
        [2 marks for correct answer, otherwise 1 mark for the temperature change of water = 37.5 °C]
   b)   Energy per gram = energy in food ÷ mass of food
        = 3050 J ÷ 0.2 g
        = **15 250 J/g** *[1 mark]*
3 a)   Accept answers between 38 °C and 40 °C *[1 mark]*.
   b)   Enzyme B, e.g. because it has an unusually high optimum temperature which it would need to work in the hot vent *[1 mark]*.
4   The food sample contains starch *[1 mark]* and lipids *[1 mark]*, but no proteins *[1 mark]*.
5 a)   To prevent the starch coming into contact with amylase in the syringe, which would have started the reaction before he had started the stop clock *[1 mark]*.
   b)   Rate = 1000 ÷ 60 = **17 s⁻¹** (2 s.f.) *[1 mark]*
   c)   Repeat the experiment using buffers with a range of different pH values and compare the results *[1 mark]*.

Page 38
Warm-Up Questions
1   Osmosis and active transport.
2   E.g diffusion is passive whereas active transport requires energy. Diffusion is movement from an area of higher concentration to an area of lower concentration, whereas active transport is from an area of lower concentration to higher concentration.
3   A partially permeable membrane only allows small molecules (e.g. water) to diffuse through it.
4   Osmosis is the net movement of water molecules across a partially permeable membrane from a region of higher water concentration to a region of lower water concentration.

Exam Questions
1 a)   The ink will diffuse / spread out through the water *[1 mark]*. This is because the ink particles will move from where there is a higher concentration of them (the drop of ink) to where there is a lower concentration of them (the surrounding water) *[1 mark]*.

244

2 a) The potato cylinder in tube D *[1 mark]*, because this tube contains the most concentrated sugar solution so this cylinder will have lost the most water *[1 mark]* by osmosis *[1 mark]*.

b) Tube A contained distilled water, so some of the water moved by osmosis into the potato cylinder *[1 mark]* from an area of high water concentration to an area of low water concentration *[1 mark]*.

Topic 2 — Cells and Control

Page 46
Warm-Up Questions
1 It's the process by which a cell changes to become specialised for its job.
2 True
3 25% of two-month-olds are lighter than the baby.
4 in the nucleus

Exam Questions
1 a) The amount of DNA is doubling *[1 mark]* so that there is one copy for each new cell *[1 mark]*.

b) The two new cells separate *[1 mark]*.

c) two *[1 mark]*

d) A change in one of the genes controlling cell division can cause cells to divide uncontrollably *[1 mark]*. This can lead to a mass of cells called a tumour, which can invade and destroy surrounding cells *[1 mark]*.

2 a) E.g. they could be grown into a particular type of cell, which can then be used to replace faulty cells *[1 mark]*.

b) Embryonic stem cells have the potential to develop into any kind of cell, whereas adult stem cells can only develop into certain types of cell *[1 mark]*.

3 3 hours = 60 × 3 = 180 minutes
180 ÷ 30 = 6 divisions
$2^6 = 2 \times 2 \times 2 \times 2 \times 2 \times 2 =$ **64 cells** *[2 marks for correct answer, otherwise 1 mark for correct working.]*

Page 50
Warm-Up Questions
1 A stimulus is a change in the environment.
2 An axon carries nerve impulses away from the cell body.
3 A myelin sheath surrounds an axon, acting as an electrical insulator.
4 sensory neurone, relay neurone, motor neurone
5 synapse

Exam Questions
1 a) Stimulus: appearance of red triangle *[1 mark]*
Receptors: cells in the eye / light receptor cells *[1 mark]*
Effectors: muscles (in hand controlling mouse) *[1 mark]*

b) 343 × 3 = 1029
1029 − 328 − 346 = **355 ms** *[2 marks for the correct answer, otherwise 1 mark for correct working.]*

2 a) motor neurone *[1 mark]*

b) Muscle *[1 mark]*, which contracts to move the baby's fingers *[1 mark]*.

c) When the electrical impulse reaches the end of the neurone, it stimulates the release of a neurotransmitter *[1 mark]*. The neurotransmitter diffuses across the synapse to activate an electrical impulse in the next neurone *[1 mark]*.

d) E.g. in a baby older than 6 months, the pathway will involve conscious parts of the brain, whereas in a newborn baby it won't. / In a baby older than 6 months, the response will not be produced as rapidly as in the newborn baby *[1 mark]*.

The response in the baby older than 6 months is not a reflex — it chooses whether it wants to grasp an object. Remember, reflexes are automatic — they don't involve conscious parts of the brain, which makes the response much faster.

Page 54
Warm-Up Questions
1 cerebellum
2 A CT scan shows the main structures in the brain of the person being scanned.
3 rods
4 The lenses refract the light rays so they focus on the retina.
5 The lens is the wrong shape and bends the light too much or the eyeball is too long. So the light from distant objects is brought into focus in front of the retina.

Exam Questions
1 a) A: cornea *[1 mark]*
B: lens *[1 mark]*

b) To control the diameter of the pupil/the amount of light entering the eye *[1 mark]*.

2 a) B *[1 mark]*

b) E.g. the doctor may be concerned that removing the tumour will cause physical damage to the brain *[1 mark]*.

3 a) The ciliary muscles relax *[1 mark]* allowing the suspensory ligaments to pull tight *[1 mark]*, which results in the lens becoming thinner/less rounded *[1 mark]*, so light is refracted less *[1 mark]*.

b) If the lens cannot form a rounded shape, light from nearby objects won't be bent enough to be focused on the retina *[1 mark]*. This means that people with presbyopia will be unable to focus on nearby objects *[1 mark]*.

Topic 3 — Genetics

Pages 63-64
Warm-Up Questions
1 two
2 A and T. C and G.
3 A section of DNA on a chromosome that codes for a particular protein.
4 A mutation is a random change in an organism's DNA base sequence.
5 A coding region.

Exam Questions
1 a) (ice cold) alcohol *[1 mark]*

b) DNA *[1 mark]*

2 a) C *[1 mark]*

b) hydrogen bonds *[1 mark]*

c) DNA contains genes *[1 mark]*. Each gene codes for a particular sequence of amino acids *[1 mark]*, which are put together to make a specific protein *[1 mark]*.

3 a) AGTCACTAC *[2 marks for completely correct sequence, otherwise 1 mark for correct order of bases but U used instead of T.]*

mRNA uses uracil (U) where DNA uses thymine (T), so to get full marks here you need to both write out the complementary sequence of bases and use 'T's instead of 'U's.

b) The mRNA base sequence contains codons/base triplets which code for different amino acids *[1 mark]*. The mRNA codons/base triplets are complementary to the anticodons in specific tRNA molecules *[1 mark]*. tRNA molecules have specific amino acids attached to them *[1 mark]*. The pairing of the anticodons in tRNA and the codons/base triplets in mRNA ensures that the amino acids are brought to the ribosome in the correct order *[1 mark]*.

4 a) three *[1 mark]*
When a cell undergoes meiosis, each new cell ends up with half the number of chromosomes as in the original cell.

b) four *[1 mark]*
Remember, when a cell undergoes meiosis, four gametes are produced — it doesn't matter whether you're talking about human cells or mosquito cells.

c) During sexual reproduction, a zygote/embryo receives a mixture of chromosomes from both parents *[1 mark]*. Each offspring inherits a slightly different mixture of chromosomes from its parents, creating genetic variation *[1 mark]*.

d) E.g. only one parent is needed *[1 mark]*. It is faster *[1 mark]*.

e) The malarial parasite reproduces sexually whilst in the mosquito, which leads to genetic variation *[1 mark]*.

5 a) A nucleotide consists of a sugar, a phosphate group, and one base attached to the sugar *[1 mark]*.

b) How to grade your answer:

Level 0: There is no relevant information. *[No marks]*

Level 1: There is some information about how the enzyme is made from the GALC gene. The points made are basic and not linked together. *[1 to 2 marks]*

Level 2: There is some explanation of how the enzyme would be made from the GALC gene. Some of the points made are linked together. *[3 to 4 marks]*

Level 3: There is a clear and detailed explanation of how the enzyme could be made from the GALC gene. The points made are well-linked and the answer has a clear and logical structure. *[5 to 6 marks]*

Here are some points your answer may include:
RNA polymerase binds to the region of non-coding DNA in front of the GALC gene.
The two DNA strands unzip and the RNA polymerase moves along one of the strands, using the coding DNA in the GALC gene as a template to make mRNA.
Base pairing ensures that the mRNA is complementary to the gene.
Once made, the mRNA molecule moves out of the nucleus and joins to a ribosome in the cytoplasm.
tRNA molecules bring amino acids to the ribosome — anticodons on the tRNA pair up with complementary codons in the mRNA to ensure that amino acids are brought to the ribosome in the correct order.
The ribosome joins the amino acids together to make the correct enzyme.

c) The mutation in the GALC gene changes its base sequence *[1 mark]*. This could alter the amino acid sequence that the bases code for *[1 mark]*. This could change the shape of the enzyme *[1 mark]* which could affect its activity *[1 mark]*.

d) The genetic variant could affect the ability of RNA polymerase to bind to the non-coding region of the GALC gene *[1 mark]*. This could affect how much mRNA is transcribed *[1 mark]* and therefore also the amount of enzyme that is produced *[1 mark]*.

Page 69
Warm-Up Questions
1 Different versions of the same gene.
2 What characteristics you have.
3 White fur, because you need two copies of the recessive allele (b) for this characteristic to be shown / if you have one recessive allele and one dominant allele (Bb) you get brown fur, so brown fur must be the dominant characteristic.
4 XX

Exam Questions
1 a)

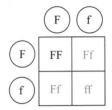

[1 mark for correct genotype of offspring, 1 mark for correct genotypes of gametes]

b) 1 in 2 / 50% *[1 mark]*
c) Has cystic fibrosis *[1 mark]*.
2 a) AA, Aa *[1 mark]*
b) E.g.

Genotypes of parents:
Genotypes of gametes:
Genotypes of offspring:

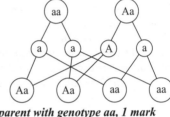

[1 mark for parent with genotype aa, 1 mark for parent with genotype Aa, 1 mark for correct genotypes of offspring]

c) 50% *[1 mark]*
Offspring with the genotype aa will have albinism.

d) Fertilisation is random/the genetic diagram only shows the probability of the outcome, so the numbers of offspring produced will not always be exactly in those proportions *[1 mark]*.

Page 73
Warm-Up Questions
1 genes
2 Scientists of the time didn't have the background knowledge to properly understand Mendel's findings because they didn't know about genes, DNA and chromosomes.
3 On the sex chromosomes / X or Y chromosomes.
4 True
Although there are multiple alleles, blood type is a still a single characteristic, meaning its inheritance follows the monohybrid pattern.

Exam Questions
1 All offspring will inherit one allele for purple flowers and one allele for white flowers *[1 mark]*.
The allele for purple flowers is dominant, so all offspring will have purple flowers *[1 mark]*.

2 a) E.g.

Parents' genotypes: X^nY X^NX^N

Gametes' genotypes: X^n Y X^N X^N

Offspring's genotypes: X^NX^n X^NY X^NX^n X^NY

*[1 mark for showing correct genotypes of gametes,
1 mark for showing correct genotypes of offspring]*
*You don't have to have used this type of genetic diagram to
get the marks here (for example you could have drawn a
Punnett square instead).*

b) No male child could inherit the colour blindness allele because they don't inherit an X chromosome from their father *[1 mark]*.

c) 0 / 0% *[1 mark]*
A daughter of this couple would inherit the recessive colour blindness allele from her father, but also a dominant allele from her mother, so she would not be colour blind.

3 a) $I^A I^O$ *[1 mark]*

b) i)

	I^B	I^B
I^A	$I^A I^B$	$I^A I^B$
I^O	$I^B I^O$	$I^B I^O$

*[1 mark for correct alleles in parents,
1 mark for correct genotypes in offspring]*

ii) 0.5 / 50% / 1 in 2 *[1 mark]*

iii) They will have blood group AB *[1 mark]*, because the I^A and I^B alleles are codominant / neither allele is dominant over the other / both alleles determine phenotype *[1 mark]*.

Page 77
Warm-Up Questions

1 Differences between members of the same species that have been caused by the environment/conditions an organism lives in.

2 a) E.g. Amy and Beth could have inherited different alleles/ genes for hair type (curly or straight) from their parents.

b) E.g. one of the sisters might use curling tongs or hair straighteners to alter their natural hair type. / Amy might use curling tongs to make her hair curly. / Beth might use hair straighteners to make her hair straight.

3 False

Exam Questions

1 a) D

b) The difference in weight must be caused by the environment *[1 mark]*, because the twins have exactly the same genes *[1 mark]*.
In this case, the environment can mean the amount of food each twin eats or the amount of exercise they each do.

c) No, because if it was caused by genes, both twins should have the birthmark *[1 mark]*.

2 a) E.g. if Eshan has the allele he could get tailored advice on lifestyle factors to reduce the likelihood of developing colorectal cancer. / He can have regular checks to ensure early treatment if he develops colorectal cancer *[1 mark]*.

b) E.g. if Eshan has the allele he could be discriminated against by life insurers / he could be discriminated against by employers / he could be put under pressure not to have children so that the gene is not passed on / he could have increased stress levels from worrying about potentially developing colorectal cancer *[1 mark]*.

3 a) Mutations change the base sequence of DNA *[1 mark]*, which can result in a new allele *[1 mark]*. New alleles can lead to differences in phenotype, increasing variation *[1 mark]*.

b) E.g the mutation could result in the production of a protein that is very different *[1 mark]*, so the activity of the protein would be affected, which would affect phenotype *[1 mark]*.

Topic 4 — Natural Selection and Genetic Modification

Pages 86-87
Warm-Up Questions

1 Organisms with the beneficial characteristic are better adapted to their environment, so they have a better chance of survival. This makes them more likely to breed successfully and pass on the alleles for the beneficial characteristic to their offspring.

2 Any trace of an animal or plant that lived a long time ago.

3 Darwin and Wallace

4 The similarity in bone structure of the pentadactyl limb in different species provides evidence that they evolved from a common ancestor.

5 E.g. RNA/DNA sequencing showed that Archaea and Bacteria were less closely related than first thought.

Exam Questions

1 a) New alleles arise though mutations *[1 mark]*.

b) i) Any two from: e.g. predation / competition for resources/food/water/mates / disease *[1 mark for each correct answer]*.

ii) They may lack the characteristics needed to adapt to the new selection pressure *[1 mark]* and so are less able to survive and reproduce *[1 mark]*.

2 a) E.g. by arranging fossils of human ancestors in chronological order / looking at differences in fossils of human ancestors from different time periods *[1 mark]*, gradual changes can be observed *[1 mark]*.

b) Any two from: e.g. stratigraphy/study of rock layers / carbon-14 dating of wooden handles / analysing structural features *[1 mark for each correct answer]*.
Stone itself cannot be carbon-14 dated. Only biological material, such as the wooden handles mentioned here in the answer, can be dated using carbon-14 dating.

c) A stone tool used by *Homo erectus* would be less complex than one used by *Homo sapiens* *[1 mark]*.

d) Over time the stone tools became more complex, which gives evidence for the evolution of the brain *[1 mark]*.

3 a) Organism C *[1 mark]* because its DNA sequence has the highest percentage similarity to humans *[1 mark]*.

b) Archaea *[1 mark]*, Bacteria *[1 mark]*, and Eukarya *[1 mark]*.

4 Variation in the population meant that some *Clostridium difficile* bacteria had alleles which gave resistance to the antibiotic *[1 mark]*. When exposed to this antibiotic, resistant bacteria were more likely to survive *[1 mark]* and pass on the resistance allele to offspring *[1 mark]*. The resistance allele became more common in the population and soon all bacteria in the population were resistant *[1 mark]*.

5 How to grade your answer:
Level 0: There is no relevant information. *[No marks]*
Level 1: There is some information about evolution by natural selection. The points are basic and not linked together. *[1 to 2 marks]*

Level 2: There is some explanation about how evolution by natural selection may have led to a change in appearance of the stingray. Some of the points made are linked together. *[3 to 4 marks]*

Level 3: There is a clear and detailed explanation of how evolution by natural selection may have led to a change in the appearance of the stingray. The points made are well-linked and the answer has a clear and logical structure. *[5 to 6 marks]*

Here are some points your answer may include:
Ancestors of this stingray showed variation in their appearance.
The stingrays that looked more like flat rocks were better camouflaged and so less likely to be seen by prey, meaning they could obtain more food / they were less likely to be seen and eaten by predators.
This means they were more likely to survive and reproduce.
As a result, the alleles that caused the stingrays to look like flat rocks were more likely to be passed on to the next generation.
Over time, the flat rock appearance became more common in the population, until all of the stingrays in the population had this appearance.

Page 93
Warm-Up Questions
1 E.g. to produce plants with bigger fruit.
2 Selective breeding reduces the gene pool. This causes an increased chance of organisms inheriting harmful genetic defects. There is also an increased chance that a population could be wiped out by a new disease.
3 Restriction enzymes and ligase enzymes.

Exam Questions
1 a) E.g. to isolate/cut the gene out of the organism's DNA / to cut open the vector DNA / to join two pieces of DNA together *[1 mark]*.
b) E.g. to make them resistant to insects/herbicides *[1 mark]*.
c) Any two from: e.g. some people are not convinced that GM crops are safe and are concerned that we might not fully understand the effects of eating them on human health. / There is concern that the transplanted genes could get out into the natural environment, which could lead to the creation of 'superweeds'. / Genetically modified crops could adversely affect food chains *[1 mark for each correct answer]*.
2 A sample of tissue is extracted from an animal *[1 mark]*. The cells are separated from each other using enzymes *[1 mark]*. The cells are placed in a culture vessel and bathed in growth medium *[1 mark]*. After several rounds of cell division, the cells can be split up again and placed into separate vessels to encourage further growth, after which the tissue culture is ready for use or storage *[1 mark]*.
3 a) The tall and dwarf wheat plants could be bred together *[1 mark]*. The best of the offspring/the offspring with the highest grain yield and highest bad weather resistance could then be bred together *[1 mark]*, and this process repeated over several generations *[1 mark]*.
b) There will be less genetic variation within the population of selectively bred wheat plants *[1 mark]*, so there is a smaller chance of disease resistance alleles being present *[1 mark]*. This means that there is a greater chance that all of the plants will be affected/killed by the disease *[1 mark]*.

Topic 5 — Health, Disease and the Development of Medicines

Pages 100-101
Warm-Up Questions
1 A state of complete physical, mental and social well-being and not merely the absence of disease of infirmity.
2 It can be spread between individuals.
3 Any two from: e.g. cholera / tuberculosis / some stomach ulcers / Chlamydia.
4 Sexual contact allows the exchange of infected bodily fluids such as semen and vaginal fluids. The exchange of such fluids transmits the virus between individuals.
5 E.g. wearing a condom when having sex. / Screening individuals so they can be treated. / Avoiding sexual contact.

Exam Questions
1 a) An organism that can cause disease *[1 mark]*.
b) D *[1 mark]*
c) The fungus is carried through the air by the wind. / Diseased ash trees are moved between areas *[1 mark]*.
2 a) Malaria is spread by vectors *[1 mark]* and not through contaminated food/surfaces / skin to skin contact *[1 mark]*.
b) E.g. mosquitoes are the vectors of malaria, so destroying mosquitoes will prevent malaria being spread between people *[1 mark]*.
c) E.g. by having clean water supplies / hygienic living conditions *[1 mark]*.
3 a) E.g. a waxy cuticle on leaves *[1 mark]*, cellulose cell walls *[1 mark]*.
b) E.g. to kill bacterial and fungal pathogens *[1 mark]*. To deter pests from feeding on their leaves *[1 mark]*.
c) E.g. chemicals can be used as drugs to treat human diseases / relieve symptoms *[1 mark]*.
d) E.g. they could change the environmental conditions *[1 mark]*. If the symptoms disappear, they are likely to have been caused by the environmental conditions rather than a pathogen *[1 mark]*.
e) E.g. analysing the distribution of the wilting crops can indicate how the pathogen is being spread / what type of pathogen is causing the disease *[1 mark]*.
f) E.g. tests involving monoclonal antibodies could be used to detect *Fusarium oxysporum* antigens in infected plant tissue. / DNA testing could be used to detect *Fusarium oxysporum* DNA in infected plant tissue *[1 mark]*.
4 a) The virus is using enzymes/proteins in the host cell to replicate its genetic material *[1 mark]* and make components of new viruses *[1 mark]*.
b) How to grade your answer:
Level 0: There is no relevant information. *[No marks]*
Level 1: There is a brief explanation of the lysogenic pathway but no explanation of how this pathway makes the HIV life cycle different from that of the Enterobacteria phage T4 virus. The points made are basic and not linked together. *[1 to 2 marks]*
Level 2: There is some explanation of the different stages of the lysogenic pathway and of how this pathway makes the HIV life cycle different from that of the Enterobacteria phage T4 virus. Some of the points made are linked together. *[3 to 4 marks]*

Level 3: There is a clear and detailed explanation of the different stages of the lysogenic pathway and of how this pathway makes the HIV life cycle different from that of the Enterobacteria phage T4 virus. The points made are well linked and the answer has a clear and logical structure.
[5 to 6 marks]

Here are some points your answer may include:
Both viruses attach to a host cell and inject their genetic material into the cell.
Unlike the Enterobacteria phage T4 virus which continues to reproduce using the lytic cycle, the HIV genetic material is incorporated into the genome of the host cell in the lysogenic pathway.
In the lysogenic pathway, the HIV genetic material gets replicated along with the host DNA every time the host cell divides.
At this stage in the lysogenic pathway, the virus is inactive and no new viruses are made.
The HIV genetic material only leaves the genome and enters the lytic pathway when triggered to do so.

Page 108
Warm-Up Questions
1   The skin acts as a barrier to pathogens, and, if it gets damaged, blood clots quickly seal cuts and keep microorganisms out.
2   To destroy specific pathogens that enter the body.
3   a (B-)lymphocyte
4   A (B-)lymphocyte and a tumour/myeloma cell.

Exam Questions
1 a)   Mucus traps particles that could contain pathogens *[1 mark]*.
  b)   They waft the mucus up to the back of the throat where it can be swallowed *[1 mark]*.
  c)   hydrochloric acid *[1 mark]*
  d)   lysozyme *[1 mark]*
2 a)   The side effects of an antibody-based drug are lower than for standard treatment methods *[1 mark]*, because monoclonal antibodies target specific cells and standard treatment methods don't *[1 mark]*.
  b)   E.g. a radioactive element is attached to monoclonal antibodies *[1 mark]* that have been developed to bind to the proteins in blood clots *[1 mark]*. These monoclonal antibodies are injected into the body *[1 mark]* and a picture is taken with a camera that picks up radiation, to locate the blood clot *[1 mark]*.
3 a)   How to grade your answer:
  Level 0:   There is no relevant information. *[No marks]*
  Level 1:   There is a brief explanation of how immunisation against rubella can prevent a person catching the disease or how having a large proportion of immunised individuals in a population reduces the risk of rubella for people who are not immunised. The points made are basic and not linked together.
[1 to 2 marks]
  Level 2:   There is some explanation of how immunisation against rubella can prevent a person catching the disease and how having a large proportion of immunised individuals in a population reduces the risk of rubella for people who are not immunised. Some of the points made are linked together. *[3 to 4 marks]*

Level 3: There is a clear and detailed explanation of how immunisation against rubella can prevent a person catching the disease and how having a large proportion of immunised individuals in a population reduces the risk of rubella for people who are not immunised. The points made are well linked and the answer has a clear and logical structure. *[5 to 6 marks]*

Here are some points your answer may include:
When a person is immunised against rubella, they are injected with dead or inactive rubella viruses.
The dead or inactive viruses carry antigens, which cause lymphocytes to produce antibodies to attack them.
The antigens also trigger the production of memory lymphocytes.
If live rubella viruses infect the body after this, memory lymphocytes can rapidly mass produce antibodies to defeat the virus.
If a large proportion of the population is immunised against rubella, then there are fewer people who are able to pass the disease on.
This means that even someone who hasn't been immunised is less likely to catch the disease.
  b)   E.g. they may be worried that they will have a bad reaction to a vaccine. / Vaccines don't always work and so the person might not be given immunity *[1 mark]*.

Page 113
Warm-Up Questions
1   False
2   A placebo is a substance that looks like the real drug but doesn't do anything.
3   To prevent contamination of a culture with unwanted microorganisms (that could affect results).
4   E.g. by looking at the relative sizes of the inhibition zones. The larger the inhibition zone around it, the more effective the antibiotic.

Exam Questions
1 a)   B *[1 mark]*
Drugs are tested on human cells, live animals and human tissue in preclinical trials. If a drug makes it through the preclinical trials, it's then tested on human volunteers in a clinical trial.
  b)   In a double blind trial neither the patient nor the doctor *[1 mark]* knows who is receiving the drug and who is receiving the placebo until all the results have been gathered *[1 mark]*.
  c)   E.g. dosage *[1 mark]*, efficacy/how well the drug works *[1 mark]*
2 a)   radius = 15 ÷ 2 = 7.5 mm
$\pi r^2 = \pi \times 56.25 = 176.7... = $ **177 mm² *[2 marks for correct answer, otherwise 1 mark for correct working.]***
  b)   The strain of bacteria used in the experiment was resistant to antibiotic Z *[1 mark]*.

Page 119
Warm-Up Questions
1   E.g. the National Health Service has to provide resources for the treatment of patients with non-communicable diseases all over the country. / People with non-communicable diseases may be unable to work, which may negatively affect the country's economy.
2   E.g. muscle weighs more than fat, so muscular people can have a high BMI even though they're not overweight.
3   E.g. they don't usually have any downsides/side effects.

Exam Questions

1 a) E.g drinking too much alcohol *[1 mark]*.

  b) E.g the cost of treating patients with liver disease in local hospitals *[1 mark]*.

2 a) A disease that cannot be spread between individuals *[1 mark]*.

  b) E.g. nicotine in cigarette smoke increases heart rate which increases blood pressure *[1 mark]*. High blood pressure damages artery walls, which contributes to the build up of fatty deposits in the arteries *[1 mark]*. Smoking also increases the risk of blood clots forming in arteries *[1 mark]*. Fatty deposits and blood clots can both restrict blood flow, increasing the risk of heart attack or a stroke *[1 mark]*.

3 a) i) $\dfrac{mass~(kg)}{(height~(m))^2} = \dfrac{76.0}{1.58^2}$
  $= \mathbf{30.4~kg~m^2}$ *[1 mark]*

  ii) $\dfrac{mass~(kg)}{(height~(m))^2} = \dfrac{73.0}{1.58^2}$
  $= \mathbf{29.2~kg~m^2}$ *[1 mark]*

  b) Before : Moderately obese *[1 mark]*,
  After : Overweight *[1 mark]*.

Topic 6 — Plant Structures and Their Functions

Page 124
Warm-Up Questions

1 False

2 A limiting factor is something that stops photosynthesis from happening any faster.

3 If the temperature's too high, the plant's enzymes will be denatured, so the rate of photosynthesis rapidly decreases.
Remember, if the temperature is too high for an enzyme, the bonds holding it together may break. This causes the shape of the enzyme's active site to change, denaturing the enzyme.

4 $light~intensity \propto \dfrac{1}{distance^2}$

Exam Questions

1 a) By counting the number of bubbles produced / by measuring the volume of gas produced, in a given time/at regular intervals *[1 mark]*.

  b) Dependent variable — rate of photosynthesis/number of bubbles in a given time/volume of gas in a given time *[1 mark]*.
  Independent variable — light intensity *[1 mark]*.

2 a) Light intensity *[1 mark]*, because between these two points increasing the light intensity increases the rate of photosynthesis *[1 mark]*.

  b) After point B, increasing light intensity did not increase the rate of photosynthesis *[1 mark]*, so light intensity was no longer the limiting factor / a factor other than light intensity (e.g CO_2 concentration or temperature) was limiting the rate of photosynthesis *[1 mark]*.

3 $light~intensity = \dfrac{1}{d^2}$
  $= \dfrac{1}{7.5^2}$
  $= \mathbf{0.018~a.u.~(2~s.f.)}$
  [2 marks for correct answer, otherwise 1 mark for correct working.]

Page 129
Warm-Up Questions

1 The lower surface of leaves.

2 False

3 light intensity, temperature, air flow

Exam Questions

1 a) xylem vessels *[1 mark]*

  b) They are made of dead cells joined end to end *[1 mark]* with no end walls between them and a hole down the middle *[1 mark]*. They're strengthened with a material called lignin *[1 mark]*.

  c) transpiration *[1 mark]*

2 a) phloem *[1 mark]*

  b) Phloem vessels are made of columns of living cells *[1 mark]*, which provide the energy needed to move substances through the vessel *[1 mark]*. The cells have small pores in the end walls *[1 mark]* to allow substances to flow through *[1 mark]*.

3 a) $(10 + 11 + 9) \div 3 = \mathbf{10\%}$ *[2 marks for correct answer, otherwise 1 mark for correct working]*

  b) How to grade your answer:
  Level 0: There is no relevant information. *[No marks]*
  Level 1: There is a brief explanation of how the increased air flow from the fan and the higher temperature increases the rate of transpiration. The points made are basic and not linked together. *[1 to 2 marks]*
  Level 2: There is some explanation of how the increased air flow from the fan and the higher temperature increases the rate of transpiration. Some of the points made are basic and not linked together. *[3 to 4 marks]*
  Level 3: There is a clear and detailed explanation of how the increased air flow from the fan and the higher temperature increases the rate of transpiration. The points made are well-linked and the answer has a clear and logical structure. *[5 to 6 marks]*
  Here are some points your answer may include:
  The movement of air from the fan moves water vapour away from plants in group D, maintaining a low concentration of water outside the leaf.
  The low concentration of water outside the leaf increases the rate at which water diffuses out of the leaf.
  Therefore, the plants in group D would lose more water, and so more mass, than the plants in group A.
  At warmer temperatures, water particles have more energy to evaporate and diffuse out of the stomata.
  The rate of transpiration will be higher in the plants at 25 °C than at 20 °C. So the plants in Group D will lose more water, and so more mass than the plants in Group A.

Page 134
Warm-Up Questions

1 palisade mesophyll tissue

2 It reduces water loss by evaporation / lowers transpiration rate.

3 auxin

4 More auxin accumulates on the side of the shoot that's in the shade. This causes the shaded side to elongate faster, so the shoot bends towards the light.
Remember in shoots auxin stimulates growth, so the side with more auxin will elongate faster.

5 E.g. to stimulate seed germination / to stimulate stem growth / to stimulate flowering / to reduce flower formation (to improve fruit quality) / to produce seedless fruit.

Exam Questions

1   C *[1 mark]*
2 a) auxin *[1 mark]*
   b) She could use a rooting powder containing auxin *[1 mark]*
       to help the cutting produce roots rapidly and
       start growing as a new plant *[1 mark]*.
3 a) The shoot has grown upwards, away from gravity *[1 mark]*.
   b) Auxin accumulated on the lower side of the shoot *[1 mark]*.
       This caused the lower side of the shoot to elongate faster,
       so the shoot bends upwards *[1 mark]*.

Topic 7 — Animal Coordination, Control and Homeostasis

Page 139
Warm-Up Questions
1   target organ
2 a) E.g. pituitary gland, thyroid gland,
       adrenal gland, pancreas, testes.
   b) ovaries
3   adrenal glands
4   thyroid

Exam Questions
1 a) a negative feedback system *[1 mark]*
   b) C *[1 mark]*
2   The pituitary gland releases a hormone/TSH which acts
       on the thyroid gland to make it release another hormone/
       thyroxine *[1 mark]*. If this hormone/TSH is not released,
       then the thyroid gland will stop releasing its hormone/
       thyroxine *[1 mark]*, so the person will experience
       symptoms linked to low thyroid hormone levels *[1 mark]*.
3   How to grade your answer:
       Level 0: There is no relevant information. *[No marks]*
       Level 1: There is a brief explanation of how the release
                 of a hormone (adrenaline) in response to seeing
                 the dog will affect the cat's heart rate and
                 blood glucose level. The answer shows basic
                 understanding, but lacks coherency.
                 [1 to 2 marks]
       Level 2: There is some explanation of how the release
                 of a hormone (adrenaline) in response to seeing
                 the dog will affect the cat's heart rate and
                 blood glucose level. There is some attempt
                 to explain why such a response is beneficial
                 to the cat. The answer shows mostly accurate
                 understanding and has some structure.
                 [3 to 4 marks]
       Level 3: There is a clear and detailed explanation of
                 how the release of a hormone (adrenaline) in
                 response to seeing the dog will affect the cat's
                 heart rate and blood glucose level. There is
                 a good explanation of why such a response
                 is beneficial to the cat. The answer shows an
                 accurate understanding of the relevant biology
                 and is well structured. *[5 to 6 marks]*
       Here are some points your answer may include:
       When the cat sees the dog a nervous impulse is sent to the
       adrenal glands.
       The adrenal glands release adrenaline.
       Adrenaline travels to the heart, where it binds to specific
       receptor cells.
       This causes the cat's heart muscle to contract more
       frequently, increasing the cat's heart rate.
       Adrenaline also binds to receptors in the liver.

This causes the liver to break down its glycogen stores,
releasing glucose.
This increases the blood glucose level.
The increased heart rate increases the rate of delivery of
oxygen and glucose to muscle cells..
The increased blood glucose increases the rate of delivery
of glucose to muscle cells.
Both these processes will help to increase respiration rate,
to produce extra energy for a 'fight or flight' response /
in case the cat needs to fight or run away.

Page 144
Warm-Up Questions
1   FSH/follicle-stimulating hormone
2   condoms
3   A fertility treatment that involves eggs
       being handled outside of the body.
4   Clomifene increases the release of FSH and LH.

Exam Questions
1 a) It inhibits it *[1 mark]*.
   b) LH/luteinising hormone *[1 mark]*
   c) day 14 *[1 mark]*
   d) It breaks down *[1 mark]*.
   e) It will maintain the lining of the uterus *[1 mark]*.
2 a) Keeping oestrogen levels permanently high inhibits
       production of FSH *[1 mark]*, so no eggs will mature /
       so egg development and production will stop *[1 mark]*.
   b) E.g. progesterone stimulates the production of thick
       cervical mucus *[1 mark]*, which will prevent any sperm
       getting through and reaching the woman's egg *[1 mark]*. /
       Progesterone inhibits the release of FSH *[1 mark]*, which
       will stop a follicle/an egg maturing in the ovaries *[1 mark]*.
       / Progesterone inhibits the release of LH *[1 mark]*,
       which will prevent ovulation from occurring *[1 mark]*.
   c) By preventing sperm from reaching the egg *[1 mark]*.
   d) Advantage: e.g. they have no unpleasant side effects. / They
       protect against sexually transmitted infections *[1 mark]*.
       Disadvantage: e.g. barrier methods are less effective at
       preventing pregnancy. / They need to be available at the
       time of intercourse *[1 mark]*.

Pages 153-154
Warm-Up Questions
1   The maintenance of a constant internal environment
       in response to internal and external changes.
2   Removes glucose from the blood and makes the
       liver turn glucose into glycogen for storage.
3   A condition in which the pancreas doesn't produce
       enough insulin, or the body becomes resistant to insulin.
4   E.g. having a high body mass index/obesity.
5   hypothalamus
6   E.g. excess ions and excess water.
7   ADH/anti-diuretic hormone

Exam Questions
1 a)

Substances	Blood	Filtrate
glucose	✗	✓
urea	✗	✓
ions	✗	✓

[2 marks — 1 mark for each correct row of the table]
*Water is also filtered out of the blood into the filtrate. However, it's not
all filtered out (otherwise the blood wouldn't be a liquid anymore) so the
missing word in the table can't be water.*
   b) B *[1 mark]*

2 a) The dialysis fluid contains the same concentration of glucose as healthy blood *[1 mark]*, so there is no concentration gradient and no net movement of glucose *[1 mark]*.

b) The dialysis machine has a selectively permeable barrier which is not permeable to molecules as large as proteins *[1 mark]*.

c) E.g. there are long waiting lists for kidneys. / There's a risk that the donor kidney will be rejected by the patient's immune system *[1 mark]*.

3 a) Organ A = pancreas *[1 mark]*, Organ B = liver *[1 mark]*

b) E.g. eating carbohydrates/sugary food *[1 mark]*.

c) The pancreas/organ A produces little or no insulin *[1 mark]*. This means that the liver/organ B is unable to remove glucose from the blood for storage *[1 mark]*. So blood glucose is able to rise to a dangerously high level *[1 mark]*.

d) It makes the liver/organ B turn glycogen into glucose increasing blood sugar levels *[1 mark]*.

4 a) Vasoconstriction *[1 mark]*. Less blood flows through the blood vessels close to the surface of the skin *[1 mark]*. This reduces the transfer of energy from the skin to the environment, helping to keep the body warm *[1 mark]*.

b) Sweat glands respond by stopping sweat production *[1 mark]*, because sweat transfers energy from the body to the environment when it evaporates, cooling the body *[1 mark]*.

5 How to grade your answer:
Level 0: There is no relevant information. *[No marks]*
Level 1: There is a brief explanation of the process that led to the runner's urine being a darker colour than normal. The points made are basic and not linked together. *[1 to 2 marks]*
Level 2: There is some explanation of the process that led to the runner's urine being a darker colour than normal. Some of the points made are linked together. *[3 to 4 marks]*
Level 3: There is a clear and detailed explanation of the process that led to the runner's urine being a darker colour than normal. The points made are well linked and the answer has a clear and logical structure. *[5 to 6 marks]*
Here are some points your answer may include:
As the runner ran, she would have become too hot.
As a response to this, her body would have started to produce lots of sweat, to try and cool her down.
This would have resulted in water loss/the runner having less water in her blood.
Her brain would have detected the decreased water content of her blood and instructed her pituitary gland to release ADH (anti-diuretic hormone) into her blood in response.
ADH made the collecting ducts of the runner's nephrons more permeable so that more water was reabsorbed back into her blood.
This resulted in less water being released in the runner's urine. So her urine was more concentrated and appeared darker in colour.

Topic 8 — Exchange and Transport in Animals

Page 162
Warm-Up Questions

1 Any two from: e.g. metabolic processes/to build up larger molecules from smaller ones. / To contract muscles. / To keep body temperature steady.

2 E.g. carbon dioxide and urea.
3 Glucose and oxygen.
4 respirometer

Exam Questions
1 a) C *[1 mark]*
b) The alveoli walls are thin *[1 mark]* which minimises the distance that gases have to move *[1 mark]*.
2 a) To release energy from the breakdown of organic compounds *[1 mark]*.
b) Any two from: e.g. aerobic respiration uses oxygen, anaerobic respiration does not. / Glucose is broken down fully during aerobic respiration but is only partially broken down during anaerobic respiration. / Aerobic respiration doesn't produce lactic acid/ethanol, anaerobic respiration does. / Aerobic respiration releases more energy than anaerobic respiration. *[2 marks]*
c) glucose *[1 mark]* → lactic acid *[1 mark]*
3 Surface area = $(2 \times 2 \times 2) + (2 \times 1 \times 4)$
$= 8 + 8 = 16 \ \mu m^2$
Volume = $2 \times 2 \times 1 = 4 \ \mu m^3$
So the surface area to volume ratio is **16 : 4**, or **4 : 1**.
[3 marks for correct answer, otherwise 1 mark for correct surface area and 1 mark for correct volume.]

Page 167
Warm-Up Questions
1 They carry blood back to the heart.
2 They help the blood to clot at a wound.
3 Any three from: e.g. red blood cells / white blood cells / platelets / glucose / amino acids / carbon dioxide / urea / hormones / proteins / antibodies / antitoxins.
4 cardiac output = heart rate × stroke volume

Exam Questions
1 a) White blood cells *[1 mark]*. They defend the body against infection *[1 mark]*.
b) Any two from: e.g. they have permeable walls *[1 mark]*, so substances can diffuse in and out *[1 mark]*. / Their walls are usually only one cell thick *[1 mark]*, which increases the rate of diffusion by decreasing the distance over which it occurs *[1 mark]*. / They are very narrow *[1 mark]*, so they can squeeze into the gaps between cells *[1 mark]*.
2 a) A — aorta, B — vena cava, C — left atrium *[1 mark]*
b) It pumps blood around the body *[1 mark]*.
c) To prevent the backflow of blood *[1 mark]*.
d) Deoxygenated blood enters the right atrium *[1 mark]* through the vena cava *[1 mark]*. The blood moves through to the right ventricle *[1 mark]* which pumps it through the pulmonary artery to the lungs *[1 mark]*.

Topic 9 — Ecosystems and Material Cycles

Page 176
Warm-Up Questions
1 a community
2 A community of living organisms (biotic) with the non-living (abiotic) conditions.
3 E.g. amount of water, light intensity, temperature, levels of pollutants.
4 Trophic levels are the different stages of a food chain.
5 A pyramid of biomass shows how much the creatures at each level of a food chain would weigh if you put them together.

Exam Questions

1 a) E.g. they could have marked out a transect/straight line from the wood to the opposite side of the field *[1 mark]* and placed quadrats along it at regular intervals *[1 mark]*. They then could have counted the number of poppies in each quadrat *[1 mark]*.

   b) E.g. the number of poppies increases with increasing distance from the wood *[1 mark]*.

2 a) At first, the population size of the cutthroat trout would decrease as the lake trout eat the cutthroat trout *[1 mark]*. This would lead to a decline in the population of the lake trout (as they'd have less to eat) *[1 mark]*. That would allow the population of cutthroat trout to increase again *[1 mark]*. The population of lake trout would then increase as they have more to eat (and the cycle would start again) *[1 mark]*.

   b) E.g. competition with other fish species *[1 mark]*.

Page 182

Warm-Up Questions

1 Biodiversity is the variety of living organisms in an ecosystem.

2 Excess nitrates cause algae in the water to grow more quickly, which stops light reaching plants growing in the water. This means that the plants cannot photosynthesise, so they die and then decompose. This provides more food for microorganisms that feed on the decomposing plants. They increase in number, using up the oxygen in the water. This leads to the death of organisms in the water that need oxygen for aerobic respiration, like fish.

3 Conservation schemes maintain biodiversity by preventing species from dying out.

4 Any two from: e.g. food is added to the nets to feed the fish, which also produce lots of waste. The food and waste can leak into the water system, causing eutrophication and the death of wild species. / Open water fish farms can be a breeding ground for parasites, which can then escape and infect wild animals, killing them. / Predators can be attracted to the nets, become trapped in them and die. / Farmed fish can escape into the wild and can out-compete indigenous species.

5 Sustainability is being able to meet the needs of today's population without affecting the ability of future generations to meet their needs.

Exam Questions

1 E.g. black rats could compete with the island's indigenous species for resources *[1 mark]*. If the rats out-compete other species this could cause them to die out, reducing biodiversity *[1 mark]*. The black rats might bring new diseases to the island habitat *[1 mark]*. These new diseases might infect and kill lots of indigenous species, reducing the habitat's biodiversity *[1 mark]*.
You don't have to have given these exact answers here. You get one mark each for giving any two sensible ways that introducing the rats could reduce biodiversity, and one mark each for explaining how each one could reduce biodiversity.

2 a) Planting only white spruce will result in low biodiversity because of the low number of tree species *[1 mark]*. A lower number of tree species will also mean that the number of different animal species using the trees for food and shelter will be lower *[1 mark]*.

   b) E.g. protect the forest so that the natural habitat of the species is preserved. / Protect the species in a safe area outside of the forest. / Use a captive breeding programme to increase their numbers *[1 mark]*.

3 a) Food security is having access to enough food that is safe to eat and has the right balance of nutrition *[1 mark]*.

   b) E.g. there's less energy and less biomass every time you move up a stage in a food chain *[1 mark]*, so for a given area of farmland, you can produce more food for humans by growing crops rather than by farming animals *[1 mark]*. This means that global food production is reduced by increasing meat production *[1 mark]*.

   c) Any two from: e.g. the increasing human population *[1 mark]*, because more people will require more food *[1 mark]*. / New pests/pathogens *[1 mark]* because these may result in a lower yield of food from crops and livestock *[1 mark]*. / Changing environmental conditions *[1 mark]* because these may result in lower yields from crops *[1 mark]*. / High input costs of farming *[1 mark]* because these can make it too expensive for people in some countries to farm *[1 mark]*. / An increase in the growth of crops to make biofuels *[1 mark]*, because they take up land that could be used for food crops *[1 mark]*.

Page 188

Warm-Up Questions

1 Fossil fuels release carbon dioxide as they are burned (to produce energy).

2 Salt water is boiled in a large enclosed vessel, so that the water evaporates. The steam rises to the top of the vessel, but the salts stay at the bottom. The steam travels down a pipe from the top of the vessel and cools and condenses back into pure water.

3 Nitrifying bacteria turn ammonia in decaying matter into nitrites and then into nitrates.

4 Using fertilisers increases the amount of nitrates in the soil. This increases the growth of the crops and so the crop yield.

Exam Questions

1 a) Animals are eating plants (and gaining nitrogen compounds from the plant proteins) *[1 mark]*.

   b) denitrifying bacteria *[1 mark]*

   c) nitrogen-fixing bacteria *[1 mark]*

2 a) transpiration *[1 mark]*

   b) Energy from the Sun evaporates water from the ocean *[1 mark]*, so the water molecule enters the atmosphere as water vapour *[1 mark]*. The warm water vapour rises, then cools and condenses into clouds *[1 mark]*. The water molecule then falls from the clouds as precipitation/rain/snow/hail into a garden pond *[1 mark]*.

3 How to grade your answer:

   Level 0: There is no relevant information. *[No marks]*

   Level 1: There is a brief description of one or two ways in which carbon stored in the vegetation could be returned to the atmosphere. The answer shows some basic understanding, but lacks coherency. The points made do not link together. *[1 to 2 marks]*

   Level 2: There is some description of more than two of the ways that carbon stored in the vegetation could be returned to the atmosphere. The answer shows mostly accurate understanding and has some structure. *[3 to 4 marks]*

   Level 3: There is a clear and detailed description of more than three of the ways that carbon stored in the vegetation could be returned to the atmosphere. The answer shows an accurate understanding of the relevant biology and is well structured. *[5 to 6 marks]*

   Here are some points your answer may include:
   Carbon stored in the small branches will be returned to the atmosphere as carbon dioxide when the branches are burnt.

The green plants could be broken down by microorganisms/decomposers, which will release carbon as carbon dioxide as they respire.
Some of the green plants may be eaten by other organisms. Some of the carbon from these plants will be released as carbon dioxide when the animals respire.
Some of the carbon from these plants will be lost as carbon compounds in the animals' waste. Microorganisms/decomposers will break this material down and release carbon dioxide as they respire.
Some of the carbon from these plants will be stored as carbon compounds in the animals' biomass.
This carbon will not be released until the animals are dead. It will be released as carbon dioxide by the microorganisms/decomposers that break down the dead material as they respire.
The wood that is taken away to be made into furniture will eventually return the carbon to the atmosphere through decay/burning when the lifespan of the furniture is over.

Page 192
Warm-Up Questions
1   A species that is very sensitive to changes in its environment, that can be studied to see the effect of human activities on an ecosystem.
2   E.g. temperature, water availability, oxygen availability.
3   Drying food removes the water that decomposers need to survive and carry out biological processes.
4   Compost is decomposed organic matter that is used as a fertiliser.

Exam Questions
1 a)   E.g. the level of sulfur dioxide in the air in Woodland B is lower than in Woodland A *[1 mark]*. There are more bushy and crusty lichen growing in Woodland B than in Woodland A *[1 mark]*. Lichen grow better in lower levels of sulfur dioxide *[1 mark]*.
  b)   E.g indicator species can't give accurate figures for the level of air pollution. / There may also be factors other than air pollution playing a role in the presence or absence of a species in an environment *[1 mark]*.
2 a)   Change in mass during last four weeks = 50 − 25
                                    = 25 % *[1 mark]*
        Rate during last four weeks = 25 ÷ 4
                                    = 6.25 % per week *[1 mark]*
        Change in rate = 12.5 − 6.25
                                    = **6.25 % per week** *[1 mark]*
  b)   How to grade your answer:
        Level 0: There is no relevant information. *[No marks]*
        Level 1: There is a brief explanation of some of the conditions needed for fast decay and how the gardener could create these conditions in the compost bin. The points made are basic and not linked together. *[1 to 2 marks]*
        Level 2: There is a good explanation of the conditions needed for fast decay and how the gardener could create these conditions in the compost bin. Some of the points made are linked together. *[3 to 4 marks]*
        Level 3: There is a clear and detailed explanation of the conditions needed for fast decay and how the gardener could create these conditions in the compost bin. The points made are well-linked and the answer has a clear and logical structure. *[5 to 6 marks]*
        Here are some points your answer may include:
        The compost bin needs to be kept warm.

A warm temperature will increase the rate of decomposition because the enzymes in decomposers will be able to work at a higher rate.
To achieve this the gardener could insulate her compost bin / put it in a warm, sunny place in her garden.
The compost should be kept moist/have a high water content.
A moist environment allows decomposition to happen faster because decomposers need water to carry out their biological processes and survive.
To achieve this, the gardener could add water to her compost when needed/keep adding plenty of fresh garden material with a high water content.
The compost needs a good supply of oxygen/good air flow. The more air flow, the greater the oxygen availability. This will increase the rate of decomposition by decomposers that respire aerobically.
To achieve this, the gardener could use a compost bin with mesh sides / turn the compost regularly with a garden fork.

Practice Paper 1
Pages 199-220
1 a)   Any two from: e.g. it has a nucleus / it contains mitochondria / it doesn't contain plasmids *[2 marks]*.
  b)   E.g. most cells have a structure that is specialised for their function, so they will contain different subcellular structures *[1 mark]*.
  c)   cell membrane *[1 mark]*
  d)   C *[1 mark]*
  e)   Similarities
        Any two from: e.g. both plant and animal cells have a nucleus. / Both plant and animal cells contain cytoplasm. / Plant cells and animal cells both have a cell membrane. / Mitochondria are found in both plant cells and animal cells. / Both plant cells and animal cells have ribosomes *[2 marks]*.
        Differences
        Any two from: e.g. chloroplasts are present in plant cells, but not in animal cells. / Plant cells have a cell wall, but animal cells do not. / Plant cells contain a permanent vacuole, but animal cells do not *[2 marks]*.
2 a)   Any two from: e.g. used sterilised Petri dishes / used sterilised growth mediums / sterilised the inoculating loop used to transfer the bacteria (by passing it through a hot flame) / used a sterile dropping pipette and spreader / lightly taped on the lids of the Petri dishes after transferring the bacteria *[2 marks]*.
  b)   Antibiotic X: 4.4 cm ÷ 2 = 2.2 cm
        $\pi \times 2.2^2 = 15.20... =$ **15 cm² (2 s.f.)** *[1 mark]*
        Antibiotic Y: 3 cm ÷ 2 = 1.5 cm
        $\pi \times 1.5^2 = 7.06... =$ **7.1 cm² (2 s.f.)** *[1 mark]*
        The inhibition zone of antibiotic X is greater than the inhibition zone of antibiotic Y, so antibiotic X is more effective against the bacteria than antibiotic Y *[1 mark]*.
  c)   Antibiotics inhibit processes inside bacterial cells *[1 mark]* but the processes antibiotics inhibit do not occur in human cells *[1 mark]*.
  d)   The bacteria could have developed resistance to the antibiotic *[1 mark]* because the allele for resistance has become widespread in the population of bacteria due to natural selection *[1 mark]*.
3 a)   The A and T bases in a DNA molecule always pair up with each other (complementary base-pairing) *[1 mark]*.
  b)   nucleus *[1 mark]*
  c)   B *[1 mark]*
Each amino acid is coded for by a sequence of three bases in DNA.

254

d) UAGUCCGAUCAA *[2 marks for correct answer, otherwise 1 mark for correct sequence using T instead of U].*

e) i) C *[1 mark]*

   ii) The mutation occurred in a non-coding region in front of a gene *[1 mark]*. The mutation makes it easier for RNA polymerase to bind to this region *[1 mark]*, increasing the amount of protein synthesis that occurs *[1 mark]*.

4 a) Any two from: e.g. stop the mosquitoes from breeding / protect people from mosquito bites using mosquito nets / protect people from mosquito bites by using insect repellent *[2 marks]*.

b) B *[1 mark]*

c) 3 days = 3 × 24 = 72 hours
72 ÷ 18 = 4 divisions
1 bacterial cell × 2^4 = 1 × 2 × 2 × 2 × 2 = **16 cells** *[2 marks for correct answer, otherwise 1 mark for correct working.]*

d) The body is injected with small amounts of dead or inactive pathogens (which are harmless) *[1 mark]*. The pathogens carry antigens, which cause the B-lymphocytes in the body to produce antibodies *[1 mark]* and cause memory lymphocytes to be made *[1 mark]*. If live pathogens of the same type are detected again, the memory lymphocytes can cause a much faster secondary immune response, so the person doesn't get ill *[1 mark]*.

5 a) B *[1 mark]*

b) E.g. research from the project about the cystic fibrosis gene could be used to develop more effective treatments for the disorder *[1 mark]*.

c) E.g.

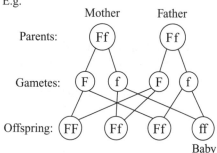

[1 mark for showing that the parents both have the Ff genotype, 1 mark for showing the gametes' genotypes as F or f, 1 mark for correctly showing all possible genotypes of the couple's offspring and identifying the baby's genotype as ff.]

d) Ff *[1 mark]*. E.g. Ian has the genotype Ff, so Leina must also have the genotype Ff in order for her children to inherit the genotypes: FF (Carys), ff (Beth) and Ff (Alfie) *[1 mark]*.

e) Environmental variation *[1 mark]*. The scar would have been caused by an environmental factor rather than being determined by genes *[1 mark]*.

6 a) Town B is the most polluted because it contains a higher percentage of dark moths *[1 mark]*.

b) 77% − 25% = **52%**
[2 marks for correct answer, otherwise 1 mark for correctly reading 77% and 25% off the graph]

c) Any one from: e.g. avoid leaving the moths inside the trap for too long. / Avoid touching the moths. / Release the moths in their original habitat *[1 mark]*.

d) The dark variety is better camouflaged in soot-polluted areas, so it is less likely to be eaten by predators *[1 mark]*. This means more dark moths survive to breed *[1 mark]* and pass the gene(s)/allele for this characteristic on to the next generation *[1 mark]*. As this process continues over time, the dark variety of moth becomes more common *[1 mark]*.

It makes sense that if an organism blends in with its background it'll be harder for predators to spot it.

7 a) Any two from: to test the drug works and produces the desired effect. / To find out about the drug's toxicity/how harmful the drug is. / To find the best dosage of drug to use *[2 marks]*.

b) E.g. to make sure it did not cause any harmful side effects when the body is working normally *[1 mark]*.

c) E.g. the trial had a large sample size *[1 mark]*. The trial had a control group/placebo *[1 mark]*. The drug and placebo were randomly allocated *[1 mark]*. Since the scientists took these steps to make their study a fair test, their conclusion should be valid *[1 mark]*.

In questions that ask you to evaluate, you need to include a conclusion that supports what you've talked about in the rest of your answer — that's what the last mark is for in the example answer shown above.

d) Giving up smoking. / Getting more exercise. / Eating less saturated fat *[1 mark]*.

8 a) B *[1 mark]*

b) To make the experiment a fair test. / To ensure the same amount of substrate was available in each experiment. / To make the results valid/repeatable *[1 mark]*.

c) They could have added the sample to a drop of iodine solution *[1 mark]*. If starch was present the iodine solution would have changed to blue-black *[1 mark]*. If starch was no longer present, the iodine solution would have remained browny-orange *[1 mark]*.

d) As the pH increases from pH 3 to pH 6, the time until the starch is no longer present decreases / the rate of reaction increases *[1 mark]*.

e) i) The result for pH 7 is anomalous *[1 mark]* because the time taken until starch is no longer present is much slower than expected *[1 mark]*.

   ii) Any two from: e.g. the student may not have used the correct volume/concentration of starch solution. / The student may have used the incorrect volume/ concentration of amylase solution. / The student may have used a buffer solution with the wrong pH. / The student may have carried out the experiment at a different temperature. / The student may have started timing the experiment too early *[2 marks]*.

9 a) Any two from: e.g. there is very little variation in the mean reaction time among all participants. / Their reaction time was very fast. / Their response was automatic *[2 marks]*.

If you have to think about what physical response to give then it's not a reflex action.

b) i) C *[1 mark]*

   ii) D *[1 mark]*

c) The men in this experiment had a faster mean reaction time than the women *[1 mark]*, so the data supports the scientist's hypothesis *[1 mark]*.

d) Any two from: e.g. the age of the participants. / The strength of the tap on the knee. / Caffeine consumption of the participants prior to the investigation / Using the same timing method/equipment *[2 marks]*.

e) i) B *[1 mark]*

   ii) How to grade your answer:

Level 0: There is no relevant information. *[No marks]*

Level 1: There is a brief description of some parts of the path taken by a nervous impulse in the reflex. The answer shows basic understanding, but lacks coherency. *[1 to 2 marks]*

Level 2: There is some description of the path taken by a nervous impulse in the reflex, but some detail is missing. The answer shows mostly accurate understanding and has some structure. *[3 to 4 marks]*

Level 3: There is a clear and detailed description of the path taken by a nervous impulse in the reflex. The answer shows an accurate understanding of the relevant biology and is well structured. *[5 to 6 marks]*

Here are some points your answer may include:
The impulse travels from the receptors, along a sensory neurone, to the central nervous system/spinal cord.
When the impulse reaches a synapse between the sensory neurone and a relay neurone, it triggers neurotransmitters to be released.
These neurotransmitters cause impulses to be sent along the relay neurone.
When the impulse reaches a synapse between the relay neurone and a motor neurone, neurotransmitters are released again.
This causes impulses to be sent along the motor neurone.
The impulse then reaches the muscle/effector, which contracts to move your hand away from the source of pain.

10a) **B** *[1 mark]*
b) i) E.g. it can produce many offspring very quickly *[1 mark]*, which means organisms can colonise an area rapidly *[1 mark]*. / Only one parent is needed *[1 mark]*, so organisms can reproduce whenever conditions are favourable, instead of waiting for a mate *[1 mark]*.
ii) E.g. there is no genetic variation between offspring *[1 mark]*, so an unfavourable change in the environment will affect all of them *[1 mark]*.
c) i) The detergent breaks down the cell membranes to release the DNA *[1 mark]*. The salt makes the DNA stick together *[1 mark]*.
ii) DNA is not soluble in cold ethanol, so it will form a precipitate *[1 mark]*.
d) How to grade your answer:
Level 0: No relevant information is given. *[No marks]*
Level 1: There is a basic description of at least two of the stages of the cell cycle or a suggestion of why disrupting the cell cycle may kill plants. The answer shows basic understanding, but lacks coherency. *[1 to 2 marks]*
Level 2: There is a clear description of at least two stages of the cell cycle and a suggestion of why disrupting the cell cycle may kill plants. The answer shows mostly accurate understanding and has some structure. *[3 to 4 marks]*
Level 3: There is a detailed description of each stage of the cell cycle and a suggestion of why disrupting the cell cycle may kill plants. The answer shows an accurate understanding of the relevant biology and is well structured. *[5 to 6 marks]*

Here are some points your answer may include:
The cell cycle involves the division of a cell to form two identical cells.
Before division takes place, interphase occurs.
This is when the cell grows and increases the amount of subcellular structures it has, such as mitochondria and ribosomes.
It then duplicates its DNA so there's one copy for each new cell.
The DNA is copied and forms X-shaped chromosomes.
Next, mitosis takes place.
The chromosomes condense (prophase).
The membrane around the nucleus breaks down.
The chromosomes line up at the centre of the cell (metaphase).
Spindle fibres pull them apart and the chromatids

are pulled to opposite ends of the cell (anaphase). Membranes form around each of the sets of chromosomes to become the nuclei of the two new cells (telophase). Finally the cytoplasm and cell membrane divide (cytokinesis) so two identical daughter cells are formed. Disrupting the cell cycle can kill plants as plants are multicellular organisms which use mitosis to grow and to replace damaged cells.
If they can no longer do this, they may die.

Practice Paper 2
Pages 221-242

1 a) **C** *[1 mark]*
b) i) **D** *[1 mark]*
ii) The biomass of the organisms decreases at each trophic level and the bars on this pyramid get smaller each time you go up one trophic level *[1 mark]*.
c) efficiency = (1.4 kg ÷ 12 kg) × 100
= 0.1166... × 100 = **12% (2 s.f.)** *[1 mark]*
d) Energy is lost at each level of a food chain *[1 mark]*. After about five levels, the amount of energy being passed on is not sufficient to support another level of organisms *[1 mark]*.

2 a) **21** *[1 mark]*
To find the median, you write out all the results from lowest to highest, e.g. 10, 21, 21, 35, 37. 21 is in the middle of the list, so it is the median.
b) To avoid bias. / To make sure the results were representative of the whole sample area *[1 mark]*.
c) (6 + 15 + 9 + 14 + 20 + 5 + 3 + 11 + 10 + 7) ÷ 10
= 100 ÷ 10
= **10 buttercups per m²** *[1 mark]*
d) i) 90 × 120 = 10 800 m²
10 × 10 800 = **108 000 buttercups**
[2 marks for correct answer, otherwise 1 mark for finding the area of the field.]
Even if you got your answer to c) wrong, you still get full marks for d)i) if you did the calculation correctly with your answer to c).
ii) E.g. take more samples from the field *[1 mark]*.
e) i) E.g. more buttercups grow where there is a higher moisture level in the soil *[1 mark]*.
ii) Use a tape measure to mark out a line/transect across the field *[1 mark]*. Place quadrats at regular intervals/next to each other along the line/transect *[1 mark]*. Record the number of buttercups in each quadrat *[1 mark]*. Measure the moisture level of the soil at each sample point and see how the number of buttercups changes as the moisture level of the soil changes *[1 mark]*.

3 a) Light coming through the hole in the box caused more auxin to accumulate on the shaded side of the shoots *[1 mark]*. This made the cells on the shaded side of the plants grow/elongate faster *[1 mark]*, so the shoots bent towards the light *[1 mark]*.
b) phototropism *[1 mark]*
c) **B** *[1 mark]*
d) The hormones in the weedkillers disrupt the normal growth patterns of broad-leaved weeds, killing them *[1 mark]* but don't affect the growth of narrow-leaved crop plants *[1 mark]*.

4 a) Organisms need to be able to break down sugars like lactose into smaller components so that they can be absorbed into the bloodstream and into cells *[1 mark]* to be used for other life processes, such as respiration *[1 mark]*.
b) The concentration of glucose is higher in the small intestine than in the blood *[1 mark]*.
c) Lactose would no longer be broken down *[1 mark]* because lactase would be denatured *[1 mark]*.

d) Their blood glucose level will not rise very much at all *[1 mark]*. This is because a person with lactose intolerance has little or no lactase to break down the lactose, so there will be little or no glucose to be absorbed from the small intestine *[1 mark]*.

5 a) C *[1 mark]*
b) To maintain the concentration gradients of oxygen and carbon dioxide *[1 mark]* to maximise the rate of diffusion of the gases into and out of the alveoli *[1 mark]*.
c) i) To carry oxygen from lungs to the cells *[1 mark]*.
ii) Their biconcave disc shape gives them a large surface area for absorbing oxygen *[1 mark]*. They don't have a nucleus, so they have more room to carry oxygen *[1 mark]*. They contain lots of haemoglobin, which combines with oxygen in the lungs to become oxyhaemoglobin *[1 mark]*.
d) E.g. the sickle-shaped cells are more rigid than normal red blood cells so they may not be able to carry as much oxygen / the sickle-shaped cells are a different shape from normal red blood cells, so they may not be able to fit through the capillaries *[1 mark]*. This could reduce the amount of oxygen transported to cells, causing an increase in breathing rate *[1 mark]*.

If you don't have enough oxygen for respiration, your breathing rate increases to get more oxygen into your blood. In a person with sickle cell anaemia, the lack of oxygen may cause their breathing rate to increase so much that they feel breathless.

6 a) Carbon compounds in the plants are being transferred to animals as they eat the plants *[1 mark]*.
b) i) light intensity *[1 mark]*, carbon dioxide concentration *[1 mark]*, temperature *[1 mark]*
ii) Energy is taken in during photosynthesis/the reaction *[1 mark]*.
c) A *[1 mark]*
d) Microorganisms break down waste products and dead organisms *[1 mark]* and release carbon dioxide into the atmosphere as they respire *[1 mark]*.
e) B *[1 mark]*

7 a) E.g. day 2 was less bright, so the stomata weren't fully open and less water could move out of the leaves. / Day 2 was colder, so the water evaporated/diffused more slowly. / Day 2 was less windy, so the water vapour was carried away more slowly, meaning that diffusion couldn't happen as quickly.
[1 mark for reason, 1 mark for explanation].

The rate of transpiration varies throughout the day due to the changing light intensity, but it can also be affected by the temperature, and the air flow around the leaves.

b) At night, the light intensity is low *[1 mark]* so the stomata close, allowing less water vapour to escape *[1 mark]*.
c) Transpiration creates a slight shortage of water in the leaf *[1 mark]*. More water is drawn up from the rest of the plant through the xylem vessels to replace it *[1 mark]*. This in turn means that more water is drawn up from the roots *[1 mark]*.
d) B *[1 mark]*
e) Each branch of a root is covered in microscopic root hair cells *[1 mark]* giving them a large surface area for absorbing water *[1 mark]*.

8 a)
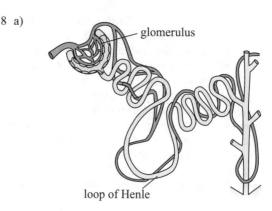

[1 mark for each correct label]
b) i) The proteins stay in the blood as they are too large to pass through the membranes of the Bowman's capsule (B) *[1 mark]*.
ii) Add potassium hydroxide to the sample *[1 mark]* followed by copper sulfate *[1 mark]*. If the mixture turns purple then protein is present in the sample *[1 mark]*. If the mixture stays blue then protein is not present in the sample *[1 mark]*.
c) The concentration of glucose at point B would be high and there would be no glucose at point C *[1 mark]*, as all the glucose is reabsorbed back into the blood in the first part of the nephron *[1 mark]*.
d) i) It sends impulses to the pituitary gland to release more ADH *[1 mark]*. This causes more water to be reabsorbed from the nephron/collecting duct *[1 mark]*.
ii) The increased level of ADH causes the kidneys to reabsorb too much water into the blood *[1 mark]*. If the water content of the blood is higher than the body cells, water may enter the cells by osmosis *[1 mark]*.
e) The person's blood flows between partially permeable membranes *[1 mark]*. Waste products/urea and excess ions and water are able to diffuse out of the blood into the dialysis fluid *[1 mark]*. The dialysis fluid contains the same concentration of glucose and salts as healthy blood, which ensures that these are not lost from the blood *[1 mark]*.

9 a) A *[1 mark]*
b) C *[1 mark]* — e.g. because the level corresponds to the thickness of the uterus lining, which is maintained by progesterone *[1 mark]*.

There are a few different ways that you can tell that this line represents progesterone. As long as you're able to justify your answer, you'll get the marks.

c) How to grade your answer:
Level 0: There is no relevant information. *[No marks]*
Level 1: There is a basic description of how at least two of the hormones help to control the menstrual cycle, but little description of how they interact with each other. The points made are not linked together. *[1 to 2 marks]*
Level 2: There is a clear description of how at least three of the hormones help to control the menstrual cycle and some description of how they interact with each other. Some of the points are linked together. *[3 to 4 marks]*
Level 3: There is a detailed description of how each of the four hormones helps to control the menstrual cycle and how they interact with each other. The points made are well linked and the answer has a clear and logical structure. *[5 to 6 marks]*

Here are some points your answer may include:
FSH is released by the pituitary gland at the start
of the menstrual cycle.
FSH causes a follicle in one of the ovaries to mature.
It also stimulates the production of oestrogen.
Oestrogen is released by the ovaries and causes the
lining of the uterus to thicken and grow.
At a high level oestrogen stimulates a surge/rapid increase
in levels of LH.
LH is released by the pituitary gland.
LH stimulates ovulation and also stimulates the
remains of the follicle to develop into a corpus luteum.
The corpus luteum secretes progesterone.
Progesterone maintains the lining of the uterus
and inhibits the release of FSH and LH.
When the level of progesterone falls and there's a
low oestrogen level, the uterus lining breaks down.
A low progesterone level allows FSH to increase
so that the menstrual cycle can begin again.

d) Advantages of the implant: e.g. it works for three years
/ protection is always available / you do not have to
remember to take a pill every day / it is highly effective.
Disadvantages of the implant: e.g. it has to be inserted by a
doctor or nurse which may be painful/inconvenient /
if certain medications are taken, a different contraceptive
method would have to be used / you could suffer from
side effects / it does not protect against STIs.
Advantages of the condom: e.g. it protects against STIs /
there are no side effects / it is not affected by medication.
Disadvantages of the condom: e.g. it needs to be available
at the time of intercourse / if it isn't used correctly it may
not be effective / it can only be used once.
Conclusion: e.g. the condom is the better method of
contraception because it prevents the spread of STIs.
*[3 marks for at least one advantage and one disadvantage
of each method, otherwise 2 marks for at least two
advantages or disadvantages of either method or
1 mark for one advantage or disadvantage of either
method. 1 mark for giving a justified conclusion.]*

10a)

*[1 mark for label and suitable scale for the x-axis,
2 marks for all points correctly plotted (or 1 mark for
8 points out of 10 plotted correctly), 1 mark for a
smooth curve of best fit.]*

b) 95 beats/min *[1 mark. Allow any value correctly
read from 30 seconds on your own graph.]*

c) B *[1 mark]*

d) How to grade your answer:
Level 0:   There is no relevant information. *[No marks]*
Level 1:   There is a basic description of how adrenaline
            affects the body. The points made are not
            linked together. *[1 to 2 marks]*
Level 2:   There is a clear description of how adrenaline
            affects the body and some explanation of how
            this prepares the body for fight or flight.
            Some of the points are linked together.
            [3 to 4 marks]
Level 3:   There is a detailed explanation of how
            adrenaline affects the body and prepares it for
            fight or flight. The points made are well linked
            and the answer has a clear and logical structure.
            [5 to 6 marks]

Here are some points your answer may include:
In threatening situations, adrenaline is released by the
adrenal glands.
Adrenaline causes the heart muscle to contract more
frequently and with more force, so that heart rate and blood
pressure increase.
This increases blood flow to the muscles, so the cells
receive more oxygen and glucose for increased respiration.
Adrenaline causes the liver to break down its glycogen
stores to release glucose.
This increases the blood glucose level, so there's more
glucose in the blood to be transported to the cells.
An increased rate of respiration and better
supply of blood to the cells mean that the body
is prepared for the sudden increase in physical
activity needed for a 'fight or flight' response.

258

Index

Index

BES41